A Practical Guide to Adopting the Universal Verification Methodology (UVM)

Sharon Rosenberg

Kathleen A Meade

ISBN 978-0-578-05995-6

Contents

List of Figures

List of Examples

Foreword

Allow me to start with a cliché: Verification is hard and only getting harder. Although trite, this statement is nonetheless true. Somewhere around the turn of the millennium, developers of systems-on-chips (SoCs) found that functional verification was consuming more than half of their time and effort. In the intervening decade, this percentage has crept up to 60% or more on many projects, and even developers of smaller chips and FPGAs are finding that past verification approaches no longer suffice. Accordingly, these engineers are constantly on the lookout for new and better ways to perform functional verification.

What they find when they start looking can be very confusing because there are so many proven and promising technologies for enhanced verification. These include simulation, simulation acceleration, emulation, object-oriented programming, aspect-oriented programming, constrained-random stimulus generation, coverage-based verification, metric-based verification, automated verification planning and management, assertion-based verification, verification reuse, linting, static formal analysis, dynamic formal analysis, hybrid formal analysis, and so forth. I could go on, but the point is clear. The problem is not that we need more verification techniques, but perhaps that we have too many.

This is precisely where methodology enters the picture. A robust and comprehensive verification methodology provides guidance on when, where, why, and how the various techniques should be applied for maximum efficiency and efficacy. The methodology should provide building-block libraries plus extensive documentation with coding guidelines, advice on verification reuse, and lots of examples. It must help novices adopt the methodology incrementally while supporting the needs of the most advanced users. Above all, it must deliver better verification results as measured by engineer productivity, schedule predictability, and profitability for the chip or system being verified.

You hold in your hands the very first book about a verification methodology that meets these lofty goals. The Universal Verification Methodology (UVM) emerging standard from Accellera is also a first; it represents an alignment on verification methodology across the industry, from the major EDA suppliers and their ecosystems to many leading-edge users. Equally importantly, the UVM represents a decade of predecessor methodologies that have produced thousands of successful chips. A quick review of the history is helpful to understand just how robust and powerful the UVM is.

UVM 1.0 EA (Early Adopter), the version used to create the examples in this book, is virtually identical to the very successful Open Verification Methodology (OVM) from Cadence and Mentor Graphics. The authors, Sharon and Kathleen, and I have been involved with the OVM since the very early days. Most key features in the OVM came from the Cadence Universal Reuse Methodology (URM), which in turn was a multi-language expansion to the *e* Reuse Methodology (*e*RM) developed at Verisity a decade ago, where Sharon was a key contributor. The OVM also contains elements of the Mentor Advanced Verification Methodology (AVM), while the UVM also has influences from the *Verification Methodology Manual (VMM) for SystemVerilog*, a book to which I contributed back in my Synopsys days.

I am making two points here. First, the people involved in the Accellera UVM and this book have been in the verification trenches for a long time. We know what works and what does not, and all the years of hard-won experience are reflected in the UVM library and documentation. In addition, because the UVM is built on an incredibly solid base, it's ready for prime time. Accellera released UVM 1.0 EA just a few weeks ago as I write this. Already, projects are adopting it, EDA tools are supporting it, and a vibrant community is developing on UVM World (**www.uvmworld.org**). Engineers can choose the UVM with confidence, and this book will be very helpful for adopting and propagating this methodology.

I'm hesitant to make bold predictions in an industry that changes as fast as electronics, but I have every expectation that the UVM will thrive, prosper, and grow. There are dozens of OVM and UVM extensions already available for Accellera to consider in future releases. The UVM will evolve to meet the ever-increasing needs of SoC verification. We can all salute the strong foundation laid by *e*RM/URM/VMM/AVM/OVM and embrace the UVM with confidence going forward.

I have seen the future of verification, and it is spelled U-V-M.

Thomas L. Anderson
Group Director, Verification Product Management
Cadence Design Systems, Inc.

May 28, 2010

Preface

The Universal Verification Methodology (UVM) was announced by Accellera on December 23rd, 2009 and introduced to the user community on May 17, 2010. After long technical debates in Accellera, UVM was born through a script that converted the Open Verification Methodology (OVM) prefixes into UVM prefixes. While some enhancements were added in terms of end-of-test and callbacks, UVM is not a huge technology leap on top of what OVM provided. The value of UVM is that it offers a single cross-industry solution to the challenges of design verification.

The timeline below illustrates the history and development of the methodologies and innovations upon which the UVM is built.

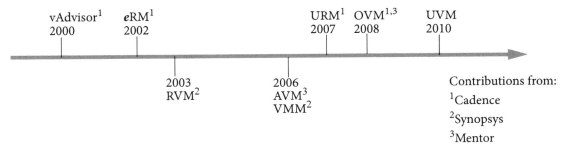

In 2000, Verisity Design (now Cadence Design Systems, Inc.) introduced a collection of best known practices for verification, called the Verification Advisor (vAdvisor). Targeted for the *e* user community, the tools included various verification design patterns in an HTML format and touched many aspects of verification, including stimuli creation, self-checking testbenches, and coverage model creation. The best practices contained in the vAdvisor consolidated Verisity's significant experience in this area and was helpful in deploying the correct methodology, speeding up development, and supporting users in performing verification tasks. In just a short time and after rapid user adoption, it was obvious that while the knowledge was useful, generic library code could be created to codify the vAdvisor best practices and enable further automation and reuse.

In 2002, Verisity announced the first verification library—the *e* Reuse Methodology (*e*RM)—which was enthusiastically adopted by users. It included packaging guidelines, architecture requirements (environments, agents, monitors, and so on), sequences and virtual sequences, messaging facilities, an objection mechanism, reset solutions, scoreboard examples, and much more. This core functionality would define the scope and content of the verification methodologies used today, especially OVM. Later, the eRM was enhanced with module-to-system reuse, system verification components, software verification components, and the first commercial register package, vr_ad.

In response, in 2003, Synopsys announced the Reuse Verification Methodology library (RVM) for the Vera verification language. The content of the RVM library included base classes, messages capabilities, and packaging guidelines, but it did not include architecture guidelines, sequences, objection mechanism, and more. As a result, many users looked at RVM as a subset of eRM. RVM's main contribution to the verification user community was the callback solution, which was borrowed from software design patterns, customized for functional verification challenges, and which helped add procedural extensions to Vera and other object-oriented languages that lacked the aspect-oriented capabilities of e. Over time, RVM was converted to the SystemVerilog (SV) Verification Methodology Manual (VMM) and was the Synopsys proprietary library that supported the evolving SystemVerilog standard.

The Advanced Verification Methodology (AVM) from Mentor was introduced in 2006. The technical capabilities of this library mainly leveraged the OSCI SystemC Transaction-Level Methodology (TLM) standard, leaving open higher-level verification needs such as test classes, complex stimuli generation, configuration, extension via a factory, and more. While not a very high-level methodology, AVM was important, since it was the first open-source verification solution.

Cadence® acquired Verisity in 2005, and began developing a SV version of eRM. While many verification concepts mapped to SystemVerilog in a natural way, some required modifications and enhancements to what was available in other existing methodologies. The Universal Reuse Methodology (URM) was introduced in early 2007. In addition to being open source and using TLM communications, URM brought many of the proven capabilities of the eRM into the SV community. Proven solutions such as the eRM architecture and packaging guidelines, sequences, and others were migrated into the SystemVerilog URM. In addition, new solutions such as an abstract factory, configuration mechanism, test classes, class automation (copy, print, compare, an so on) and others provided a significant upgrade for SystemVerilog users.

In January 2008, Cadence and Mentor joined forces to release OVM. The fact that URM and AVM were already using TLM as the standard inter-component communication mechanism made the library unifications relatively smooth. Because URM has uniquely provided high-level methodology infrastructure, it was a logical choice to adopt the majority of that high-level methodology from URM into OVM. OVM's primary advantage over URM was that it was the first multi-vendor verification solution tested against more than a single vendor simulator. Given the early stages of the SystemVerilog language standard, the differing language implementation order between the simulators and the lack of clarity on some of the constructs, this was important to many users who wanted to keep their testbench vendor-neutral.

The collaborative OVM proved to be a very good solution. Not only did it provide an open-source library, examples, and documentation, it also set up a user community site, **www.ovmworld.org**, where OVM users could share ideas, ask questions and make their own contributions to the methodology. As a result, many companies chose OVM as the verification methodology for their teams. Cadence also extended OVM for integration of multi-language testbenches using e, SystemVerilog and SystemC. This was relatively easy since the abstract concepts of OVM were originated from eRM.

Here we are in 2010: The OVM 2.1.1 was chosen as the basis for the UVM standard, and now the era of UVM has begun. No more long technical comparisons between OVM and VMM are needed. No more obstacles for internal and commercial reuse stand in the way. The UVM is tested by all vendors and is an emerging Accellera standard. A **www.uvmworld.org** portal was created as a resource for both UVM and OVM users, and serves the entire SV community. To be sure, the work is not complete; there are still features to be added. Over time, and in a methodical fashion, they will be added to UVM to enable a better verification platform for the benefit of the industry.

This book covers the concepts and motivation from which the design and implementation of UVM was derived. We also share challenges and proven solutions that did not formally make it to UVM-SystemVerilog but that users frequently ask about and are likely to be added to the library in the future. This book is written primarily for verification engineers tasked with verifying complex IP blocks or entire system-on-chip (SoC) designs. However, much of material will also be of interest to SoC project managers as well as designers inclined or required to learn more about verification. See "How to Use This Book" on page 4 for further information about the audience and the content of each chapter.

1 What is the Universal Verification Methodology (UVM)?

The Universal Verification Methodology (UVM) is a complete methodology that codifies the best practices for efficient and exhaustive verification. One of the key principles of UVM is to develop and leverage reusable verification components—also called UVM Verification Components (UVCs). The UVM is targeted to verify small designs and large-gate-count, IP-based system-on-chip (SoC) designs.

The UVM has all of the verification features and capabilities your management may ask for to justify its use.

- It is **mature**—The UVM code is based on the Open Verification Methodology (OVM) library, with some modifications made on top of the proven OVM code.

- It is **open**—It is an emerging Accellera standard (and targeted for the IEEE) delivered in an open-source format.

- It is **compatible** and **portable**—It is tested to work on all major commercial simulators.

On the technical side, UVM delivers a common objected-oriented UVM verification component (UVC) use model and ensures that all UVM-compliant UVCs will inter-operate, regardless of origin or language implementation. Key features of the UVM include:

- **Data Design**—Provides, via methodology and library code, the ability to cleanly partition your verification environment into a set of specific data items and components. In addition, UVM provides many built-in capabilities that simplify activities such as textually printing and graphically viewing objects, hierarchically setting and getting data values in objects, and automating commonplace activities such as copying, comparing, and packing items. Together, this allows engineers to focus on what the objects contain and how they work, instead of the mundane supporting code.

- **Stimulus Generation**—Provides classes and infrastructure to enable fine-grain control of sequential data streams for module- and system-level stimulus generation. Users can randomize data based on the current state of the environment, including the design under test (DUT) state, interface, or previously-generated data. The UVM provides built-in stimulus generation, which can be customized to include user-defined hierarchical transactions and transaction stream creation.

- **Building and Running the Testbench**—Creating a complete testbench (verification environment) for an SoC containing different protocols, interfaces, and processors is becoming more and more difficult. UVM base classes provide automation and help streamline usage of the UVM. A well-defined build flow allows creation of hierarchical reusable environments. A common configuration interface enables users to customize run-time behavior and testbench topology without modifying the original implementation, which is key for facilitating reuse.

- **Coverage Model Design and Checking Strategies**—Enabling best-known practices for incorporating functional coverage, and physical and temporal, protocol, and data checks into a reusable UVC.

- **User Example**—Including a golden SystemVerilog example, which is based on an easy-to-understand, yet complete protocol called the XBus. The example includes tests, sequences, testbench structures, and derived UVCs using the methodology and base classes.

1.1 Verification Planning and Coverage-Driven Verification

The ultimate goal of the UVM is to help you find more bugs earlier in the design process. In over 14 years of working with customers who have been building verification environments, we have learned that the best way uncover unanticipated bugs is by using *controlled randomness*. In fact, we have seen more users have ultimate success in finding unanticipated bugs using controlled randomness than any other verification technique. In many technical engagements, we would work with users who had already verified their design and we would ask them, *"Will you let us try to find a bug in a week?"*

Most engineers agreed right away. But how can you find bugs in a system that you are not familiar with, that was tested for a long period of time by capable engineers who are much more experienced in the specific verification requirements of the project than you? As you can probably guess, the solution is *randomness!* We would consult the local engineers, abstract a protocol and system attributes that can be randomized, and let the random solver do the rest. Success was inevitable.

UVM also provides the best framework to achieve coverage-driven verification (CDV). CDV combines automatic test generation, self-checking testbenches, and coverage metrics to significantly reduce the time spent verifying a design. The purpose of CDV is to:

- Ensure thorough verification using up-front goal setting

- Eliminate the effort and time spent manually creating hundreds of tests

- Use run-time self-checking to simplify error analysis and debugging, and to receive error notifications as early as possible

The CDV flow is different from the traditional directed-testing flow. With CDV, you start by setting verification goals using an organized planning process. You then create a *smart* verification environment—one that generates random legal stimuli and sends it to the DUT. Coverage monitors are added to the environment to measure progress and identify non-exercised functionality. Checkers are added to identify undesired DUT behavior. Finally, simulations are launched when both the coverage model and testbench are implemented. Then a more complete verification can be achieved.

Using CDV, you can thoroughly verify your design by changing testbench parameters or changing the randomization seed. Test constraints can be added on top of the smart infrastructure to guide stimulus generation to meet verification goals sooner. Ranking technology allows you to identify the tests and seeds that contribute to the verification goals, and to remove redundant tests from a test-suite regression. Figure 1-1 is a graphical representation of this flow.

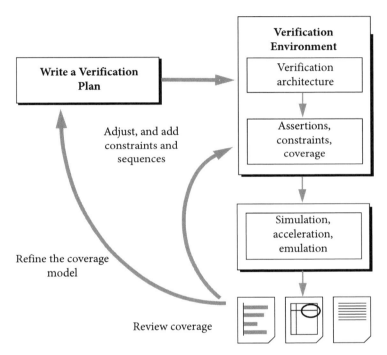

Figure 1-1   The Verification Planning and Execution Flow

CDV environments support both directed and automated testing. The recommended approach is to focus first on automated testing and let it do most of the work, before devoting effort to writing time-consuming, deterministic tests intended to reach specific scenarios that are too difficult to reach randomly. Proper planning can enable significant efficiencies and high visibility into the verification process. Creating an executable verification plan containing concrete metrics enables you to accurately measure your progress and thoroughness throughout a design and verification project. Using this proven method, sources of coverage can be planned, observed, ranked, and reported at the feature level. Using an abstracted, feature-based approach (and not relying on implementation details) results in a more readable, scalable, and reusable verification plan. You can find out more about this well-defined process and relevant automation capabilities in various vendor-specific materials.

1.2 Multi-Language and Methodologies

Multi-language design and verification is usually not a project or corporate goal, but it is a fact of life and it provides an opportunity for companies to share and leverage more proven verification assets. No one really starts a new project with the goal of writing a multi-language verification environment from scratch. But many users want to save time by leveraging available verification code without rewrites. Depending on whether you already have multiple internal VIP components implemented in multiple languages, or if you may run into this requirement in the future, you probably need to consider a multi-language methodology now. With the number of acquisitions and joint-development activities in the industry today, we have seen that many users who have never dealt with reuse before now find it a common and necessary activity.

UVM uses Transaction-Level Modeling (TLM) APIs to facilitate transaction-level communication between verification components written in SystemVerilog as well as between components written in other languages such as *e* and SystemC. Using the same API in all languages, it reduces the need to learn and bridge between facilities with different semantics. However, TLM is just the basics of multi-language (ML) interoperability. The UVM uses TLM for all standard languages. Examples of multi-language usage for both TLM 1.0 and TLM 2.0 are demonstrated in the Cadence OVM contribution and in Cadence product releases. Other facilities required for practical multi-language simulation include: a central configuration mechanism, traffic randomization and coordination, messages, and more.

1.3 What is Unique about This Book?

For some users, books are the preferred way to build knowledge; they provide an easy entry point for learning a topic. This book is based on many years of experience in multiple application domains and saves the users the expensive trial-and-error process to adopt a solution that works. It provides real-life tips and guidelines for successful methodology deployment, and suggests effective coding habits you can adopt from the beginning. The book does not cover the entire class library features, but focuses on the important ones that enable the concepts that make UVM users successful.

When users go through multiple deployments of UVM, guidelines that looked insignificant at first can make a big difference. For example, it is important to establish a standard directory structure for reusable components. While the nature of the directory structure is always arguable, experience shows that this seemingly-small matter can have a huge impact on team collaboration. Another example is the need for consistency. While some guidelines look less critical for a single user or small scale projects, they quickly grow into real pain points during collaboration, or when training new engineers.

1.4 How to Use This Book

A typical verification team consists of multiple contributors with different skill sets and responsibilities. The different roles of developers and environment users require different depths of verification knowledge. The organization of this user guide is based on the way a typical verification team divides its responsibilities:

- **UVC developers** create the reusable testbench infrastructure.
- Environment users (or integrators) write tests for and configure the testbench infrastructure created by the developers to meet project-specific verification goals. We also differentiate between **testbench**

integrators who instantiate and configure testbenches and **test writers** who create the tests on top of an already-assembled testbench.

In some companies the UVC developer, testbench integrator and the test writer are the same person. To gain a thorough understanding of UVM, we highly recommend that you read this entire book regardless of your individual role. However, the organization of the book allows environment users to quickly learn what they need to know without having to read and understand all of the methodology.

This book is structured as follows:

To Learn About ...	Read ...
The structure of UVM testbenches and components	Chapter 2 "UVM Overview"
The basics of object-oriented programming	Chapter 3 "Object-Oriented Programming (OOP)"
The mechanics and basic facilities of the UVM library	Chapter 4 "UVM Library Basics"
The basic concepts and components that make up a standard reusable interface environment	Chapter 5 "Interface UVCs"
A technology and development flow that expedites UVC development and usage	Chapter 6 "Automating UVC Creation"
The creation of simple testbenches—collections of reusable components with additional glue logic **Note** This is about initial interface UVC integration concepts and usage. Chapter 10 "System UVCs and Testbench Integration" covers the complete integration and how to leverage the register package and other testbench elements in a reusable way.	Chapter 7 "Simple Testbench Integration"
Various techniques for sequence and randomization control	Chapter 8 "Stimulus Generation Topics"
A methodology and automation to enable productive and reusable register-related verification logic	Chapter 9 "Register and Memory Package"
How to wrap device-specific logic and reuse it in block, subsystem and system integration	Chapter 10 "System UVCs and Testbench Integration"
An overview of both the short-term and longer term areas in which the UVM will likely be enhanced	Chapter 11 "The Future of UVM"

1.4.1   How to Run the Examples

The main example used throughout this book is the development of a testbench for a UART Controller device. This design and testbench are based on the UART module testbench from the UVM Reference Flow, available in the contributions area of **www.uvmworld.org**. The UVM Reference Flow applies the UVM to the block and cluster verification in a SoC design.

The smaller examples are also downloadable from **www.uvmworld.org** and are available in the contributions area, listed as UVM Book Examples. Each chapter has its own directory, and example numbers are on the files. The examples are self contained and easy to run. To run the examples with IUS, use the following command:

```
% irun -f run.f example-name.sv
```

Some examples provided in the example files are not fully described in the chapters. These are still a good source of reference. A complete list of examples is provided at the beginning of this book (see page xiii).

We encourage you to download the reference flow and examples, review them, run them, and experiment with them.

1.4.2   Conventions in This Book

This book uses typeface variations to help you locate and interpret information easily. These type variations are explained in the following table.

Table 1-1   Typographical Conventions

Typeface	Represents
courier font	The Courier font indicates code. For example, the following line is UVM code: `uvm_object_utils(uart_config_reg)`
courier bold	In examples, Courier bold highlights important lines of code to which you should pay attention. `// Control field - does not translate into signal data` **`rand apb_delay_enum delay_kind;`**
italic	The italic font represents either user-defined variables or titles of books. In this example, *example-name* is the beginning of the filename for your SystemVerilog file: `% irun -f run.f example-name.sv`
%	Denotes the UNIX prompt. For example: `% irun -f run.f example-name.sv`

1.4.3 Abbreviations

The following table documents the abbreviations used in this book.

Abbreviation	Definition
AHB	Advanced High-performance Bus
AMBA	Advanced Microcontroller Bus Architecture
AOP	Aspect-Oriented Programming
APB	AMBA Advanced Peripheral Bus
API	Application Programming Interface
ATM	Asynchronous Transfer Mode
AVM	Advanced Verification Methodology
BFM	Bus Functional Model
CDV	Coverage-Driven Verification
CPU	Central Processing Unit
DMA	Direct Memory Access
DUT	Device Under Test
*e*RM	*e* Reuse Methodology
ESL	Electronic System Level
FPGA	Field-Programmable Gate Array
HDL	Hardware Description Language
HVL	High-Level Verification Language
HW	Hardware
IES	Incisive® Enterprise Simulator
IP	Intellectual Property
LRM	Language Reference Manual
ML	Multi-Language
OOP	Object-Oriented Programming
OSCI	Open SystemC Initiative

Abbreviation	Definition
OVM	Open Verification Methodology; see Preface for more information
PCI-E	Peripheral Component Interconnect Express
RDB	Register Database
RTL	Register Transfer Level
RVM	Reuse Verification Methodology
SC	SystemC
SoC	System-on-Chip
SV	SystemVerilog
SW	Software
TCP	Transmission Control Protocol
TLM	Transaction-Level Modeling
UART	Universal Asynchronous Receiver/Transmitter
URM	Universal Reuse Methodology
UML	Unified Modeling Language
UVC	Universal Verification Component
VIF	Verification Interface
VIP	Verification IP
VMM	Verification Methodology Manual

2   UVM Overview

This chapter provides an overview of the structure of UVM testbenches and components. This chapter describes:

- How to use the UVM to create SystemVerilog testbenches
- The recommended architecture of a UVM verification component

2.1   UVM Testbench and Environments

A UVM testbench is composed of reusable UVM-compliant universal verification components (UVCs). A UVM-compliant UVC is an encapsulated, ready-to-use and configurable verification environment intended for an interface protocol, a design sub-module, or even for software verification. Each UVC follows a consistent architecture and contains a complete set of elements for sending stimulus, as well as checking and collecting coverage information for a specific protocol or design.

The interface UVC is applied to the device under test (DUT) to verify implementation of the design protocol logic or as a means to program the DUT. For example, in bus UVCs, the UVC can emulate a central processing unit (CPU) that programs a direct memory access (DMA) device. Module UVCs contain internal verification logic for a subsystem or a module and enable the subsystem verification in a larger system. UVM-compliant UVCs expedite creating efficient testbenches for the DUT, and are structured to work with any hardware description language (HDL) and high-level verification language (HVL), including Verilog, VHDL, *e*, SystemVerilog, and SystemC.

Figure 2-1, UVM Testbench Example, shows an example of a verification environment with three UVM-compliant interface UVCs and a module UVC. These UVCs might be stored in a company repository and reused for multiple verification environments. The UVCs are instantiated and configured for a desired operational mode. The verification environment also contains a multi-channel sequence mechanism (a virtual sequencer) that synchronizes the timing and the data between the different interfaces and allows fine control of the test environment for a particular test. For example, a virtual sequencer can ask the BUS interface UVC to execute the `configure_dut` sequence, and then ask external interface UVCs to drive traffic for some time while polling the DUT status through the DUT.

The repository block on the right illustrates a company UVC repository that can contain internally implemented or commercial UVCs which can be leveraged by all verification projects.

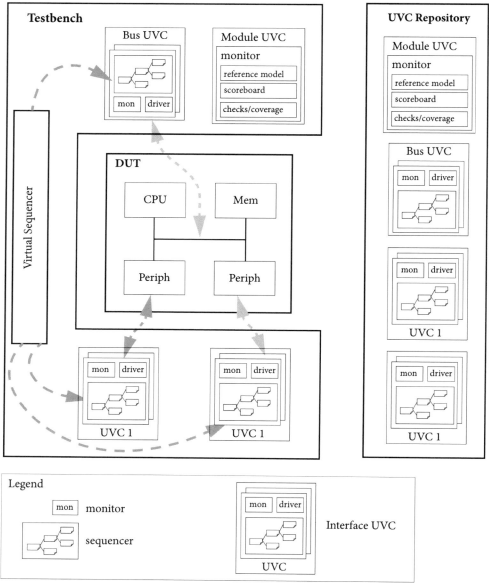

Figure 2-1   UVM Testbench Example

2.2   Interface UVCs

The interface UVCs standard structure includes the following elements:

2.2.1   Data Items

Data items represent stimulus transactions that are input to the DUT. Examples include networking packets, bus transactions, and instructions. The fields and attributes of a data item are derived from the data item's specification. For example, the Ethernet protocol specification defines valid values and attributes for an Ethernet data packet. In a typical test, many data items are generated and sent to the DUT. By intelligently randomizing data item fields using SystemVerilog constraints, you can create a large number of meaningful tests and maximize coverage.

2.2.2   Driver/Bus Functional Model (BFM)

A driver is an active entity which emulates logic that drives the DUT. A typical driver repeatedly pulls data items generated by a sequencer (advanced generator) and drives it to the DUT by sampling and driving the DUT signals. For example, a driver controls the read/write signal, address bus, and data bus for a number of clock cycles to perform a write transfer. (If you have created a verification environment in the past, you probably have implemented driver functionality.)

2.2.3   Sequencer

A sequencer is an advanced stimulus generator that controls the items provided to the driver for execution. By default, a sequencer behaves similarly to a simple stimulus generator and returns a random data item upon request from the driver. This default behavior allows you to add constraints to the data item class in order to control the distribution of randomized values. Unlike generators that randomize arrays of transactions or one transaction at a time, a sequencer includes many important built-in features. A partial list of the sequencer's built-in capabilities includes:

- Ability to react to the current state of the DUT for every data item generated
- Capture of the order between data items in user-defined sequences, which forms a more structured and meaningful stimulus pattern
- Enabling time modeling in reusable scenarios
- Support for declarative and procedural constraints for the same scenario
- System-level synchronization and control of multiple interfaces

2.2.4   Monitor

A monitor is a passive entity that samples DUT signals but does not drive them. Monitors collect coverage information and perform checking. Even though reusable drivers and sequencers drive bus traffic, they are not used for coverage and checking—monitors are used instead. A monitor performs the following functions:

- Collects transactions (data items). A monitor extracts signal information from a bus and translates the information into a transaction that can be made available to other components and to the test writer. Note that this activity might be performed by a collector component that is described below.

- Extracts events. The monitor detects the availability of information (such as a transaction), structures the data, and emits an event to notify other components of the availability of the transaction. A monitor also captures status information so it is available to other components and to the test writer.

- Performs checking and coverage

    - Checking typically consists of protocol and data checkers to verify that the DUT output meets the protocol specification.

    - Coverage is also collected in the monitor.

- Optionally prints trace information

Note   We recommend splitting the monitor activity into signal- and transaction-level activities. This is done by splitting the monitor class into a low-level collector class and a high-level monitor that does transaction-level coverage and checking. See more information about the collector in "Collector" on page 12.

On a protocol-by-protocol basis, an environment can instantiate a separate monitor per device (for example, a monitor per master or slave in an AHB bus), or a single bus monitor. A bus monitor handles all the signals and transactions on a bus, while an agent monitor handles only signals and transactions relevant to a specific device.

Typically, drivers and monitors are built as separate entities (even though they may use the same signals) so they can work independently of each other. However, you can reuse code that is common between a driver and a monitor to save time.

Note   To enable an agent to operate passively when only the monitor is present, do not make monitors depend on drivers for information.

2.2.5   Collector

In use models such as transaction-level modeling or acceleration, the signal-level activity is abstracted away completely, or placed into the accelerator box. In addition, advanced protocols include transaction-level state machines, which need to be checked and covered. When driving stimuli, the UVM enforces a good separation between the transaction level (sequencer) and the signal-level activity (driver). The collector enables a similar separation for the monitoring path. The collector is also a passive entity. It follows the specific protocol in order to collect bits and bytes and form transactions. An analysis port is used to send the collected transaction to the monitor, where coverage and checking are performed. While not mandatory, We recommend that you dedicate the monitoring path to a monitor and a collector. Figure 2-2, Monitor-Collector Interaction, demonstrates the interaction between the monitor and the collector.

Note   UVM 1.0 EA does not currently include a separate collector class.

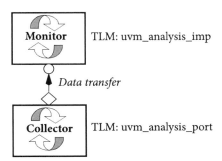

Figure 2-2   Monitor-Collector Interaction

2.2.6   Agents

Sequencers, drivers, monitors, and collectors can be reused independently, but this requires the environment integrator to learn the names, roles, configuration, and hookup of each of these entities. To reduce the amount of work and knowledge required by the test writer, UVM recommends that environment developers create a more abstract container called an *agent*.

Agents can emulate and verify DUT devices. They encapsulate a driver, sequencer, monitor, and collector (when applicable). UVCs can contain more than one agent. Some agents are proactive (for example, master or transmit agents) and initiate transactions to the DUT, while other agents (slave or receive agents) react to transaction requests. Agents should be configurable so that they can be either active or passive. Active agents emulate devices and drive transactions according to test directives. Passive agents only monitor DUT activity.

2.2.7   The Environment

The environment (env) is the top-level component of the UVC. It contains one or more agents, as well as other components such as a bus monitor. The env contains configuration properties that enable you to customize the topology and behavior to make it reusable. For example, active agents can be changed into passive agents when the verification environment is reused for system verification.

Figure 2-3, Typical Interface UVC, illustrates the structure of a reusable verification environment. Notice that a UVM-compliant UVC may contain an environment-level monitor. This bus-level monitor performs checking and coverage for activities that are not necessarily related to a single agent. An agent's monitors can leverage data and events collected by the global monitor.

The environment class (uvm_env) is designed to provide a flexible, reusable, and extendable verification component. The main function of the environment class is to model behavior by generating constrained-random traffic, monitoring DUT responses, checking the validity of the protocol activity, and collecting coverage. You can use derivation to specialize the existing classes to their specific protocol. This book describes the process and infrastructure that UVM provides to replace existing component behavior with IP-specific behavior.

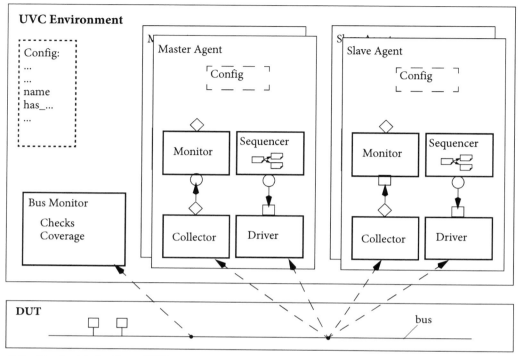

Figure 2-3 Typical Interface UVC

2.2.8 Testbench

A testbench is an environment that instantiates the rest of the reusable verification components. Interface, system, and SW environments are instantiated, configured, and connected in a testbench component. If the next generation of a device uses exactly the same interfaces of an existing device, the testbench can be re-applied and reused. But usually the testbench is specific to the DUT and to the project, and is typically not reused in vertical reuse scenarios. Refer to Figure 2-1 to see the integration of multiple UVCs in a UVM testbench.

2.3 System and Module UVCs

As already discussed, an interface UVC captures protocol-related verification aspects. But where would you place a device-specific set of verification aspects? For example, where would you place end-to-end coverage of multiple interfaces? Or a DUT-specific checker? For these purposes, a module UVC is needed. A module UVC is an environment that contains verification logic for a specific module or subsystem. It assists in verifying this subsystem, as it is vertically reused in a larger environment.

A system UVC makes use of interface, module, and software UVCs (UVCs that can dynamically control software execution). A system UVC might not contain its own agents, in which case it merely instantiates other UVCs and connects them to create a larger verification environment. System UVCs are targeted at system verification—for example, a CPU, bridge, or a cell phone. Relatively small system UVCs sometimes are called module UVCs. A system UVC typically makes use of other UVCs, including:

- Interface UVCs for connecting to the system interfaces
- Other module or system UVCs, which are subsystems or modules of the current system being verified

Any system UVC can be reused in a larger system verification environment. The system UVC architecture is similar to the interface UVC architecture and contains:

- A collector for signals that connect to the DUT.
- A monitor that is fed by the collector and other interface UVCs' monitors. Virtual (multiple channel) sequencers connected to the sequencers of the interface and subsystem UVCs. While interface UVC sequencers control a single interface, a virtual sequencer controls multiple sequencers and orchestrates the system-level scenario. Its sequence library defines multiple-channel sequences, which simultaneously control all of the system interfaces.
- A scoreboard—an untimed reference model that allows end to end checking. The scoreboard receives input from the interface UVCs and compares the DUT responses to the testbench prediction for the same input. We recommend using a scoreboard in the system UVC.
- An address map and register files. Most systems use memory and registers, which can be modeled using a register package. With UVM, you will have a pointer to the register database address map and register files.

2.3.1   Software UVCs

Verification poses requirements such as *How can you ensure that an interrupt occurred while visiting all the software states?* Or, *How can you steer the simulation to visit this specific HW/SW corner cases?* SW UVCs are elegant solutions for requirements such as these.

A SW UVC expands the coverage-driven verification (CDV) capabilities of a testbench to control and monitor software. The software UVC provides run-time control to the execution of driver routines. It can control the type, time, and parameters of routine calls, and can collect desired coverage for software state variables. Virtual sequences can be used to seamlessly control HW interfaces and SW execution. Coverage monitors can collect coverage for HW, SW and their associations.

Note   We do not cover SW UVCs in this book. If you are interested in additional information regarding these, please contact a Cadence representative.

Figure 2-4, Typical System-Level UVM Testbench, shows how interface, module, and system UVCs can be reused to compose a specific verification environment, including HW/SW co-verification. Later in this book we cover the details of how to develop this type of environment.

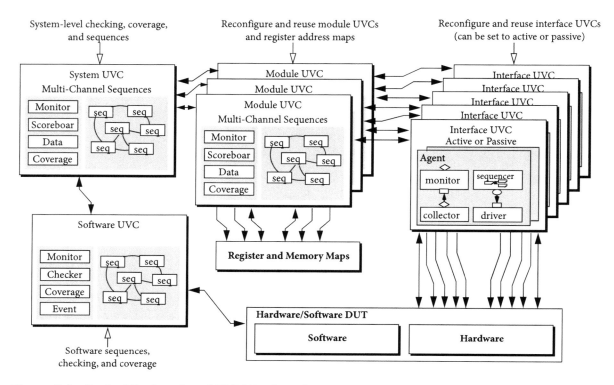

Figure 2-4 Typical System-Level UVM Testbench

2.4 The SystemVerilog UVM Class Library

The SystemVerilog UVM Class Library provides all of the building blocks you need to quickly develop well-constructed, reusable, verification components and test environments (see Figure 2-5). The library consists of base classes, utilities, and macros. Components may be encapsulated and instantiated hierarchically and are controlled through an extendable set of phases to initialize, run, and complete each test. These phases are defined in the base class library but can be extended to meet specific project needs. See the *UVM Class Reference* for more information.

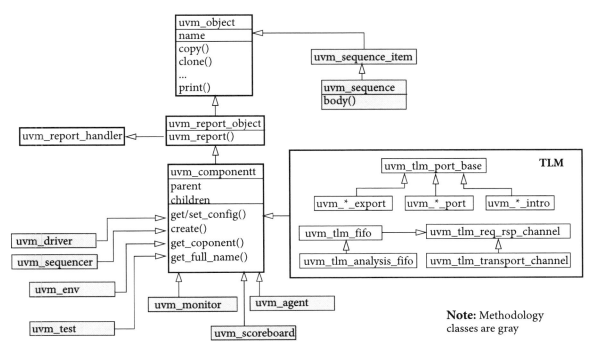

Figure 2-5 (Partial) UVM Class Hierarchy

The advantages of using the SystemVerilog UVM Class Library include:

- **A robust set of built-in features**—The SystemVerilog UVM Class Library provides many features that are required for verification, including complete implementation of printing, copying, test phases, factory methods, and more.

- **Correctly-implemented UVM concepts**—Each component in the block diagram in Figure 2-3 is derived from a corresponding SystemVerilog UVM Class Library component. Figure 2-6, Typical UVM Environment Using UVM Library Classes, shows the same diagram using the derived SystemVerilog UVM Class Library base classes. Using these base-class elements increases the readability of code since each component's role is predetermined by its parent class.

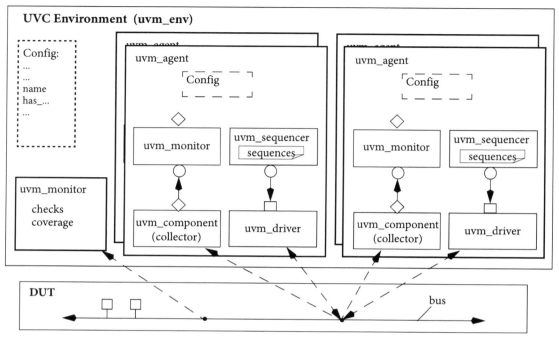

Figure 2-6 Typical UVM Environment Using UVM Library Classes

2.4.1   UVM Utilities

The SystemVerilog UVM Class Library also provides various utilities to simplify the development and use of verification environments. These utilities support debugging by providing a user-controllable messaging utility. They support development by providing a standard communication infrastructure between verification components (TLM) and flexible verification environment construction (UVM factory).

The SystemVerilog UVM Class Library provides global messaging facilities that can be used for failure reporting and general reporting purposes. Both messages and reporting are important aspects of ease of use.

2.4.1.1   The UVM Factory

The *factory* method is a classic software design pattern used to create generic code, deferring to run time the exact specification of the object that will be created. In functional verification, introducing class variations is frequently needed. For example, in many tests you might want to derive from the generic data item definition and add more constraints or fields to it; or you might want to use the new derived class in the entire environment or only in a single interface; or perhaps you must modify the way data is sent to the DUT by deriving a new driver. The factory allows you to substitute the verification component without having to change existing reusable code.

The SystemVerilog UVM Class Library provides a built-in central factory that allows:

- Controlling object allocation in the entire environment or for specific objects

- Modifying stimulus data items, as well as infrastructure components (for example, a driver)

Use of the UVM built-in factory reduces the effort of creating an advanced factory or implementing factory methods in class definitions. It facilitates reuse and adjustment of predefined verification IP in the end-user's environment. One of the biggest advantages of the factory is that it is transparent to the test writer and reduces the object-oriented expertise required from both developers and users. See "UVM Factory" on page 62 for more information and examples of the UVM factory.

2.4.1.2   Transaction-Level Modeling (TLM)

UVM components communicate by way of standard TLM interfaces, which improves reuse. Using a SystemVerilog implementation of TLM in UVM, a component may communicate, by way of its interface, to any other component which implements that interface. Each TLM interface consists of one or more methods used to transport data. TLM specifies the required behavior (semantic) of each method but does not define their implementation. Classes inheriting a TLM interface must provide an implementation that meets the specified semantic. Thus, one component may be connected at the transaction level to others that are implemented at multiple levels of abstraction. The common semantics of TLM communication permit components to be swapped in and out without affecting the rest of the environment. See "Transaction-Level Modeling in UVM" on page 52 for more information.

3 Object-Oriented Programming (OOP)

Unless you are an OOP expert, we encourage you to review this chapter and make sure you understand the terminology. While you can learn the UVM library and pick up the details as you go along, it is more efficient to build some OOP foundations before going through the verification methodology and the use model.

Many books have been written about OOP; this brief chapter covers only the basics of OOP. Our goals are to show the motivation behind OOP, introduce basic concepts, and demonstrate these concepts using simple SystemVerilog examples in a HW verification context.

This chapter includes:

- Distributed development environments
- Polymorphism in OOP
- Libraries and inheritance reuse
- UML block diagrams
- SW design patterns
- Why OOP isn't enough
- Aspect-Oriented Programming

3.1 Introduction

In the early days of software engineering there were epic struggles with project complexity, growth, and the challenge of managing large development teams. Object-Oriented Programming (OOP) introduced a revolution to the software community to help deal with these problems. OOP focuses on modularity, change tolerance, code reuse, ease of understanding, and distributed development. Most projects today use object-oriented concepts.

Since C++ introduced OOP, user experience has generated more knowledge about how best to make use of OOP. There is a lot of agreement and even more debate about OOP. *Which features should be encouraged? Does C++ define which features are object-oriented?*

As reuse and verification IP become prevalent in hardware verification, OOP is applicable. In fact, functional verification provides ideal conditions for reuse, as standard protocols, systems, and even tests and interesting sequences of transactions take advantage of OOP.

3.2   Designing Large Software Applications

Traditionally, a program is seen as a collection of functions. This works well for small applications, but hinders reusing a subset of the program or making use of distributed parallel development process in which different engineers own different aspects of the program. So how can we design a large application? OOP suggests using a "divide and conquer" approach in which applications are a set of related, interacting objects. For example, an application that emulates traffic would involve cars, drivers, and traffic lights. Instead of designing an application for the complete traffic system, we should focus on separate modules to capture cars, drivers, and traffic light operations. The same is true for a testbench or verification project. Instead of focusing on the complete application, we focus on data items or protocol-specific components that eventually comprise the testbench.

3.3   What is an Object in OOP?

An object is an entity that holds data and methods that operate on that data. Each object can be viewed as an independent little machine or actor with a distinct role or responsibility. In our traffic emulation example, the cars, drivers, and traffic lights are all objects.

3.4   Distributed Development Environment

One of the challenges in OOP is defining the objects and the interaction between them. This initial agreement is key for allowing individuals and teams to collaborate. The objects provide services via an agreed upon public interface (contract). Other objects can use this public API. The object's internal implementation can be independently developed and refined. Languages provide information-hiding facilities to limit object use to its public methods. Figure 3-1 demonstrates two developers working in an OOP environment, using an agreed-upon interface between separate objects.

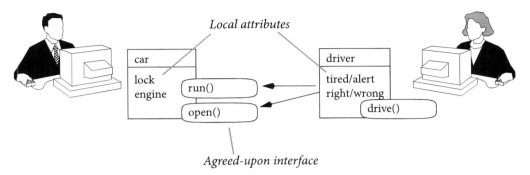

Figure 3-1 OOP Interface Objects Enable Parallel Development

3.5 Separation of Concerns

Can we use the same objects to create other systems? Or copy one object and leverage it in a different system? This requires building independent objects. No functionality overlap should exist between the objects. For instance, our traffic emulation example may also include a race track. In a typical race track, there are no traffic lights, no turn signals, and the cars are much faster. If the implementation of a car assumes the existence of traffic lights, it cannot take part in a race track system that has no traffic lights. In the same vein, a functional verification example can have a packet that should not send itself or commit to a specific protocol/driver. If it does, it cannot be used in an environment that requires a different driving protocol or protocol layering.

3.6 Classes, Objects, and Programs

A class defines the abstract characteristics (attributes) and behavior (methods) of an object. It is a blueprint that allows creating one or more objects of the same type. For example, there might be a class for cars that defines all of the things a car object can contain. Then, a particular make of car, say a ... *Plorsche*, is a sub-class (specialization) of the car class, with its own particular attributes above and beyond a general car class. Finally, a car object is a particular instance of a car with specific color and engine attributes, such as a silver Plorsche coupe. There could be many Plorsche cars that share these attributes; all these would be objects of the Plorsche sub-class, or specialization, of cars.

Objects hold run-time data and are used as a building block of a program. A program or application instantiates objects and triggers their interaction.

Figure 3-2 below illustrates how a program is made of class object instantiations.

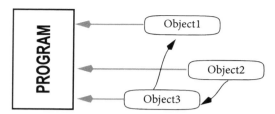

Figure 3-2   Program and Object Interaction

```
class car;  // class definition
   local lock my_lock; // internal implementation
   local engine my_engine;
   task void run();  // public interface
   task void open();
endclass: car

module top;
   car my_car = new; // object of instance creation
   my_car.run();
endmodule: top
```

Note   SystemVerilog classes are different from the Verilog module instances in their dynamic nature. The module instances, their number, and hierarchy are created at the time of elaboration in Verilog, and are static throughout the simulation. Objects can be created during run time upon request. This allows for the creation of modular and optimized data structures.

In functional verification, the build process of a testbench is dynamic, which makes it more flexible. It uses procedural flow control to instantiate the needed testbench structure. Dynamic objects are used to represent data items such as packets, frames or transactions that are created during run time, as required, and often take into account other environment variable values.

3.7   Using Generalization and Inheritance

Humans perceive the world using generalization. An abstract notion of a car means: four wheels, an engine, at least two doors, a steering wheel, and so on. This ability to abstract allows us to organize data and enables efficient communication. For example, you can say "I drove my car to work yesterday" and listeners would understand without the need for you to define a car, and talk about the specific car you drove, or the way that you "drive." These details are unnecessary to understanding the intent of your simple statement.

Object-oriented programming allows us to do the same thing with software design. You can define a generic class notion and, using inheritance, create specializations of that abstract class. A sports car could be a specialization of the generic car notion. As well as having all car attributes, it has more horsepower, better handling, and often attracts attention. A user can express the desired functionality—for example, drive() a car—without knowing the specific details of what driving means in a specific car.

Using inheritance allows objects with sufficiently similar interfaces to share implementation code. A parent class that should never be instantiated—meaning it exists only for modeling purposes to enable reuse and abstraction—is declared as a virtual class.

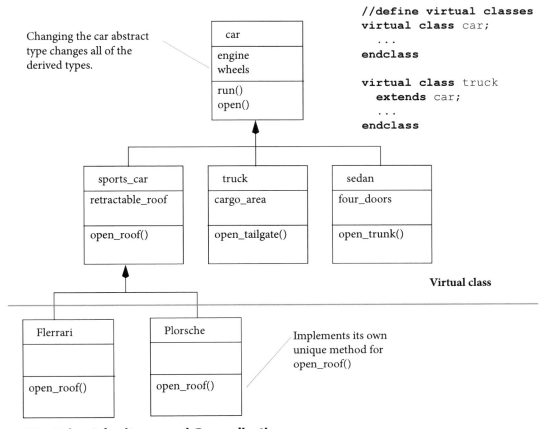

Figure 3-3   Using Inheritance and Generalization

Example 3–1   Generalization and Inheritance

```
virtual class car;  // note that car is a virtual class
   local lock my_lock;
   local engine my_engine;
   task run(); endtask
   task open(); endtask
endclass: car

virtual class sports_car extends car;
   task run(); … endtask;
endclass: sports_car

class plorsche extends sports_car;
   task run(); … endtask; // plorsche's run()
endclass: plorsche
```

3.8   Creating Compact Reusable Code

If you have an overlap between objects, consider creating an abstract class to hold the common functionality and derive a class to capture the variation. This will reduce the amount of code needed for development and maintenance. For example, request and response packets may have similar attributes, but the data generated in the request is collected at the response, and vice versa.

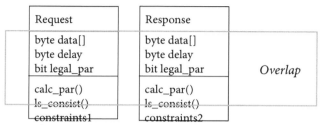

Figure 3-4   The Overlap between Request and Response

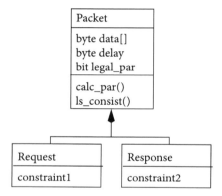

Figure 3-5   Using an Abstract Class to Model the Request and Response

3.9   Polymorphism in OOP

Programs may require manipulating sets of objects in a procedural way. For example, you might want to have an abstract handle to car, and in a loop call the `run()` method of all the cars in an array. Each car class has a different run() method implementation. The ability to execute run() on an abstract class and have the specific `run()` executed is called "polymorphism." The programmer does not have to know the exact type of the object in advance. Example 3–2 below demonstrates how Plorsche and Flerrari cars are derived from an abstract sport car class. Polymorphism allows the `print()` task of the program to hold a pointer to the virtual class array that may consist of both Plorsche and Flerrari cars, but execute the correct `print()` function for each item.

Example 3–2   Inheritance and Polymorphism

```
typedef enum {RED, BLUE, BLACK, WHITE} color_t;
virtual class sports_car;
  rand color_t color;
  virtual function void print(); // virtual keyword
    $display("I'm a %s sports car", color.name());
  endfunction
endclass: sports_car

class plorsche extends sports_car;
  virtual function void print();
    $display("I'm a %s plorsche", color.name());
  endfunction
endclass: plorsche

class flerrari extends sports_car;
  virtual function void print();
    $display("I'm a %s flerrari", color.name());
  endfunction
endclass: flerrari

module top;
  ...
  task print_all(sports_car cars[]);
    for (int i=0;i<cars.size();i++)
      cars[i].print();
  endtask
endmodule: top
```

3.10 Downcast

Imagine that a new car with an ability to fly is invented, while other cars cannot fly. A car user would not want to discover that their car cannot fly after they drive it into a chasm. An early warning is needed before you start driving to ensure that your car has the ability to fly.

In these kinds of situations, you need to get a compile time error message before the simulation starts. For example, you do not want an illegal assignment to break the simulation after two days of execution. Compilers force users to explicitly *downcast* a generic reference before using one of its subtype features or attributes. (The term downcast means going down in the inheritance tree.)

Note   In our car example, the user needs to explicitly state that the pointer holds a car with a fly() method. Assigning a generic handle into a specific handle is called downcast.

Example 3–3   Downcast

```
class flying_car extends sports_car;
  virtual function void fly();
    ...
```

```
      endfunction
   endclass: flying_car

   module top;
      task fly_if_you_can(sports_car cars[]);
         flying_car this_car;
         for (int i = 0; i < cars.size(); i++)
         begin
   // cars[i].fly(); a compile-time error!
            if ($cast(this_car, cars[i]))
               this_car.fly();
         end
      endtask
   endmodule: top
```

3.11 Class Libraries

A class library is a collection of classes to expedite system implementation. Instead of starting the implementation from scratch, a user can derive new classes from the library classes by customizing them, or simply instantiate and use them. Examples include mathematical libraries, graphical libraries and even verification-oriented libraries.

UVM has a class library. An important benefit of a class library is that it codifies best practices and enables standardization and reuse. A downside of using a class library is the need to learn the class library specifications. Though class libraries come with API specifications, it is a good practice to go through class library implementation and get a sense of the capabilities and suggested implementation.

Figure 3-6 below shows class library usage, as library classes are directly instantiated or derived and instantiated to build the final program.

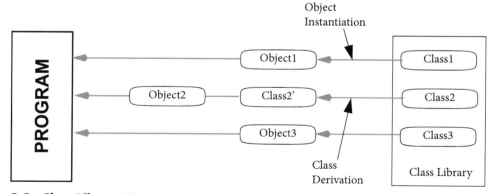

Figure 3-6   Class Library Usage

3.12 Static Methods and Attributes

Objects have attributes that hold their specific data and status. For example, one Plorsche status can be "being driven" while a different Plorsche can be "parked." However, SystemVerilog supports static attributes that belong to a class and not a specific instance. These attributes can be accessed even if no instance exists and allows multi-instance booking and settings. For example, you can count the number of instances of a specific class using a static attribute. You can also have static methods that can manipulate static attributes. The static methods cannot access non-static properties, as these may not even exist.

Example 3–4   Static Methods and Attributes

```
virtual class car;
    static int counter = 0; // shared by all instances
    static local function void increment_counter();
        counter ++;
        $display("creating item %0d ...", counter);
    endfunction

    function new();
        increment_counter(); // increment on construction
    endfunction: new
endclass: car
```

Note   Calling a static method does not involve a specific instance and is achieved by using the *class_name*::*method_name*(). For example, we can use the car's static method like this:

```
car::increment_counter()
```

3.13 Parameterized Classes

Parameterized classes are used when similar logic for different data types or sizes are needed. Classic usage of parameterized classes is for containers. The following example shows a container of different types of objects:

```
class stack #(type T = int);   // parameterized class syntax
    local T items[$];
    task push( T a ); ... endtask
    task pop( ref T a ); ... endtask
endclass

stack int_stack;              // default: stack of ints
stack #(bit[9:0]) bit_stack;  // stack of 10-bit vectors
stack #(real) real_stack;     // stack of real numbers
```

3.14 Packages and Namespaces

A typical application leverages many classes from multiple origins. Chances are that some type, class, or function names may collide and result in a compilation error. The cost of modifying class and type names for uniqueness can be substantial. Furthermore, the issue is more challenging when using encrypted code, such as for verification IP (VIP).

To keep the global namespace free of collisions, object-oriented languages add the package or namespace feature. This creates a different scope for each package definition. In cases where no collision exists, users can import all of the definitions into the joint namespace using the import command. If collisions exist and inclusive import is not possible, users can import specific types or use the fully-qualified type name of the class (a combination of the package name and the class name).

For example, let's assume that in our system, two types of car classes (sports_car) were developed, one by Brand A and another by Brand Z. Without packages, two classes called "sports_car" (one each from Brand A and Brand Z) cannot be compiled:

```
// file: branda_pkg.sv
package branda_pkg;
class sports_car;... endclass
endpackage: branda_pkg

// file: brandz_pkg.sv
package brandz_pkg;
class sports_car; ... endclass
endpackage: brandz_pkg

// file: race.sv;
`include "brandz_pkg.sv"
`include "branda_pkg.sv";
module race;
    branda_pkg::sports_car my_m5 = new; // use the full name of package::class
    brandz_pkg::sports_car my_convertible = new;
endmodule: race
```

In the following example, we import the package into a single module scope. This is possible because within the package, there are no collisions with the names. You can import all the symbols in a package or just use selected ones that do not collide.

```
// file: branda_pkg.sv
package branda_pkg;
class m5;... endclass: m5
endpackage: branda_pkg

// file: brandz_pkg.sv
package brandz_pkg;
class convertible; ... endclass: convertible
endpackage: brandz_pkg

// file: race.sv;
```

```
`include "brandz_pkg.sv"
`include "branda_pkg.sv"
module race;
    import brandz_pkg::*;
    import branda_pkg::*;
    convertible my_convertible = new; // use class name directly
    m5 my_m5 = new;
endmodule: race
```

It is critical to use packages for all reusable code to enable coexistence with other similar classes in other packages and prevent code modifications.

3.15 Unified Modeling-Language Diagrams

The Unified Modeling Language (UML) defines standardized graphical notation to create an abstract model of a system. It includes several diagram types to describe applications. It includes structure, behavior and interaction diagrams. The most important diagram in UML, and the only diagram we cover in this book, is for class diagrams. A class diagram is a type of static structure diagram that describes the structure of a system. It shows the system's classes, their attributes, and the relationships between the classes.

Class diagrams are used both for system modeling and design, and to understand an existing application. In a class diagram, a class is represented by a rectangle. The class name is on top, the attributes are in the middle, and the list of methods is on the bottom.

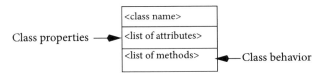

Figure 3-7   Class Box in a Class Diagram

Figure 3-8 shows a few UML graphical notations, relationships between classes, including containment of classes and derivation of classes from parent classes.

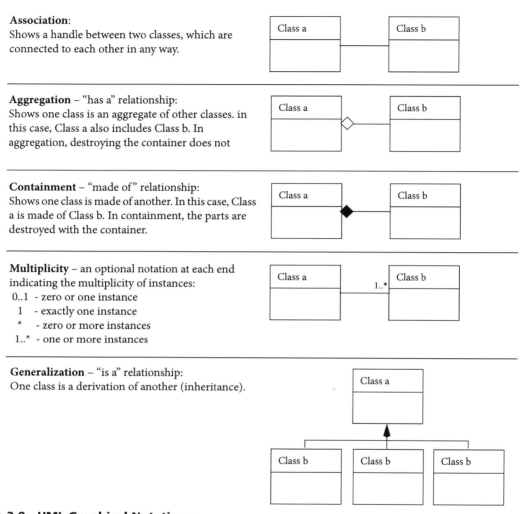

Association:
Shows a handle between two classes, which are connected to each other in any way.

Aggregation – "has a" relationship:
Shows one class is an aggregate of other classes. in this case, Class a also includes Class b. In aggregation, destroying the container does not

Containment – "made of" relationship:
Shows one class is made of another. In this case, Class a is made of Class b. In containment, the parts are destroyed with the container.

Multiplicity – an optional notation at each end indicating the multiplicity of instances:
0..1 - zero or one instance
1   - exactly one instance
*   - zero or more instances
1..* - one or more instances

Generalization – "is a" relationship:
One class is a derivation of another (inheritance).

Figure 3-8   UML Graphical Notations

3.16 Software Design Patterns

Creative solutions to software problems can produce both random benefits and consequences. Alternatively, already-proven solutions produce more consistent results. We are not against creativity, but most verification challenges require both creativity and common sense without the need to reinvent the wheel.

Design patterns are general, repeatable solutions to commonly occurring problems in software design. The book *Design Patterns: Elements of Reusable Object-Oriented Software* (often referred to as the "Gang of Four," or "GoF" book), published in 1995, coined the term "design patterns" and became an important source for object-oriented design theory and practice. These best known practices are captured in a template that includes names, challenge, code samples, and so on.

For more information, read the book *Design Patterns: Elements of Reusable Object-Oriented Software,* by Gamma, Helm, Johnson, and Vlissides.

SW Design Patterns: A Singleton Design Pattern

Many systems require system resources that should be instantiated only once. This could be a memory manager, global coordinators, or other system-level facilitators. The question is how to create a class with a built-in restriction to be instantiated only once? The singleton solution works by making the constructor function private to the class, which prevents the class from being instantiated. The only way to instantiate the class is by calling a static method that, on first call, allocates a local instance of the class and returns an object handle for the caller. Consecutive calls to this static method return the instantiated instance handle without allocating a new class. An example of a singleton in the UVM library is the reporting server that has a protected constructor to limit the creation of the server to a single instance.

3.16.1 Software Design Anti-Patterns

Anti-patterns, also called pitfalls, are commonly reinvented bad software solutions to problems. The term was coined in 1995 by Andrew Koenig inspired by the Gang of Four book. There are multiple reasons why bad practices are being used. In some cases, it involves lack of planning; in others, a perfectly good solution is used under the wrong circumstances, making it counter-productive. Like design patterns, anti-patterns have a formal template with the name, cause, implications and more. Anti-patterns also include recovery process (refactoring) to mend the misused practice. An example of an anti-pattern is "spaghetti" code—source code that has a complex and tangled control structure.

For more information, read the book *AntiPatterns: Refactoring Software, Architectures, and Projects in Crisis,* by Brown, Marley, McCormick, and Mowbray.

3.17 Why Isn't the Existing OOP Methodology Enough?

Mentioned above are some books that document knowledge from years of aggregated and proven experience in Object-Oriented Programing. So, why do we need more methodology? Most of the generic concepts are applicable and valid for the functional verification task. But functional verification introduces unique challenges and is different from software development. As opposed to programs that are released every six months, the result of functional verification is the final test, several of which may be created in a single day.

Consider the testbench in Figure 3-9 and the three tests that use it. Each test touches different aspects of the testbench. It may change the configuration, introduce different sequences, use constraints on top of the generated data items and more to achieve its goals. Object-oriented programming was not intended for such extreme reuse, nor it was taking into account the openness of classes to be further modified by tests.

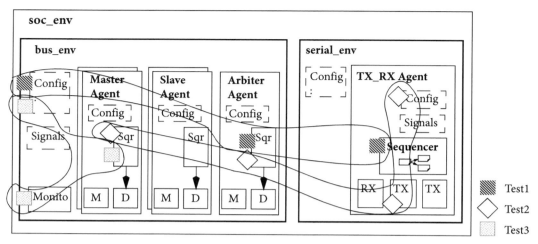

Figure 3-9   Unique Tests and Testbench Reuse in Functional Verification

3.18   Aspect-Oriented Programming

Recently, software design patterns have been criticized for suggesting complex recipes, as opposed to improving the tools or the languages. OOPSLA (Object-Oriented Programming, Systems, Languages & Applications), an annual ACM conference mainly in the United States, conducted a panel that was called "The Trial of the Gang of Four" on exactly this topic.

The *e* language was introduced by Verisity to solve verification challenges and uses this approach of built-in solutions rather than design patterns. Without expanding too much on the aspect-oriented nature of *e*, which is a superset of OOP, aspect-oriented programming offers simple solutions to many of the SystemVerilog language limitations. In SystemVerilog UVM, we use the factory solution, callbacks, field macros, configuration mechanism and much more; in *e* these are not required. Also, *e* allows other capabilities, such as coverage and enumerated-type extensions, much stronger modeling capabilities for data-item randomization, and other language features that significantly simplify the verification task. There were several efforts in the industry to provide limited AOP extensions to other HVLs, but these were limited and missed the target, both in understanding the challenges and the solutions. We can only hope that at some point, SystemVerilog will adopt these capabilities and simplify the verification effort for the benefit for the SystemVerilog user community.

Summary

Object-oriented programming introduces a way to handle the complexity of large software applications. It focuses on modularity, accommodating changes, and reuse that is key for functional verification. Knowing the theory and the motivation is beneficial, but there is no need to master the theory in order to use the UVM library. One of the advantages of using the UVM library is that it codifies the best verification practices into the library base classes, enabling you to do the right things just by following the recommended instructions.

4   UVM Library Basics

The UVM is first and foremost a methodology and collection of best practices for functional verification. As mentioned before, the UVM library is a capable and mature enabler of this high-level methodology. While the library classes and engines can be used in arbitrary ways, we highly recommend following the UVM as prescribed in the following chapters, as they suggest a proven recipe for successful verification.

This chapter covers the mechanics and basic facilities of the library. It focuses on the features that are needed for most verification environments and their use model.

Note   For simplification and educational purposes, the examples here do not necessarily follow UVM-recommended architecture or methodology.

The topics that are covered in the chapter are:

- Using the UVM Library
- Library Base Classes
- TLM ports
- Factory
- Messages and reporting facilities
- Configuration mechanism

4.1   Using the UVM Library

To use the UVM Library, a user needs to:

- Compile the UVM package top file `uvm_pkg.sv`
- Import the `uvm_pkg` into the desired scope
- Include the UVM macros

4.1.1 Hello World Example

The following example displays the message "Hello World!" to the screen:

```
1   // Compile the UVM package
2   `include "uvm_pkg.sv"
3   module hello_world_example;
4       // Import the UVM library and include the UVM macros
5       import uvm_pkg::*;
6       `include "uvm_macros.svh"
7       initial begin
8           `uvm_info("info1","Hello World!", UVM_LOW)
9       end
10  endmodule: hello_world_example
```

Lines 1-2: The comment is a reminder to compile the UVM library. The `uvm_pkg.sv` is the top UVM library file that includes the rest of the UVM files into a single SystemVerilog package. Note that SystemVerilog packages need to be compiled outside of modules or other scopes. We recommend using a command line to compile it, as packages tend to be shared by multiple scopes and you do not want to bind the compilation of the package to a specific scope.

Line 5: When the library has been compiled, the user imports the package into any scopes that use the library features.

Line 6: The UVM macros need to be included separately because they are compiler directives that do not survive multiple compilation steps. To avoid recompiling the entire library multiple times, they are included separately.

Line 8: The `uvm_info` macro is part of the UVM message capabilities that allow printing, formatting and controlling screen messages. In this case, we just print the message "Hello World!"

4.1.2 Guidelines for Using the UVM Library

- To prevent name collisions, avoid importing the uvm_pkg into the global scope. This is true for any package being imported.

- The top UVM files are typically enclosed by the following:

```
`ifndef <FILE_NAME>_SVH
`define <FILE_NAME>_SVH
... body of the file
`endif
```

This allows including the UVM library from multiple locations and avoids multiple declarations by compiling the files only once. We recommend using this technique in the user's UVC files.

- To run this test on the Cadence® Incisive® Enterprise Simulator (IES) with the UVM package that is delivered with IES:

```
% irun -uvm myfile.sv
```

To use an alternate UVM, use:

```
% irun -uvmhome $UVM_HOME myfile.sv
```

4.2   Library Base Classes

The Figure 4-1 class diagram below represents selected classes of the UVM library. These classes provide automation that can be leveraged by deriving user-defined classes and customizing their behavior. In addition to automation, the base classes provide an API that enables uniformity and thus reuse.

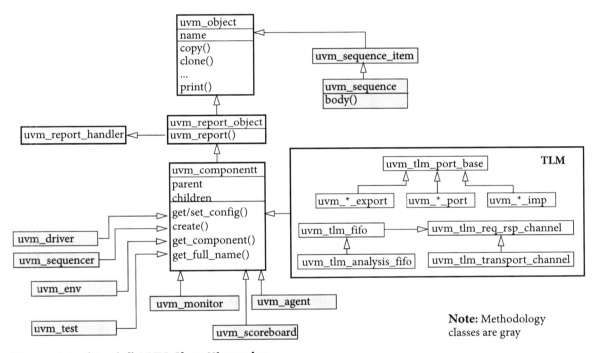

Figure 4-1   (Partial) UVM Class Hierarchy

Note   We do not show the uvm_transaction class in this diagram. While this class is still part of the library, it was voted to be deprecated by the Accellera TSC.

In the following sections, we discuss the uvm_object and uvm_component abstract classes.

4.3   The uvm_object Class

The abstract uvm_object class is the base class for all UVM data and hierarchical classes. Its primary role is to define and automate a set of methods for common operations such as create, copy, pack/unpack, compare, print, and record. Classes deriving from uvm_object must implement the pure virtual methods such as create() and get_type_name(). The code below demonstrates a simple example of an AMBA advanced peripheral bus (APB) transfer class definition that does not use the UVM object class definition.

Example 4–1   Non-UVM Class Definition

```
1  typedef enum bit {APB_READ, APB_WRITE} apb_direction_enum;
2  class apb_transfer;
3    rand bit [31:0] addr;
4    rand bit [31:0] data;
5    rand apb_direction_enum direction;
6    function void print();
7      $display("%s transfer: addr=%h  data=%h", direction.name(), addr,
   data);
8    endfunction : print
9  endclass : apb_transfer
```

The simple example above includes a `print()` method common to almost all transactions. Most data items require print, copy, compare, pack, unpack, and other utility functions. Leaving it up to the class developer to define the signatures of these services is an obstacle to reuse. The environment integrator will have to learn the signatures (names, parameters, return values) and behaviors of multiple classes coming from different resources. The UVM library solves this issue by introducing the `uvm_object` base class that defines the signature of these commonly needed services. All objects in the testbench should be directly or indirectly derived from `uvm_object`. The UVM SystemVerilog class library also includes macros that automatically implement the print, copy, clone, compare, pack, and unpack methods, and more.

Example 4–2 below shows the APB transfer class derived from UVM object.

Example 4–2   APB Transfer Derived from uvm_object

```
1  typedef enum bit {APB_READ, APB_WRITE} apb_direction_enum;
2  class apb_transfer extends uvm_object;
3    rand bit [31:0] addr;
4    rand bit [31:0] data;
5    rand apb_direction_enum direction;
6    // Control field - does not translate into signal data
7    rand int unsigned transmit_delay;  //delay between transfers
8    //UVM automation macros for data items
9    `uvm_object_utils_begin(apb_transfer)
10     `uvm_field_int(addr, UVM_DEFAULT)
11     `uvm_field_int(data, UVM_DEFAULT)
12     `uvm_field_enum(apb_direction_enum, direction, UVM_DEFAULT)
13     `uvm_field_int(transmit_delay, UVM_DEFAULT | UVM_NOCOMPARE)
14   `uvm_object_utils_end
15   // Constructor - required UVM syntax
16   function new (string name="apb_transfer");
17     super.new(name);
18   endfunction : new
19 endclass : apb_transfer
```

Lines 9-14: The UVM automation macros

Lines 16-18: The constructor is not mandatory in data objects. If the constructor is used, it must have defaults for all of the arguments.

4.3.1   UVM Field Automation

The `uvm_object_utils_begin(TYPE)` and `uvm_object_utils_end` macros are used to declare common operations declared for UVM objects.

- Implements `get_type_name()` which returns the object type as a string
- Implements `create()` which allocates an object of the specified type by calling its constructor
- Registers the `type` with the factory so it can be overridden elsewhere in the testbench (more details on this later)
- Implements a static `get_type()` method needed for the factory operation

The `uvm_field_*` macros include the given fields in implementations of the `print()`, `copy()`, `clone()`, `pack()`, `unpack()`, `compare()`, and `record()` methods for an object. The automation supports nested objects and user customization. The syntax of the macros is:

Syntax: `uvm_field_*(field_name, flags)`

The *field_name* must be an existing property identifier of the class and *flags* specifies the automation required for that field. Flags are numeric and can be combined using the bitwise OR "|" or plus "+" operators. Syntax exists for objects, strings, events, real numbers, queues, and different types of arrays.

A wide variety of field automation macros is available; they are described in the *UVM Reference Manual*.

4.3.2   uvm_object Definition Guidelines

- It is desirable to derive objects from `uvm_sequence_item`. Such derivation adds a few extra fields to the object, but allows the object to be randomized as part of a `uvm_sequence`.
- Use `UVM_DEFAULT` as the flag argument (instead of `UVM_ALL_ON`) for all `uvm_field_*` macros. This allows the UVM architects to add automation that by default might not be enabled by default. Other flags are used to remove undesired automation.
- Set the class name as the default value in the constructor argument.
- Do not forget to call `super.new(name)` as the first statement in every constructor declaration.
- There is a different macro for classes that have type parameters `uvm_object_param_utils*`
- `uvm_field_object` defaults to deep operations. If you are using a reference to another object, make sure to use the `UVM_REFERENCE` flag so that deep operations are not done.

Example 4–3 demonstrates additional usage of the field automation, including class composition and dynamic arrays. In this example, the `yapp_packet` has a `pkt_header` field.

Example 4–3   uvm_object Fields Automation

```
1   class packet_header extends uvm_object;    // Packet Header class
2     rand bit [5:0]  length;
3     rand bit [1:0]  addr;
4     `uvm_object_utils_begin(packet_header)
5       `uvm_field_int(length, UVM_DEFAULT)
6       `uvm_field_int(addr, UVM_DEFAULT)
7     `uvm_object_utils_end
8   endclass : packet_header

9   typedef enum bit { BAD_PARITY, GOOD_PARITY } parity_e;
10  class yapp_packet extends uvm_object;
11    // Physical Data
12    rand packet_header header;     // pkt_header class contains: addr, length
13    rand bit [7:0]  payload []; // dynamic array in the range [1:63]
14    bit      [7:0]  parity;     // calculated in post_randomize()
15    // Control Knob
16    rand parity_e parity_type;   // randomized to determine parity type
17    rand int packet_delay;
18    // UVM macros for built-in automation - These declarations enable
    automation
19    // of the data_item fields and implement create() and get_type_name()
20    `uvm_object_utils_begin(yapp_packet)
21      `uvm_field_object(header, UVM_DEFAULT)
22      `uvm_field_array_int(payload, UVM_DEFAULT)
23      `uvm_field_int(parity, UVM_DEFAULT)
24      `uvm_field_enum(parity_e, parity_type, UVM_DEFAULT)
25      `uvm_field_int(packet_delay, UVM_DEFAULT | UVM_DEC | UVM_NOCOMPARE)
26    `uvm_object_utils_end

27    // Constructor - required syntax for UVM automation and utilities
28    function new (string name = "yapp_packet");
29      super.new(name);
30        header = packet_header::type_id::create("header"); // allocation
    using the factory
31      endfunction : new
32    endclass : yapp_packet
```

Line 1: `header_packet` is derived from `uvm_object`

Line 21: If this were just a reference object, we would use the `UVM_REFERENCE` flag to avoid deep operations. The payload is a dynamic array and uses a special macro to print all the array items.

Line 24: Enumeration types syntax has an extra parameter:
```
`uvm_field_enum(<enum_type>, <field_name>, <flags>)
```

Line 30: Instead of using "`header = new("header")`" we use the factory. The `create()` implementation is achieved by the `uvm_object_utils` macros and allows extending the transaction in other projects or tests. For more information about this, see "UVM Factory" on page 62.

4.3.3   UVM Object Automation Usage Examples

The following example demonstrates the built-in automation features in the UVM library. It assumes that apb_transfer was defined as shown in Example 4–2.

Example 4–4   UVM Object Automation Usage

```
1   module automation_example;
2     // Import the UVM library and include the UVM macros
3     import uvm_pkg::*;
4     `include "uvm_macros.svh"
5     // Include the APB transfer class
6     `include "apb_transfer.sv"

7     apb_transfer my_xfer, tx1, tx2, tx3;

8     initial begin
9       my_xfer = apb_transfer::type_id::create("my_xfer");

10      if (!my_xfer.randomize())
11        `uvm_fatal("RANDFAIL","can not randomize my_xfer")
12      tx1 = my_xfer;          // tx1 and my_xfer share the same memory
13      // Create a new apb_transfer
14      tx2 = apb_transfer::type_id::create("tx2");
15      tx2.copy(tx1);          // Copies fields from tx1 to tx2
16      $cast(tx3, tx1.clone()); // Creates a new apb_transfer and copy all
17                              //   specified fields from tx1 to tx3
18      if(!tx3.compare(tx2))
19        `uvm_error("CompareFailed", "The comparison failed")
20      my_xfer.print();        // Prints my_xfer in a table format
21      my_xfer.print(uvm_default_tree_printer); // Prints in "tree" format
22    end
23  endmodule: automation_example
```

To use the UVM library, you need to import the UVM package and include the uvm_macros.svh.

The example creates, randomizes, copies, clones, and prints an apb_transfer using the example code above. The macros will automatically implement a print() method for a table format and a tree format:

Default table format:

```
----------------------------------------------------------
Name              Type             Size      Value
----------------------------------------------------------
my_xfer           apb_transfer     -          @560
   addr           integral         32        'hb2cbb864
   data           integral         32        'heba598d7
```

```
    direction          apb_direction_enum  1          APB_WRITE
    transmit_delay     integral            32               'h6
    ------------------------------------------------------------
```

Default tree format:

```
my_xfer: (apb_transfer@560)  {
  addr: 'hb2cbb864
  data: 'heba598d7
  direction: APB_WRITE
  transmit_delay: 'h6
}
```

The printout below shows a randomized yapp_packet from Example 4–3 on page 40. The packet includes a header class object and a dynamic array for the payload. These values are easily formatted and printed in the table below.

```
-------------------------------------------------------------
Name                  Type             Size        Value
-------------------------------------------------------------
my_packet             yapp_packet      -            @570
  header              pkt_header       -            @596
    length            integral         6            'h30
    addr              integral         2             'h2
  payload             da(integral)     48             -
    [0]               integral         8            'h7b
    [1]               integral         8            'he7
    [2]               integral         8            'h8c
    ...               ...              ...           ...
    [45]              integral         8            'hf3
    [46]              integral         8            'h78
    [47]              integral         8            'he1
  parity              integral         8            'h74
  parity_type         parity_e         1        GOOD_PARITY
  packet_delay        integral         32            'd8
-------------------------------------------------------------
```

The field automation macros will also implement a string print method, sprint(), which returns a string that can be used in a formatted display statement. The print formats are customizable; see the *UVM Reference Manual* for more details.

Note   The table printer uses the most formatting and therefore is the most expensive in run time. If your simulation will be printing a large number of transactions, it is a good idea to use the tree format.

4.3.4   Using UVM Field Automation

Using the UVM field automation is optional. Though users can implement the set of routines on their own, we recommend using the automation macros. Using the macros provide:

- Productivity—It takes time to implement the routines and the rich set of control options that they provide.

- Extensibility—Adding a field in case of nested objects requires understanding the UVC original implementation and sometimes the logic is tricky, as opposed to the single line of field declaration of the macros.

- Implementation consistency that is important for reuse—For example, if each developer implements their own format for the `print()` method, the poor integrator who uses multiple packages will have to analyze an inconsistent log file, where the field headers, values, radices, and structure are subject to the developer's imagination.

- Maintainability—Maintaining fewer lines of code simplifies the UVC developer's job.

- Code correctness—For large data objects, it is difficult to get all the logic for all the routines correct. A bug may show up at an inopportune time.

Keep in mind that these macros are an internal implementation of the library, are very mature, and should never be debugged by users. Debugging the default object `print()` methods is equivalent to debugging the internal `$display` function in the Verilog simulator.

In summary, we have seen users who initially were concerned about the usage of macros, but later became fans once they tried them, saying, "They just work!"

4.4   The uvm_component Class

All of the infrastructure components in a UVM verification environment, including environments and tests, are derived either directly or indirectly from the `uvm_component` class. The component class is quasi-static and should only be created at the beginning of the simulation (build phase). User-defined classes derived from this class inherit additional built-in automation.

Note   Typically, you will derive your classes from the methodology classes, which are themselves extensions of `uvm_component`. However, understanding the `uvm_component` is important because many of the facilities that the methodology classes offer are derived from this class.

The following sections describe some of the capabilities provided by the `uvm_component` base class and how to use them. The key pieces of functionality provided by the `uvm_component` base class include:

- Phasing and execution control
- Hierarchy information functions
- Configuration methods
- Factory convenience methods
- Hierarchical reporting control

4.4.1   Simulation Phase Methods

In HDL, such as Verilog and VHDL, static elaboration of the instances hierarchy occurs before simulation starts. This ensures that all instances are in place and connected properly before run-time simulation. In SystemVerilog, classes are instantiated at run time. This raises a few questions: *When is it safe to start traffic generation and execution? When is a good time to assume that all the UVC components have been created? and that TLM ports can be connected?*

While each developer can devise their own synchronization points for these operations, the SystemVerilog UVM Class Library provides a set of standard built-in simulation phase methods that allow synchronization of environments without up-front planning. These phases are hooks for users to include logic to be executed at critical points in time. For example, if you need checking logic to be executed at the end of the simulation, you can extend the check() phase and embed procedural code in it. Your code will then be executed at the desired time during simulation. All built-in phases are executed in zero time except the run phase. See uvm_phase documentation in the *UVM Class Reference* for more information on using built-in phases.

From a high-level view, the existing simulation phases (in simulation order) are:

- **new()**—While this is not a UVM phase, the component constructor is the first function to be executed when a component is being allocated. The uvm_component constructor includes two parameters: a string name parameter that holds the component name, and a reference to the component's parent. We recommend against using default values for constructor parameters of components. This ensures that the user provides meaningful values for the name and parent. The constructor signature should look as follows:

  ```
  class street extends uvm_component;
    `uvm_component_utils(street)
    function new(string name, uvm_component parent);
      super.new(name, parent);
    endfunction : new
  endclass : street
  ```

Tip   Some guidelines about the usage of the constructor include:

- You must define a constructor that takes a name and parent argument for all component types because the factory provides the name and parent argument when constructing the components.

- Do not use default values for the name and parent argument to the constructor so that the user is forced to give meaningful values for these parameters.

- Name components with short but meaningful names.

- For arrays of components, use indexes in their names: agent[*index*], which will form names like env.agent[0].monitor, env.agent[1].monitor, and so on.

- **build()**—The first phase of the UVM phasing mechanism is the build() phase, which is called automatically for all components in a top-down fashion. This method optionally configures and then creates a component's child components. We use this method for building child components and not the constructor, since the constructor is not fully polymorphic. Since build() is called top-down, the parent's configuration calls are completed before the child's build() method is called.

Some guidelines about the usage of build are:

- Every build() implementation should call super.build() as the first statement of build() unless the component is explicitly turning off automatic configuration. Calling super.build() updates the component configuration field values by invoking a function called apply_config_settings. Also though not recommended, a parent component may explicitly call build() on its children as part of the parent.build(). Calling the super.build() ensures that build() does not get called twice.

- Allocate all sub-components in the build() phase rather than in the constructor. This allows the component to be configured before it allocates the hierarchy underneath it. Also, the constructor is not polymorphic, so it is not possible for a derivative class to change the structure unless the structure is created in the build function.

- If a component is allocated after the build phase, UVM will generate an error message.

- Configuration settings for a components descendents should be done in the build method just before the component's children are created.

- If you are changing the structure of a component by overriding the build method, you cannot call super.build() as this will cause the super classes build to be executed. However, if you still want the behavior of uvm_component's build method, you can get this by calling uvm_component::build(). This effectively jumps over the super class' build method.

```
class my_derived_comp extends mycomp;
    function new(string name, uvm_component parent);
        super.new(name,parent);
    endfunction
    function void build();
        uvm_component::build(); //doesn't call super.build()
        ...//do other stuff
    endfunction
endclass
```

- **connect()**—The connect() phase is executed after build(). Because all sub-components of the environment are created during build() in a top-down fashion, users may rely on the fact that the hierarchical test/environment/component topology has been fully created when connect() is called. Use this method to make TLM connections, assign pointer references, and make virtual interface assignments.

- **end_of_elaboration()**— The end_of_elaboration() phase ensures that all of your connections and references are properly set up from the connect phase. Just before the end_of_elaboration phase is executed, UVM completes the TLM bindings so that, during this phase, all port bindings are established and can be examined.

- **start_of_simulation()**—The start_of_simulation() phase provides a mechanism to avoid zero time dependencies as components start up. Component initializations can be done in this phase so that when the components start their run phase, everything is properly initialized.

- **run()**—The run() phase is the only predefined time-consuming phase, which defines the implementation of a component's primary run-time functionality. Implemented as a task, it can perform time-consuming operations. When a component returns from its run task, it does not signify completion of its run phase. Any processes that it may have forked *continue to run*. The run phase terminates by execution of the global_stop_request(), calling the kill method, if time-out was set and reached, or if the objection mechanism was used.

- **extract()**—This phase can be used to extract simulation results at the end of a simulation run, but prior to checking in the next phase. This phase can be used to collect assertion-error count, extract coverage information, extract the internal signals and register values of the DUT, extract internal variable values from components, or extract statistics or other information from components. This phase is a function and executes in zero time. It is called in bottom-up order.

- **check()**—Having extracted vital simulation results in the previous phase, the `check` phase can be used to validate such data and determine the overall simulation outcome. This phase is a function and executes in zero time. It is called in bottom-up order.

- **report()**—This phase executes last and is used to output results to files and/or the screen. This phase is a function and executes in zero time. It is called in bottom-up order.

Although all of these hook methods are defined for `uvm_component` and its derivatives, you only need to implement the methods you will use.

Components do not need to use the `` `uvm_field_object `` macro for their child components. The component hierarchy is created by the fact that the parent object is always provided when a component is constructed.

Examples of the phases and hierarchy construction are provided below.

4.4.2 Hierarchy Information Functions

Because the component tree is static throughout the simulation, components are aware of their hierarchy location and can query for their parent class, child classes or their location within the hierarchy. Some of the functions that `uvm_component` class provides are:

- **get_parent()**—Returns a handle to this component's parent, or null if it has no parent

- **get_full_name()**—Returns the full hierarchical name of this object. The default implementation concatenates the hierarchical name of the parent, if any, with the leaf name of this object.

- **get_child**(*string_name*)—Returns a handle to this component's child, based on its name

The following example demonstrates the UVM simulation phases and component hierarchy information methods. It includes a composition of street, city, and state, and illustrates the `get_child()`, `get_parent()`, and `get_full_name()` capabilities. Allocating components using `new()` is discouraged. See more on this in "UVM Factory" on page 62.

Example 4–5   uvm_component Simulation Phases and Hierarchy Methods

This example illustrates a hierarchy of components that includes state, city, and street instances. Note the use of the constructor and the `build()`, `run()`, and `end_of_elaboration()` phases. The user implements the desired logic within the phases hooks. The `run_test()` call at Line 50 triggers the automatic phases execution. The example also demonstrates the hierarchical information functions `get_child()`, `get_parent()`, and `get_full_name()`.

```
1   module test;
2   import uvm_pkg::*;
3   `include "uvm_macros.svh"
```

```
 4  class street extends uvm_component;
 5    `uvm_component_utils(street)
 6    function new(string name, uvm_component parent);
 7      super.new(name, parent);
 8    endfunction : new
 9    task run ();
10      `uvm_info("INFO1", "I vacationed here in 2010", UVM_LOW)
11    endtask : run
12  endclass : street

13  class city extends uvm_component;
14    street Main_St;
15    `uvm_component_utils(city)
16    function new(string name, uvm_component parent);
17      super.new(name, parent);
18    endfunction : new
19    function void build(); // note that we allocate in the build()
20      super.build();
21      Main_St = street::type_id::create("Main_St", this);
22    endfunction : build
23    task run();
24     uvm_component child, parent;
25     string pr, ch;
26     child = get_child("Main_St");
27     parent = get_parent();
28     pr = parent.get_full_name();
29     ch = child.get_name();
30      `uvm_info(get_type_name(), $psprintf("Parent:%s  Child:%s", pr, ch), UVM_LOW)
31    endtask : run
32  endclass : city

33  class state extends uvm_component;
34    city Capital_city;
35    `uvm_component_utils(state)
36    function new(string name, uvm_component parent);
37      super.new(name, parent);
38    endfunction : new
39    function void build();
40      super.build();
41      Capital_city = city::type_id::create("Capital_city", this);
42    endfunction : build
43    function void end_of_elaboration();
44      this.print();
45    endfunction : end_of_elaboration
46  endclass : state
```

```
47  state Florida = state::type_id::create("Florida", null);
48  state New_York = state::type_id::create("New_York", null);

49  // Start UVM Phases
50  initial run_test();
51  initial #100 global_stop_request();
52  endmodule : test
```

Line 4: A street class definition. Since the street has no child components, a `build()` method is not needed. The `new()` and the `build()` methods call `super.new()` and `super.build()`.

Line 9: The run method prints an informational message.

Line 13: The city component contains a street child component.

Line 19: The street is created in the `build()` phase using the factory.

Line 26: From within the `run()` phase, the city calls `get_child()` to receive information about the street child component.

Line 27: `get_parent()` returns the parent component of the city that is in this case the state.

Line 28: `get_full_name()` returns the full hierarchical path of the parent all the way to the top.

Lines 47-48: Instantiation and creation of two states; these are also created using the factory.

Line 50: `run_test()` call to start the UVM phases.

The result of executing the code above looks like this:

```
--------------------------------------------------------------------------
Name                    Type              Size              Value
--------------------------------------------------------------------------
Florida                 state              -                @580
  Capital_City          city               -                @711
    Main_St             street             -                @712
--------------------------------------------------------------------------

--------------------------------------------------------------------------
Name                    Type              Size              Value
--------------------------------------------------------------------------
New_York                state              -                @638
  Capital_City          city               -                @776
    Main_St             street             -                @769
--------------------------------------------------------------------------
UVM_INFO @0: New_York.Capital_City [city] Parent:New_York  Child:Main_St
UVM_INFO @0: New_York.Capital_City.Main_St [INFO1] I vacationed here in 2010
UVM_INFO @0: Florida.Capital_City [city] Parent:Florida  Child:Main_St
UVM_INFO @0: Florida.Capital_City.Main_St [INFO1] I vacationed here in 2010
Simulation complete via $finish(1) at time 100 NS + 0
./uvm_st_ci_st.sv:75 initial #100 $finish;
```

4.4.3 uvm_top Component

There is a special component in UVM called `uvm_top`. This component is a singleton instance of the `uvm_root` type which is derived from `uvm_component`. The `uvm_top` component is responsible for the phasing of all components, and provides searching services (`uvm_top.find()` and `uvm_top.find_all()`) to allow you to locate specific components or groups of components in the verification hierarchy. The `uvm_top` component also provides a place to store global configuration settings; calling `set_config_*` from outside of a component is equivalent to calling `uvm_top.set_config_*`. This is true for messages as well; calling `uvm_report_*` (or `` `uvm_info/warning/error/fatal ``) from outside of a component is equivalent to calling `uvm_top.uvm_report*`.

4.5 UVM Configuration Mechanism

An important aspect of a generic reusable verification component is the ability to configure it for a desired operation mode. The UVM provides a flexible configuration mechanism that allows configuring run-time attributes and component topology without derivation or use of the factory. The configuration of component attributes is achieved via `set_config*` API that includes three functions:

```
virtual function void set_config_int (string inst_name,string field_name,
                uvm_bitstream_t value )
virtual function void set_config_string (string inst_name,string field_name,
                string value )
virtual function void set_config_object (string inst_name,
                string field_name,uvm_object value, bit clone = 1 )
```

Argument description:

- *inst_name*: A hierarchical path to a component instance. Use of wildcards is allowed as part of the instance name.
- *field_name*: The name of the field that needs to be configured. This field is defined in the instance.
- *value*: The value to be assigned to the field. Depending on the set_config call, it can be either `uvm_bitstream`, **string**, or `uvm_object`.
- *clone*: Valid only for set_config object and indicates whether a different copy of the object is provided or just a reference to the value object.

Properties that are registered as UVM fields using the `uvm_field_*` macros are automatically updated by the components `super.build()` method. These properties can then be used to determine the `build()` execution for the component. You can also use the manual `get_config_*` method to get the configuration values before the `build()` phase (for example, in the component constructor).

Note To influence the testbench topology, the configuration settings must be provided before the component build occurs.

The following example illustrates the use of the configuration mechanism. Instead of using class derivation, we use the configuration mechanism to set the state names and number of votes for each state.

Example 4–6   Configuration Mechanism

```
1   module test;
2   class state extends uvm_component;
3     string state_name;
4     int unsigned num_votes;
5   // Configurable fields must use the field declaration macros. Use the
6   // UVM_READONLY flag if the property should not be configurable.
7     `uvm_component_utils_begin(state)
8       `uvm_field_string(state_name, UVM_DEFAULT)
9       `uvm_field_int(num_votes, UVM_DEFAULT | UVM_DEC)
10    `uvm_component_utils_end
11    function new(string name, uvm_component parent);
12      super.new(name, parent);
13    endfunction : new
14    function void end_of_elaboration();
15      this.print();
16    endfunction : end_of_elaboration
17  endclass : state

18    state my_state1, my_state2;
19    initial begin
20      // configure BEFORE create
21      set_config_string("my_state1", "state_name", "GEORGIA");
22      set_config_string("my_state2", "state_name", "CONNECTICUT");
23      set_config_int("*", "num_votes", 7);
24      // create
25      my_state1 = state::type_id::create("my_state1", null);
26      my_state2 = state::type_id::create("my_state2", null);
27      fork
28        run_test();
29        #100 global_stop_request();
30      join
31    end
32  endmodule : test
```

Line 23: We used the "*" notation to configure the num_votes field. All states will use that configuration value.

The log information below shows the component configurations in the end_of_elaboration phase().

```
-------------------------------------------------------------
Name                  Type            Size          Value
-------------------------------------------------------------
my_state1             state           -                @16
   state_name         string          7             GEORGIA
   num_votes          integral        32               'd7
-------------------------------------------------------------
```

```
my_state2              state              -                    @18
   state_name          string            11            CONNECTICUT
   num_votes           integral          32                   'd7
------------------------------------------------------------------
```

The example below demonstrates a use for the `get_config_*` API. You can use this API if you do not use the automation macros, or you want to query the configuration settings before or after the `build()` phase. In the example we use the `get_config_int` to decide if the coverage group needs to be constructed.

```
1   module test;

2   typedef enum bit [2:0] {FLORIDA, NEW_YORK, GEORGIA, CALIFORNIA, MICHIGAN,
3                           TEXAS, MARYLAND, CONNECTICUT} state_name_enum;
4   class state extends uvm_component;
5     bit coverage_enable = 1;
6     state_name_enum = FLORIDA;
7     `uvm_component_utils_begin(state)
8        `uvm_field_string(state_name_enum, state_name, UVM_DEFAULT)
9        `uvm_field_int(coverage_enable, UVM_DEFAULT|UVM_READONLY)
10    `uvm_component_utils_end

11    covergroup state_cg;
12       coverpoint state_name;
13    endgroup : state_cg

14    function new(string name="state", uvm_component parent);
15      super.new(name, parent);
16      void'(get_config_int("coverage_enable", coverage_enable));
17      if (coverage_enable)
18        state_cg = new(); // covergroup must be new'ed in constructor
19    endfunction : new
20    function void end_of_elaboration();
21      if(coverage_enable) state_cg.sample();
22      this.print();
23    endfunction : end_of_elaboration
24  endclass : state

25  state my_state;

26  initial begin
27    set_config_int("my_state", "state_name", NEW_YORK);
28    set_config_int("my_state", "coverage_enable", 0);
29    my_state = state::type_id::create("my_state", null);
30    fork
31      run_test();
32      #100 $finish;
33    join
34  end
```

```
35 endmodule : test
```

Line 16: Since a covergroup can only be created in the constructor, we must call the `get_config_int()` method to retrieve the `coverage_enable` field. The other fields will be retrieved in the `build()` method.

Line 28: Sets `coverage_enable` to 0 for `my_state`. In this example, the coverage group will not be created.

4.6 Transaction-Level Modeling in UVM

Over two decades ago, designers shifted from gate-level to RTL design. This shift was driven by the development of standard Verilog and VHDL RTL coding styles, as well as the availability of RTL synthesis and implementation tools. A major benefit of moving to RTL was that it enabled designers to focus more on the intended cycle level behavior designs and design correctness at this level, and much less on gate-level considerations.

Transaction-level modeling (TLM) is a similar shift in abstraction levels that has been occurring for both design and verification engineers. With transaction-level models, the focus is on modeling distinct transactions flowing through a system, and less on clock cycle level behavior.

TLM has been used within testbenches for many years. In general, any testbench is at the transaction-level if it has components that create stimulus or that do coverage or checks using transactions rather than using clock cycle level behavior. To verify RTL DUTs, such testbenches use transactors (sometimes called "bus functional models" or BFMs) to convert between the transaction level and the RTL. In UVM, such transactors are also called drivers and collectors.

In TLM, transactions in the system are modeled using method calls and class objects. There are several significant benefits that come from modeling at the transaction level rather than at the signal level:

- TLM models are more concise and simulate faster than RTL models.

- TLM models are at a higher level of abstraction, and more closely match the level of abstraction at which the verification engineer or design engineer thinks about the intended functionality. This makes it easier to write the models and easier for other engineers to understand them.

- TLM models tend to be more reusable since unnecessary details which hinder reuse are moved outside of the models. Also, TLM enables use of object-oriented techniques such as inheritance and separation of interfaces from implementation.

The adoption of TLM is dependent on the availability of standard TLM modeling approaches, just as the adoption of RTL synthesis flows was dependent on the availability of standard RTL coding styles. Fortunately, in recent years, several important standardized TLM APIs have been defined. Two particularly prominent standards in the EDA and ESL area are the Open SystemC Initiative (OSCI) TLM 1.0 and TLM 2.0 standards.

The OSCI TLM 1.0 standard is a simple, general-purpose TLM API that is designed to model message passing. In message passing, objects (in this case transactions) are passed between components in a manner similar to packets being passed on a network.

In message passing as in packet transmission, there is no shared state between sender and receiver—rather, the only communication is contained within the messages that are passed.

The OSCI TLM 2.0 standard is designed to enable the development of high speed virtual platform models in SystemC. The TLM 2.0 standard is specifically targeted at modeling on-chip memory mapped buses, and contains many features to enable integration and reuse of components which connect to on-chip buses.

OSCI TLM 1.0 and TLM 2.0 are separate and distinct standards, each serving different purposes. Some people may assume that TLM 2.0 supersedes TLM 1.0 due to their naming, but this is not the case.

The UVM provides TLM APIs and classes which are based on the TLM 1.0 standard. This is because the general purpose message passing semantics of TLM 1.0 are well suited to the needs of transaction-level modeling for many verification components. TLM 1.0 is also well suited to modeling communication between different languages, for example between models in SystemVerilog, SystemC, and *e*. The TLM 1.0 interfaces in UVM can even be used to communicate with TLM 2.0 models in SystemC.

This section presents some of the key concepts for using TLM within UVM so that you can understand how to use TLM to construct reusable verification components. More detailed information on the various TLM classes in UVM is also available within the *UVM Reference Manual*.

4.6.1   Key TLM Concepts in UVM

4.6.1.1   Modeling Transactions

In UVM, a transaction is any class that extends from `uvm_sequence_item`. A transaction is defined by the user to contain whatever fields and methods are required to model the information that needs to be communicated between different components within the verification environment. For example, a simple packet might be modeled as follows:

```
1   class simple_packet extends uvm_sequence_item;
2     rand int src_addr;
3     rand int dst_addr;
4     rand byte unsigned data[];
5     constraint addr_constraint { src_addr != dst_addr; }
6     ...
7   endclass
```

A transaction typically contains sufficient data fields to enable a driver or transactor to create the actual signal-level activity that is required to represent the transaction data. A transaction may also contain additional data fields to control how randomization occurs, or for any other purposes within the verification environment. You can extend from transactions to include additional data members, functions, and constraints. Later sections show how you can use the concept of extending from transactions to accomplish specific verification tasks with minimum effort.

4.6.1.2   TLM Ports and Exports

The TLM API in UVM specifies a set of methods that are called by models to communicate transactions between components. In UVM, a port object specifies the set of methods that can be called, while an export object provides the implementation of the methods. Ports and exports are connected together via `connect()` calls when the verification environment is constructed, and subsequent calls to the TLM methods on the port will execute the TLM methods implemented within the export.

Example 4–7   Transaction from a Producer to a Consumer Using put

In UVM TLM, the `put` interface can be used to send a transaction from a producer to a consumer. A simple example of such a producer in UVM follows:

```
class producer extends uvm_component;
  uvm_blocking_put_port #(simple_packet) put_port;

  function new(string name, uvm_component parent);
    put_port = new("put_port", this);
  endfunction

  virtual task run();
    simple_packet p = new();
    ..
    put_port.put(p);
  endtask
endclass
```

As mentioned before, the `put` port is connected via a `connect()` call to a `put` export. The implementation of the `put` method that is called above is provided in the consumer component:

```
class consumer extends uvm_component;
  uvm_blocking_put_imp #(simple_packet, consumer) put_export;

  task put(simple_packet p);
    // consume the packet
  endtask
endclass
```

The result of connecting the port to the export and then calling the `put` method in the producer above is that the `put` implementation in the consumer will execute with the `simple_packet` object passed from producer to consumer.

TLM also include standard graphical notation to illustrate different type of communication. The `put` communication flow is captured in the block diagram below:

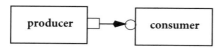

Figure 4-2   Simple Producer/Consumer put Communication

The TLM interfaces in UVM specify some simple rules that the producer and consumer both must follow. In this case, for the `put` interface, the rules are:

- The implementation of the put method may block execution until the put completes. Therefore, the caller of the put method must work properly if the implementation of the put method blocks execution.

- The producer is responsible for creating the packet transaction, and the consumer must not modify it (if it needs to it must copy it first).

By following these rules, it becomes possible to easily swap either the producer or consumer with alternative models that also adhere to the same simple TLM interface. The TLM API serves as a simple interface contract that promotes interoperability, much as standards such as USB and Ethernet do in the hardware world. By allowing easy swapping of models, UVM TLM plays a key role in enabling you to reuse models and meet verification goals, as we see in later chapters.

In the above example, there is a single process that runs in the producer, and when the put method is called, the flow of control passes to the put task within the consumer. The put method passes the transaction in the same direction as the control flow of the put method call itself.

In some modeling situations, it is necessary to have the transaction data flow happen in the opposite direction from the control flow of the TLM method call, because the consumer contains the process that requires the transaction data. A producer/consumer example in this case would instead use the get interface, and would be written as:

```
1   class producer_2 extends uvm_component;
2     uvm_blocking_get_imp #(simple_packet, producer_2) get_export;

3     task get(output simple_packet p);
4       simple_packet p_temp = new();
5       ...
6       p = p_temp;
7     endtask
8   endclass

9   class consumer_2 extends uvm_component;
10    uvm_blocking_get_port #(simple_packet) get_port;

11    function new(string name, uvm_component parent);
12      get_port = new("get_port", this);
13    endfunction

14    virtual task run();
15      simple_packet p;
16      ...
17      get_port.get(p);
18    endtask
19  endclass
```

As in the case of the put interface above, UVM specifies rules that the producer and consumer must follow while using the get interface:

- The implementation of the get method may block execution until the get completes. Therefore, the caller of the get method must work properly if the implementation of the get method blocks execution.

- The implementation of the get method must create and return a new simple_packet object to the caller of get.

The graphical notation for get communication scheme looks like this:

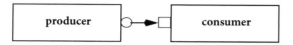

Figure 4-3   Consumer gets from Producer

4.6.1.3   Connecting Ports to Exports

In the example above, the port-to-export connection needs to be created by calling the connect() method. To make the connection, the user needs to invoke the connect method within the user-supplied connect callback in the parent component of the producer and consumer components:

```
class parent_comp extends uvm_component;
  producer producer_inst;
  consumer consumer_inst;
  ...
  virtual function void connect();
    producer_inst.put_port.connect(consumer_inst.put_export);
  endfunction
endclass
```

The general rule is that when connecting ports to exports, the connect method of the child component port is always invoked with the child component export as the argument.

4.6.1.4   Connecting Ports to Ports and Exports to Exports

In Verilog RTL, modules have ports which represent their signal level interface to the outside world. Verilog RTL modules also may contain internal structure such as child modules, which themselves may have signal ports. However, it is the ports that exist on the parent module which represent the interface specification of the parent module—any child modules and ports of the child modules are considered implementation details that should be kept hidden.

Similarly, in UVM TLM, it is the ports and exports of a given component that represent that component's TLM interface to the outside world. Any child components and ports and exports of such child components should be considered implementation details that should be hidden. Such hiding of internal structure enhances modularity of the overall verification environment and enables easier reuse and swapping of particular components.

But what if you have a port or an export on a child component within a parent component that needs to be made visible as a port or an export of a parent component? In this case, you need to connect a child port to a parent port, or a child export to a parent export.

Example 4–8   Connecting a Child Port to a Parent Port

```
class parent_producer extends uvm_component;
  uvm_blocking_put_port #(simple_packet) put_port;
  producer child_producer_inst;

  function new(string name, uvm_component parent);
    put_port = new("put_port", this);
    child_producer_inst = new("child_producer_inst", this);
  endfunction

  virtual function void connect();
    child_producer_inst.put_port.connect(put_port);
  endfunction
endclass
```

The general rule is that when connecting child ports to parent ports, the connect() method of the child port is called with the parent port as the argument.

Example 4–9   Connecting a Child Export to a Parent Export

```
class parent_consumer extends uvm_component;
  uvm_blocking_put_export #(simple_packet) put_export;
  consumer child_consumer_inst;

  function new(string name, uvm_component parent);
    put_export = new("put_export", this);
    child_consumer_inst = new("child_consumer_inst", this);
  endfunction

  virtual function void connect();
    put_export.connect(child_consumer_inst.put_export);
  endfunction
endclass
```

The general rule in this case is that when connecting child exports to parent exports, the connect() method of the parent export is called with the child export as the argument. Note this is different from the connection rule for child port to parent port immediately above.

4.6.1.5   Using uvm_tlm_fifo

In the original producer and consumer example above, there is a single process located in the producer, and the consumer does not contain any process—rather, the put method in the consumer is executed when put is called in the producer.

In the subsequent producer_2 and consumer_2 example above, there is a process in consumer_2, and consumer_2 has a get_port that it calls to get each packet.

You might encounter modeling situations where you need to connect components such as the first producer with components such as consumer_2. Such situations arise frequently because many TLM components require their own processes for modeling purposes, and yet they still must be connected together to pass transactions.

How can components such as producer and consumer_2 be connected? A very common way to connect them is to use the uvm_tlm_fifo component within UVM. The UVM uvm_tlm_fifo is a parameterized FIFO that has both put and get exports. The uvm_tlm_fifo is instantiated with a parameter that indicates the type of objects that are stored in the fifo, and the constructor for uvm_tlm_fifo has an argument that indicates the maximum depth of the fifo (which defaults to one).

Example 4–10   uvm_tlm_fifo Usage

```
class producer_consumer_2 extends uvm_component;
  producer producer_inst;
  consumer_2 consumer2_inst;
  uvm_tlm_fifo #(simple_packet) fifo_inst;   // fifo stores simple_packets

  function new(string name, uvm_component parent);
    producer_inst = new("producer_inst", this);
    consumer2_inst = new("consumer2_inst", this);
    fifo_inst = new("fifo_inst", this, 16);  // set fifo depth to 16
  endfunction

  virtual function void connect();
    producer_inst.put_port.connect(fifo_inst.put_export);
    consumer2_inst.get_port.connect(fifo_inst.get_export);
  endfunction
endclass
```

When this model runs, the process in the producer component creates and stores packets into the fifo, and the process in the consumer_2 component consumes the packets when it calls the get method.

Because of the fifo, the synchronization between the two processes is now decoupled. Either process may execute arbitrary delays, yet the usage of the fifo and the blocking put and get calls ensure that no packets are ever lost. In many verification modeling situations, this insensitivity to various delays within models and guaranteed delivery of transactions is desirable. The UVM TLM makes it easy to model such systems.

The figure below illustrates a fifo connection.

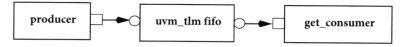

Figure 4-4   Using a uvm_tlm_fifo

4.6.1.6   Analysis Ports and Exports

The put and get ports described so far require that exactly one export be connected to them before simulation starts. If the ports are left unconnected, you get an error message from UVM that tells you to connect them.

Sometimes when you are constructing components such as monitors, you may need a port that can either be left unconnected, or connected to one or more components. This is because monitors are typically passive components in the overall verification environment, and do not directly affect the generation of stimulus or affect any synchronization with the DUT. Instead, monitors passively collect data transactions and pass them on to any other components which have registered an interest in the data transactions.

Analysis ports exist in UVM for this type of situation. Analysis ports are similar to regular TLM ports, but it is okay to leave them unconnected, and they also allow any number of analysis exports to be connected to them.

For those familiar with callbacks, analysis ports are essentially structured callbacks (callbacks with port connectivity).

An analysis port has a single void function `write()` that can be called with a single transaction argument. Every analysis port maintains a list of analysis exports that have been connected to it. When the write method of an analysis port is called with a transaction, the analysis port calls the write method of every connected analysis export with the same transaction. Because the write method is a function, it is guaranteed that the analysis port write will return without blocking. And, because the write method is a void function, the component containing the analysis port does not have any status returned after the write is done. The overall effect is that from the perspective of the component containing the analysis port, one does not need to know or care about any downstream components that may be connected to the analysis port.

Example 4–11   Monitor with an Analysis Port

```
class packet_monitor extends uvm_component;
  uvm_analysis_port #(simple_packet) analysis_port;

  function new(string name, uvm_component parent);
    analysis_port = new("analysis_port", this);
  endfunction

  virtual task run();
    simple_packet p = new();
    .. // reassemble packet here from lower level protocol
    analysis_port.write(p); // write the collected packet to the analysis port
  endtask
endclass
```

Example 4–12   Component with an Analysis Export

```
class packet_checker extends uvm_component;
  uvm_analysis_imp #(simple_packet, packet_checker) analysis_export;

  function new(string name, uvm_component parent);
    analysis_export = new("analysis_export", this);
  endfunction

  function void write (simple_packet p);
    // check the packet here
  endfunction
```

```
endclass
```

These two components can be instantiated in a parent component and the analysis port and export can be connected using the normal UVM TLM connection rules. And, as mentioned above, since the analysis port allows more than one export to be connected to it, it is okay to instantiate multiple components that have analysis exports and connect them to the analysis port within the `packet_monitor` component.

Sometimes the transactions that are being passed through an analysis port cannot be processed immediately by the downstream component. Instead, they may need to be stored for some period of time before they can be consumed. For example, this situation might arise in a scoreboard which needs to compare actual packets coming from a DUT versus expected packets coming from a reference model. In this case the packets coming from the reference model may need to be stored since the packets from the DUT will encounter various delays.

The `uvm_tlm_fifo` might seem like a good way to solve this sort of problem, by storing the packets until they are needed. However, `uvm_tlm_fifo` does not have an analysis export, so you cannot directly connect it to an analysis port. There is a good reason for this—any implementation of the write method in an analysis export must pass the transaction and return immediately, but this is not always possible if the fifo has a fixed size. UVM has the `uvm_tlm_analysis_fifo` to address this need. The `uvm_tlm_analysis` fifo has an analysis export, so that it can be directly connected to analysis ports, and it has an unbounded size so that writes always succeed.

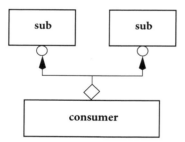

Figure 4-5   Analysis Communication

4.6.1.7   `uvm_*_imp_decl Macros

Sometimes there are situations where a component needs to have multiple implementations of the same interface. A classic example of this is a scoreboard that has to monitor multiple interfaces (for instance, two inputs and one output). When such situations arise, you must provide some means for dealing with the multiple interfaces. There are three potential solutions:

- Create a component for each implementation with that component having responsibility for the specific interface.

- If the transaction type is the same for each interface, use a single implementation; this requires that the transaction object provide some way of disambiguating where the transaction came from.

- Create additional _imp types for each port where each _imp type calls to a different implementation function.

In UVM, the third option is the simplest because of the `uvm_*_imp_decl` macros. These macros are used to create new implementation types which forward to different implementation functions. For example, if you use `uvm_analysis_imp_decl(_1)`, you will get a new implementation class call `uvm_analysis_imp_1#(type T)` which will have an implementation function called `write_1()`.

Tip Guidelines for using the `uvm_*_imp_decl` macros:

- Because these declarations create new class types, it is best to put the macros in some shared scope, such as a package.

- Use these classes in cases where a component really needs to have to implementations of the same interface (as with a typical scoreboard).

- Use generic, but meaningful names for the suffix. For example, `_inport1` and `_outport1` are reasonable names because they provide some information about the connectivity of the implementation.

- Start the suffix with an underscore so that the implementation functions will have the underscore separator (for example, `write_inport1`).

Example 4–13 `uvm_*_imp_decl` Macros

Below is a simple example of a scoreboard which uses the macros.

```
1    package my_analysis_imps_pkg;
2      import uvm_pkg::*;
3      `include "uvm_macros.svh"
4      `uvm_analysis_imp_decl(_inport1)
5      `uvm_analysis_imp_decl(_inport2)
6      `uvm_analysis_imp_decl(_outport2)
7      `uvm_analysis_imp_decl(_outport2)
8    endpackage: my_analysis_imps_pkg

9    package scoreboard_pkg:
10     import uvm_pkg::*;
11     `include "uvm_macros.svh"
12     import my_analysis_imps_pkg::*;
13     import mytx_pkg::*;
14     mytx q1[$], q2[$];
15     class myscoreboard extends uvm_component;
16       uvm_analysis_imp_inport1#(my_tx, myscoreboard) in_export_1;
17       uvm_analysis_imp_inport2#(my_tx, myscoreboard) in_export_2;
18       uvm_analysis_imp_outport1#(my_tx, myscoreboard) out_export_1;
19       uvm_analysis_imp_outport2#(my_tx, myscoreboard) out_export_2;
20       function new(string name, uvm_component parent);
21         super.new(name,parent);
22         in_export_1 = new("in_export_1", this);
23         in_export_2 = new("in_export_2", this);
24         out_export_1 = new("out_export_1", this);
```

```
25          out_export_2 = new("out_export_2", this);
26       endfunction
27       function void write_inport1(mytx t);
28         q1.push_back(t);
29       endfunction
30       function void write_inport2(mytx t);
31         q2.push_back(t);
32       endfunction
33       function void write_outport1(mytx t);
34         mytx t1, t2;
35         t1 = q1.pop_front();
36         t2 = t.transform1(); //execute some transformation function
37         if(!t1.compare(t.transform1()))
38           `uvm_error("SBFAILED", $psprintf("Expected: %s  Got: %s",
                   t1.sprint(), t2.sprint()))
39       endfunction: write_outport1
40       function void write_outport2(mytx t);
41         mytx t1, t2;
42         t1 = q2.pop_front();
43         t2 = t.transform2(); //execute some other transformation function
44         if(!t1.compare(t.transform1()))
45           `uvm_error("SBFAILED", $psprintf("Expected: %s  Got: %s",
                   t1.sprint(), t2.sprint()))
46       endfunction
47     endclass
48  endpackage: scoreboard_pkg;
```

4.7   UVM Factory

As part of the verification task and in order to follow the verification plan, a user may need to extend the generic verification environment behavior beyond its original intent. Unlike design, where specifications can capture the desired functionality in a complete and deterministic form, the verification process is fluid, dynamic and unpredictable. A reusable environment developer cannot foresee each and every corner case test for a certain project, or future projects. The global UVM factory is an advanced implementation of the classic software factory design pattern that is used to create generic code, deferring to run-time to decide the exact subtype of the object that will be allocated. Consider the following classes definitions that may be targeted for reuse:

Example 4–14   UVM Non-Factory Allocation

This first example uses a direct allocation using new(). After the example we explain why calling the new() is not recommended and limits reuse.

```
1   class driver extends uvm_component
2       `uvm_component_utils(driver)
3       function new(string name, uvm_component parent);
```

```
4           super.new(name, parent);
5        endfunction
6        virtual task drive_transfer();
7        ...
8        endtask
9    endclass: driver

10   class agent extends uvm_component; // bad example that uses new()
11       `uvm_component_utils(agent)
12       driver my_driver;

13       function new(string name, uvm_component parent);
14         super.new(name, parent);
15         // create the driver
16         my_driver = new ("my_driver",this); // using new()
17       endfunction
18   endclass: agent
```

For our discussion purposes let's say that the user wants to integrate an agent that is part of an interface UVC into a testbench and would like to specialize the drive_transfer() task implementation to print an information message. OOP recommends the user derive a new driver component, as follows.

```
1    class my_project_driver extends driver;
2      `uvm_component_utils(my_project_driver)
3      virtual task drive_transfer();
4         super.drive_transfer();
5         `uvm_info("MYINFO1","Finished driving transfer", UVM_LOW)
6      endtask
7      function new(string name, uvm_component parent);
8      ....
9      endfunction
10   endclass: my_project_driver
```

This new class extension is not enough to cause the desired effect, since the agent instantiates the previous definition of the driver and not the extended my_project_driver component. To fix this, the integrator is forced to extend the definition of the agent class and potentially other classes that instantiate the driver. Since the driver parent components definition needs to be extended, the interface UVC definition needs to be extended and we experience a ripple effect of many code modifications all over the testbench. UVM factory introduces an elegant solution that allows overriding the exact driver from outside the agent class. Instead of allocating using new(), the user uses a create() method, which uses a central facility that allocates the driver and returns a handle. A more reusable version of the agent that uses the factory is illustrated below:

Example 4–15 Using the UVM Factory

```
1    class agent extends uvm_component;
2        `uvm_component_utils(agent)
3        driver my_driver;
```

```
4       function new(string name, uvm_component parent);
5          super.new(name, parent);
6   // create the driver
7         my_driver = driver::type_id::create("my_driver",this);
8      endfunction
9   endclass: agent
```

When this code is created, the user can override all of the drivers in the system using:

```
set_type_override_by_type(driver::get_type(), my_project_driver::get_type());
```

Or the user can override drivers in the system by replacing a specific instance of the driver using:

```
set_inst_override_by_type("env0.agent0.driver", driver::get_type(),
        my_project_driver::get_type());
```

Factory allocation is not limited to components and is extremely important for objects and sequence items. The scenario in which data items need to be extend to follow verification plan requirements is further discussed in the interface UVC section.

To use the factory, these steps should be followed:

1. Register all classes within the factory.

    This is automatically achieved by using the utility macros `uvm_object_utils and `uvm_component_utils for objects and components, respectively.

2. Create objects and components using the create() API. This API is the same for both data objects and components.

    ```
    my_driver = driver::type_id::create("my_driver",this);
    ```

3. Use the type and instance override calls to override the base types with a derived types. Remember, you must set the desired type before you create the class

There are more capabilities to UVM factory, such as selecting the instances to be overridden using a wildcard expression string, providing a soft override that is ignored if other overrides exist, and much more. For more details please see the *UVM SystemVerilog User Guide*.

The example below illustrates the same example as above but with factory calls instead of hard-coded allocation.

Example 4–16   UVM Factory Usage

This example defines a state component that has florida and new_york sub-types. We demonstrate how the factory is used to control the allocated state using a create() call, and type overrides.

```
1   class state extends uvm_component;
2     `uvm_component_utils(state)
3     function new(string name, uvm_component parent);
4       super.new(name, parent);
```

```
 5     endfunction : new
 6     function void end_of_elaboration();
 7       this.print();
 8     endfunction : end_of_elaboration
 9   endclass : state

10  class florida extends state;
11  `uvm_component_utils(florida)
12    function new(string name, uvm_component parent);
13      super.new(name, parent);
14    endfunction : new
15  endclass : florida

16  class new_york extends state;
17  `uvm_component_utils(new_york)
18    function new(string name, uvm_component parent);
19      super.new(name, parent);
20    endfunction : new
21  endclass : new_york

22  state my_state1, my_state2;

23  // Start UVM Phases
24  initial begin
25    my_state1 = state::type_id::create("my_state1", null);
26    `uvm_info("INFO1",{ my_state1.type=", my_state1.get_type_name()},
                        UVM_LOW)
27    // set factory to allocate new_york state whenever a state is created
28    factory.set_type_override_by_type(state::get_type(),
      new_york::get_type());
29    my_state2 = state::type_id::create("my_state2", null);
30    `uvm_info("INFO2",{"my_state2.type=",my_state2.get_type_name()},UVM_LOW)
31    #100 $finish;
32  end
```

Line 1: Definition of a state base class

Lines 10-21: florida and new_york are derived from the state component.

Line 22: Declares two states handles, state1 and state2.

Lines 25-26: Allocating a state using the factory API state::type_id::create(...). Since no overrides were provided to the factory a state object will be allocated and printed in line 30.

Line 28: The factory is used to return the new_york sub-type upon a request to create a state.

Line 29: Create the state using the factory.

Line 30: Now the printed component name is new_york.

And the resulting printout is:

```
UVM_INFO ./test.sv(51) @ 0: reporter [INFO1] my_state1.type=state
UVM_INFO ./test.sv(54) @ 0: reporter [INFO2] my_state2.type=new_york
```

Note We cannot stress enough how important it is to use the factory to create both components and objects. For some users, the factory may be a new concept, but using the factory is simple, and the implementation is built in within the UVM library.

4.8   UVM Message Facilities

While developing or using environments, users will need to print information or issue error messages. A user may want to get trace messages from a suspect component or filter out undesired errors. Verilog's $display does not allow nonintrusive filtering and control of messages. Changing the verbosity on the command line or via Tcl run-time commands does NOT require that you recompile and re-elaborate the design to observe different trace messages. UVM reporting services are built into all components and are derived from a parent uvm_report_object class. The services can also be used in SystemVerilog modules, interfaces and programs. The mechanism provides a simple solution for most requirements and the ability to customize them with flags, parameters and user-defined hooks.

4.8.1   UVM Message APIs

The messages facilities have a routine interface:

```
uvm_report_info(string id, string message, int verbosity = UVM_MEDIUM, string
filename = "", int line = 0);
uvm_report_warning(string id, string message, int verbosity = UVM_MEDIUM,
string filename = "", int line = 0);
uvm_report_error(string id, string message, int verbosity = UVM_LOW, string
filename = "", int line = 0);
uvm_report_fatal(string id, string message, int verbosity = UVM_NONE, string
filename = "", int line = 0);
```

They also have a macro API:

```
`uvm_info(string id, string message, int verbosity)
`uvm_warning(string id, string message)
`uvm_error(string id, string message)
`uvm_fatal(string id, string message)
```

The macro API is recommended because it checks if a message needs to be printed before executing expensive string manipulation. The macros also automatically add the filename and line numbers.

The string id is a tag that can be used for filtering. The verbosity level is an integer value to indicate the relative importance of the message. If the value is smaller or equal to the current verbosity level, then the report is issued. For example, if the verbosity is set to 100, all messages coded with 101 and higher will not print.

An enumerated type called uvm_verbosity provides several standard verbosity levels including:
UVM_NONE=0, UVM_LOW=100, UVM_MEDIUM=200, UVM_HIGH=300, UVM_FULL=400, UVM_DEBUG=500.

Note   When using the message macros, verbosity is ignored for warnings, errors and fatal errors. This prevents verbosity modifications from hiding bugs. The verbosity parameter is retained in the routines for backward compatibility purposes. If a warning, error, or fatal error needs to be turned off, this can be done by setting the action to UVM_NOACTION. For example, to turn off a specific message in component mycomp that is an UVM_ERROR with id MYTAG, you might do the following in a test or testbench:

```
mycomp.set_report_severity_id_action(UVM_ERROR, "MYTAG", UVM_NO_ACTION);
```

4.8.2   Guidelines for Using UVM Messages

- The run-time differences between using the macro API and the routines has proven to be significant in many testbenches. Use the macros API whenever you can.

- To enable easy message control of a testbench that contains multiple components, use only the enumerated values. Also use this standard interpretation of verbosity levels:

  - UVM_NONE—For non-maskable and critical message

  - UVM_LOW—For maskable messages that are printed only rarely during simulation (for example, when is reset done)

  - UVM_MEDIUM—Short messages that happen once per data item or sequence

  - UVM_HIGH—More detailed per-data-item information, including printing the actual value of the packet and printing sub-transaction details

  - UVM_FULL—Anything else, including message prints in specific methods (just to follow the algorithm of that method)

  - UVM_DEBUG—Debug mode with internal developer debug messages

- For information messages we recommend using the get_type_name() as the id argument. It is easy to see how many messages came from the different components during a simulation run, and it can be a quick sanity check that all components operated properly. This usage also allows filtering by type.

- Sometimes users need to ignore warnings for a particular project needs or a certain test requirements. For malfunction-related reports (warnings, errors, and fatals), use a unique name as the id argument. This allows fine control of ignoring errors.

4.8.3   Modifying Message Verbosity

There are three ways to change the verbosity for debug:

- Command-line argument (simulator-dependent). For example, use:
  ```
  % irun … +UVM_VERBOSITY=UVM_NONE
  ```
- Procedurally in SystemVerilog. For example:
  ```
  set_report_verbosity_level_hier(UVM_MEDIUM);
  ```

- Tcl (run time). For example, use:

```
uvm_message uvm_test_top.uart_ctrl_tb.apb0 UVM_FULL
```

Note   Changing the verbosity on the command line or by way of Tcl run-time commands does *not* require that you recompile and re-elaborate the design to see different trace message recording.

You can use the same message macros in the context of non class-based code too. The following example illustrates this in the context of an initial block inside a module:

Example 4–17   Using the Info Message within Modules

```
1   module test;
2     import uvm_pkg::*;
3     `include "uvm_macros.svh"

4     initial begin
5       uvm_report_info("TEST", "I am in the top-level test", UVM_NONE);
6       `uvm_info("TEST", "I am in the top-level test", UVM_NONE)
7     end
8   endmodule : test
```

The output of the previous snippet looks like this:

```
----------------------------------------------------------------------
UVM_INFO @ 0: reporter [TEST] I am in the top-level test
UVM_INFO ./messages.sv(13) @ 0: reporter [TEST] I am in the top-level test
----------------------------------------------------------------------
```

4.9   Callbacks

Callbacks, as with the factory, are a way to effect or monitor an environment from the outside. Callbacks are different from the factory in that an object developer must insert calls to specific callback methods/tasks inside of this class at points where he deems it appropriate for the user to take action. The callback users can then create their derived callback class and attach to one or more desired objects.

4.9.1   Using Callbacks

The use model of callbacks is broken into two parts, the developer piece and the user piece.

4.9.1.1   Developer

The first thing the developer must do is decide on an interface to make available. Often the callback function will include a reference to the object that is issuing the callback. And, it will include other information that is necessary for the callback user.

Using our example from "Hierarchy Information Functions" on page 46, we may want to add a callback to the city class which gets executed before it prints its parent/child information. To do this we would do something like:

```
1   typedef class city;
2   virtual class city_cbs extends uvm_callback;
3     function new(string name="city_cb");
4       super.new(name);
5     endfunction
6     pure virtual function void pre_info (city c);
7   endclass
```

Next, the developer must register their callback type with the type which will use the callback. This registration enables UVM to do type checking when a user tries to add a callback to a specific object. If the registration is left out, the user will get a warning from UVM that the callback type was not registered with the object type they are attempting to add it to.

```
1   class city extends uvm_component;
2     `uvm_register_cb(city, city_cbs)
3     ...
4   endclass
```

Note   If the type using the callback is derived from a class which also used callbacks, you must use the `uvm_set_super_type macro so that UVM is aware of the class hierarchy and can properly manage the callbacks.

Finally, the developer inserts a call to the callback functions in their code. A utility macro, `uvm_do_callbacks, is provided to simplify the process. A developer may choose to manually iterate the callbacks using the uvm_callback_iter class as well; this provides ultimate flexibility as to how the callbacks are executed.

```
1   task run();
2     uvm_component child, parent;
3     string pr, ch;
4     child = get_child("Main_St");
5     parent = get_parent();
6     pr = parent.get_full_name();
7     ch = child.get_name();
8     `uvm_do_callbacks(city, city_cbs, pre_info(this))
9     `uvm_info(get_type_name(), $psprintf("Parent:%s Child:%s", pr, ch),
    UVM_LOW)
10    endtask : run
```

For convenience, the developer should also create a callback typedef.

```
typedef uvm_callbacks#(city, city_cbs) city_cb;
```

4.9.1.2   User

Now that a callback class has been defined and used within an object, a user may use the callback as necessary. For the end user, the first thing to do is to extend the callback class with the desired behavior.

```
1  class my_city_cb extends city_cbs;
2    function new(string name="my_city_cb");
3      super.new(name);
4    endfunction
5    virtual function void pre_info(city c);
6      `uvm_info("my_city_cb", $psprintf("pre_info called for city %s",
   c.get_full_name()), UVM_LOW)
7    endfunction
8  endclass
```

Next, the user attaches the callback to a specific instance or to all instances of the type. A null handle specifies a type-wide callback.

```
1  my_city_cb cb = new;
2  initial begin
3    city_cb::add(null, cb);
4    run_test();
5  end
```

Running this code with the previous example results in the following:

```
UVM_INFO @ 0: reporter [my_city_cb] pre_info called for city
New_York.capital_city
UVM_INFO @ 0: New_York.capital_city [city] Parent:New_York Child:Main_St
UVM_INFO @ 0: New_York.capital_city.Main_St [INFO1] I vacationed here in 2010
UVM_INFO @ 0: reporter [my_city_cb] pre_info called for city
Florida.capital_city
UVM_INFO @ 0: Florida.capital_city [city] Parent:Florida Child:Main_St
UVM_INFO @ 0: Florida.capital_city.Main_St [INFO1] I vacationed here in 2010
```

4.9.2   Guidelines for Using Callbacks

4.9.2.1   Developer Guidelines

- Create an abstract (virtual) class for the callbacks with pure virtual methods for the interface.

- Pass a reference of the object making the callback call.

- Take care when passing references to data objects, as they can be changed (this is okay as long as that is your intent).

- Provide a typedef for the uvm_callbacks#(T,CB) class with the name T_cb.

- Use the `uvm_set_super_type macro if a super class utilizes callbacks.

4.9.2.2   User Guidelines

- Create a callback implementation class which implements all of the pure virtual methods in the callback class.

- Allocate a new callback object for each callback you add.

- Use type-wide callbacks if you want your callback to effect all types and instance specific callbacks if you only want to affect specific instances of an object.

Note   Instance-specific callbacks cause the instance handle of the object to be stored in a queue until all objects are removed. Care must be taken when associating instance specific callbacks with transient data objects because those data objects cannot be garbage collected until all references are removed. For callbacks to transient objects, prefer using type-wide callbacks if they meet your needs.

4.9.3   The Report Catcher Built-In Callback

UVM has a handful of built-in callbacks. One such callback is the report catcher. The report catcher callback is called just before a message is to be issued. In this callback, it is possible to catch a message so that it is not processed further; modify the message type (demote errors, and so forth), or modify the message text.

Below is an example of how a report catcher can be used to demote a specific type of error message to an info message. This may be done in a test that is specifically attempting to create an error condition.

```
1   module test;
2     import uvm_pkg::*;
3     `include "uvm_macros.svh"

4     class my_catcher extends uvm_report_catcher;
5       virtual function action_e catch();
6         if(get_severity() == UVM_ERROR && get_id() == "MYID") begin
7           set_severity(UVM_INFO);
8         end
9         return THROW;
10      endfunction
11    endclass

12    my_catcher catcher = new;
13    initial begin
14      uvm_report_cb::add(null,catcher);
15      `uvm_error("MYID", "This one should be demoted")
16      catcher.callback_mode(0);  //disable the catcher
17      `uvm_error("MYID", "This one should not be demoted")
18    end
19  endmodule
```

This example results in the following output:

```
UVM_INFO @ 0: reporter [MYID] This one should be demoted
```

```
UVM_ERROR @ 0: reporter [MYID] This one should not be demoted
```

Summary

The chapter introduces key feature of the UVM library. While the UVM features are capable and flexible, they were created as enablers to the higher-level methodology that is needed to speed up verification for large and small designs. The next chapters introduce the UVM methodology for developing reusable verification components for design interface protocols.

5   Interface UVCs

Interface UVCs are key building blocks of a verification testbench. Extra effort and design at the interface UVC level simplifies the integration and test writing and enables large-scale reuse. Many library capabilities, introduced in the previous chapter, were designed to enable the creation of interface UVCs. This chapter describes the basic concepts and steps needed to create a standard reusable interface UVC.

5.1   Stimulus Modeling and Generation

5.1.1   Modeling Data Items

The first step in developing a verification component is describing the data item class. Data items are high-level transactions that will eventually be used to control how a particular interface on the DUT is driven. When generating this stimulus, realistic values that follow the protocol are generated and sent. Examples of data items are transactions, packets, and instructions. You may want to generate a stream of stimulus up front and apply the transactions one by one, or generate transactions whenever they are needed. Many times you want to generate sequences of transactions that relate to each other.

To create a user-defined data item, first you will want to review the interface's transaction specification and identify the data fields for that transaction. Some transaction attributes are derived from the protocol specifications and are required to specify how the transaction is represented on the bus. Other attributes are there to enable interesting data and easy control of the data randomization. Users can control how the value of those fields are set via constraints, control fields, and methods associated with the transaction. The UVM SystemVerilog class library provides the `uvm_sequence_item` base class for describing data items. Every user-defined data item should be derived directly or indirectly from this base class. The UVM SystemVerilog class library also includes macros that automatically implement the print, copy, clone, compare, pack/unpack methods, and more. The example below illustrates an APB transfer.

Note   The transfer is derived from `uvm_sequence_item` and not from `uvm_object`, as demonstrated in the previous chapter. Deriving the data items from a `uvm_sequence_item` allows them to be randomized as part of a sequence where the order to the data items makes a difference.

Example 5–1   APB Transfer

```
1  typedef enum bit {APB_READ, APB_WRITE} apb_direction_enum;
2  class apb_transfer extends uvm_sequence_item;
3    rand bit [31:0] addr;
4    rand bit [31:0] data;
5    rand apb_direction_enum direction;
6  // Control field - does not translate into signal data
7    rand int unsigned transmit_delay;  //delay between transfers
8  // Constraints
9    constraint c_delay { transmit_delay inside {[0:100]}; }
10   constraint c_addr  { addr[1:0] == 2'b00; }

11   //UVM automation macros for data items
12   `uvm_object_utils_begin(apb_transfer)
13     `uvm_field_int(addr, UVM_DEFAULT)
14     `uvm_field_int(data, UVM_DEFAULT)
15     `uvm_field_enum(apb_direction_enum, direction, UVM_DEFAULT)
16     `uvm_field_int(transmit_delay, UVM_DEFAULT|UVM_NOCOMPARE|UVM_NOPACK)
17   `uvm_object_utils_end

18   // Constructor UVM sequence items require a single string argument
19   function new (string name="apb_transfer");
20     super.new(name);
21   endfunction : new
22 endclass : apb_transfer
```

Line 1: We use enumerated types for ease of reading.

Line 2: Derive data items from uvm_sequence_item so they can be generated in a procedural sequence. See "Configuring the Sequencer's Default Sequence" on page 116 for more information.

Lines 9-10: Add constraints to a data item definition in order to:

- Specify the default distribution for generated traffic. For example, the delay between transfers should be fewer than 100 clocks.

- Reflect specification rules. In this example, the address must be on a word boundary.

Lines 12-17: Use the UVM macros to automatically implement frequently needed class functions. The UVM provides built-in macros to simplify development of the verification environment. The macros automate the implementation of functions defined in the base class, such as copy(), compare(), and print(), saving many lines of code. Use of these macros is optional but recommended. Refer to the previous chapter for more details.

Line 16: While comparison is done between two transfers, this field need not be compared. Hence, UVM_NOCOMPARE. Also because the transmit delay does not go directly to the DUT the NO_PACK flag is used to exclude it from the pack() and unpack() functions.

Line 18: The constructor syntax for UVM sequence items is a single string argument "name" with an optional default string value.

5.1.2   Defining Control Fields

Some of the attributes can be directly constrained to a desired value. For example, the direction of the apb_transfer can be either read or write. The generation of all values of the input space is often impossible and usually not required. However, it is important to be able to generate a few samples from ranges or categories of values. In Example 5–1 on page 74, the delay property could be randomized to anything between zero and 100. It is not necessary (nor practical) to cover the entire legal space, but it is important to try back-to-back items along with short, medium, and large delays between the items, and combinations of all of these. To do this, define control fields (often called "knobs") to enable the test writer to control these variables. These same control knobs can also be used for coverage collection. For readability, use enumerated types to represent various generated categories.

Example 5–2   Defining a Transaction Control Field

```
1    typedef enum bit {APB_READ, APB_WRITE} apb_direction_enum;
2    typedef enum {ZERO, SHORT, MEDIUM, LONG, MAX} apb_dly_enum;
3    class apb_transfer extends uvm_sequence_item;
4      rand bit [31:0] addr;
5      rand bit [31:0] data;
6      rand apb_direction_enum direction;
7      // Control fields - do not translate into signal data
8       rand apb_dly_enum delay_kind;
9      rand int unsigned transmit_delay;  //delay between transfers
10     // Constraints
11     constraint c_addr_valid { addr[1:0] == 2'b00; }
12     constraint c_delay { solve delay_kind before transmit_delay;
13                 transmit_delay >=0; transmit_delay <=100;
14             (delay_kind == ZERO) -> transmit_delay == 0;
15             (delay_kind == SHORT) -> transmit_delay inside { [1:10] };
16             (delay_kind == MEDIUM) -> transmit_delay inside { [11:29] };
17             (delay_kind == LONG) -> tramsmit_delay inside { [30:100] };
18             (delay_kind == MAX) -> transmit_delay == 100; }
19     //UVM utilities and automation macros for data items
20     `uvm_object_utils_begin(apb_transfer)
21       `uvm_field_int(addr, UVM_DEFAULT)
22       `uvm_field_int(data, UVM_DEFAULT)
23       `uvm_field_enum(apb_direction_enum, direction, UVM_DEFAULT)
24       `uvm_field_enum(apb_dly_enum, delay_kind,
25                     UVM_DEFAULT| UVM_NOCOMPARE | UVM_NOPACK)
26       `uvm_field_int(transmit_delay,
27                     UVM_DEFAULT | UVM_NOCOMPARE | UVM_NOPACK)
28     `uvm_object_utils_end
29     // Constructor - required UVM syntax
```

```
30   function new (string name="apb_transfer");
31     super.new(name);
32   endfunction : new
33 endclass : apb_transfer
```

Using this method allows you to create more abstract tests. For example, you can specify distribution as:

```
constraint c_delay_kind_dist {delay_kind dist {ZERO:=2, SHORT:=1, MEDIUM:=1,
                                                LONG:=1, MAX:=2};}
```

When creating data items, keep in mind what range of values are often used or which categories are of interest to that data item. Then add knobs to the data items to simplify control and coverage of these data item categories.

Notes

- Control knobs that are added for generation and coverage purposes should not be compared, packed or unpacked since they are not sent to the DUT.

- We do not discuss here data-item attributes that are added for coverage purpose only, such as adding a start_time and an end_time to cover a transfer processing time. These attributes are best captured by the monitor to enable passive operation mode and are discussed in the coverage section below.

5.1.3   Inheritance and Constraint Layering

For a specific test, you might want to adjust the randomness, disable existing constraints or further change the generation using additional constraints. This is achieved using class inheritance. You create a new class which extends from the original class. All the original fields, methods and constraints are available in the extended class. You override an existing constraint by adding a constraint with the same constraint name. Or you can add a constraint with a different name to specify additional constraints:

```
class short_delay_transfer extends apb_transfer;
  // further constrain the transmit_delay
  constraint c_short_delay {transmit_delay <= 3; }
endclass : short_delay_transfer
```

Note   In the code snippet above, the constructor and UVM automation macros have been omitted for brevity. In future examples, the constructor and macros will be shown only when needed. Please remember to include a constructor and UVM automation macros for all components and data items derived from uvm_object.

In this example, the constraint block in the class `short_delay_transfer` will be solved together with the constraint blocks from the class `apb_transfer` during randomization, and the value of `transmit_delay` will be constrained between 0 and 3. In a larger environment, you will often want to replace `apb_transfers` with `short_delay` transfers. The UVM factory greatly simplifies the replacement of a type with a derived type such as `short_delay_transfer`. This is one of the major reasons for using the factory. Such constraint layering requires usage of the UVM factory.

To enable this type of extensibility:

- Make sure constraint blocks are organized so that users are able to override or disable constraints for a random variable without having to rewrite a large constraint block.

  Note   Many users find that writing a larger number of short constraint blocks is easier than a small number of long constraint blocks.

- Do not use the `protected` or `local` keywords to restrict access to properties that may be constrained by the user. This will limit your ability to constrain them with an inline constraint.

- Use descriptive names for constraints. This will make it easier for users not familiar with the original definition to understand and override constraints in derived types.

5.1.4   Using Empty Constraint Blocks for Tests

A user can leave in a class an empty constraint block that later can be filled with constraints by the test writer. This technique is not SystemVerilog-compliant, but is supported by all of the simulators. Using an empty constraint block is an ad hoc layering technique. As well as not being part of the language reference manual (LRM), it has the limitations of not supporting instance overrides; not supporting multiple extensions, as no new class is created; and no ability to turn off or override existing constraint blocks. Further, you can only compile one set of constraints at a time, so it makes it difficult to manage for all but the smallest projects. We recommend using the factory solution over external implementation of constraint blocks. For more information on the factory, see "UVM Factory" on page 62.

5.1.5   A Simple Data Item Test

When you have captured your data item with its control knobs and constraints, you can write a simple test to create, randomize and print a few items to verify the results you expect are produced.

Example 5–3   Test for the apb_transfer Data Item

```
1   module test;
2     // import the UVM library and include the UVM macros
3     import uvm_pkg::*;
4     `include "uvm_macros.svh"

5     // include the data item class
6     `include "apb_transfer.sv"

7     apb_transfer my_xfer;
8     initial begin
9       my_xfer = apb_transfer::type_id::create("my_xfer");
10      repeat (5) begin
11        if (!my_xfer.randomize())
12            `uvm_fatal("RANDFAIL","Can not randomize my_xfer")
13        my_xfer.print();
```

```
14    end
15 endmodule : test
```

Notes

- To run this test on the Cadence IES simulator, first set UVM_HOME to the location of your UVM library installation, then run the following command:

  ```
  % irun $UVM_HOME/src/uvm_pkg.sv -incdir $UVM_HOME/src test.sv
  ```

  This simple test will also verify that you have access to the UVM library and macros.

- If you forgot to specify a field with the `uvm_field_*` macros, it will not be printed.

- Check your constraints by randomizing with additional constraints:

  ```
  if(!my_xfer.randomize() with { addr inside {['h0000:'hFFFF]};
                                 direction == APB_WRITE; })
  ... additional code ...
  ```

- As well as looking at the generated values, try to look at the distribution of the values. Some constraint sets can create an undesired bias to the generated values. It is useful to define a transaction coverage group and use it for such analysis. Randomize and cover the transaction multiple times in a loop and review the generation result. *Do you have too many reads vs. write transfers? Is the length delay between transactions reasonable? Are the generate transaction kinds evenly distributed?* Fix the constraints needed to achieve the desired results.

5.2   Creating the Driver

When data items are generated, the driver's role is to drive them to the bus following the interface protocol. The driver obtains data items from the sequencer for execution. Once the driver is finished sending the data item, it may return a value back to the sequencer. For example, the sequencer can randomize a read bus transaction and send it to the driver for delivery to the DUT. The driver performs the read operation on the bus and returns the result value back to the sequencer.

The SystemVerilog UVM Class Library provides the `uvm_driver` base class, from which all driver classes should be extended. The uvm_driver class is parameterized by both the request type (the data that is randomized by the sequencer) and the response (the DUT result that goes back to the sequencer). Built-in TLM ports are provided to communicate with the sequencer.

To create a driver:

1. Derive a driver class from the `uvm_driver` base class. It is parameterized with the request and response data item type(s), so ensure that your driver class provides types for these parameters.

2. Declare a virtual interface in the driver to connect the driver to the DUT interface.

3. Add the UVM infrastructure and automation macros for class properties to provide implementations for print(), copy(), compare(), and so on.

4. In the `run()` task, get the next data item from the sequencer and drive it on the virtual interface.

Refer to "Configuring the Sequencer's Default Sequence" on page 116 for a description of how a sequencer, driver, and sequences synchronize with each other to generate constrained random data.

The example below defines an AMBA advanced peripheral bus (APB) master driver. The example derives apb_master_driver from uvm_driver (parameterized to use the apb_transfer transaction type) and uses the methods in the seq_item_port object to communicate with the sequencer. As always, include a constructor and the `uvm_component_utils macro to register the driver type with the common factory.

Example 5–4   APB Master Driver Definition

```
1   class apb_master_driver extends uvm_driver #(apb_transfer);
2     // Virtual interface used to drive and view HDL signals
3     virtual apb_if vif;
4     // UVM utility and automation macros for general components
5     `uvm_component_utils(apb_master_driver)
6     // Constructor
7     function new (string name, uvm_component parent);
8       super.new(name, parent);
9     endfunction : new
10    // Additional class methods
11    extern virtual task run();
12    extern virtual protected task get_and_drive();
13    extern virtual protected task reset_signals();
14    extern virtual protected task drive_transfer(apb_transfer trans);
15  endclass : apb_master_driver

16  task apb_master_driver::run();
17    fork
18      get_and_drive();
19      reset_signals();
20    join
21  endtask : run

22  task apb_master_driver::get_and_drive();
23    forever begin
24      // Get the next data item from sequencer (may block).
25      seq_item_port.get_next_item(req);
26      drive_transfer(req);              // Execute the item
27      seq_item_port.item_done(req);   // Return the request.
28    end
29  endtask : get_and_drive

30  task apb_master_driver::drive_transfer (input apb_transfer trans);
31    ... // Add your logic here.
32    endtask : drive_transfer
```

Line 1: Derive the driver from `uvm_driver`. By parameterizing the driver with a class type, it will have a built-in variable named `req` of the type `apb_transfer` (the data item). This is the data type you will retrieve from the sequencer.

Notes

- By default, the response field accepts the same type as the request field. So this driver accepts `apb_transfer` types and returns `apb_transfers` back to the sequencer. For a different request and response type, use:

  ```
  class apb_driver extends uvm_driver #(apb_transfer_req, apb_transfer_res);
  ```

- Your driver class can optionally provide a second parameter for the type of response sent back to the sequencer. If you chose not to provide a second parameter, the response type will be the same as the request type. In this example, we are providing only a single parameter for the request type.

Line 5: Add the UVM component utilities macro.

Line 7: The constructor for `uvm_components` has two arguments: a string name and a reference to the component's parent.

Note In the data item section, we had several fields registered with macros. It is common for components to have a small number of fields. And in many instances, there are no fields registered at all.

Line 25: Call `get_next_item()` to get the next data item for execution from the sequencer.

Line 27: Signal the sequencer that the execution of the current data item is done.

Line 31: Add your application-specific logic to the `drive_transfer()` method to execute the data item. When first developing the UVC, you may want to only print the transaction until you have integrated a SystemVerilog interface.

More flexibility exists on connecting the drivers and the sequencer. See "Connecting the Driver and Sequencer" on page 86.

- We recommend that you use extern virtual protected tasks in the driver; this allows a concise view of the driver's API. We also recommend that you place the external implementation of these in the same file. This allows a quick review of the class interfaces without introducing too many files.

- A driver should not randomize parameters and, as much as possible, the traffic control should be reserved for the sequencer. This allows reusing the test logic, even if the driver does not exist (for example, when verifying the TLM model). Timing and injection-related parameters, such as delay between data items or timing-related error injection, should be randomized by the sequencer and delivered to the driver as part of the request.

5.2.1   The SystemVerilog Interface and Virtual Interface

The driver interacts with the DUT using a virtual interface. The SystemVerilog interface construct is used to bundle the DUT signals that will be connected to the UVM testbench. The interface definition is part of the reusable UVC. SystemVerilog interfaces are defined outside a module boundary, are instantiated in a module, and the interface signals are references via a " ." operator *(interface.sig_name)*. In addition to signals, the interface can contain assertions, parameters, functions, tasks, module ports (`modports`) and clocking blocks. The example code below shows a simple interface declaration for an APB bus.

Example 5–5   APB Interface Definition

```
interface apb_if (input pclock, input preset);

   // APB Bus Protocol Signals
   logic [31:0] paddr;
   logic        prwd;
   logic [31:0] pwdata;
   logic        penable;
   logic [15:0] psel;
   logic [31:0] prdata;
   logic   pslverr;
   logic   pready;

   // Control flags
   bit     has_checks = 1;
   bit     has_coverage = 1;

  // Checking and coverage (via assertions) would follow here

endinterface : apb_if
```

The `pclock` and the `preset` are ports as they are always input to the interface UVC. This makes the interface more modular and simplifies the connectivity especially if interface arrays are used.

An interface cannot be instantiated inside of a class. Instead, SystemVerilog provides an additional keyword "virtual" which enables you to place a reference to an interface inside of a class. This allows you to instantiate an interface and connect it up to the signals of your DUT and then in your driver make a reference to the instantiated interface.

A SystemVerilog virtual interface provides the mechanism for connecting abstract signals to the actual signals. A virtual interface can be referenced inside classes anywhere inside the dynamic testbench. The virtual interface must be connected to an actual interface instance and signals are referenced using a hierarchical reference to the virtual interface. The syntax for a virtual interface inside a class is shown in Example 5–4 on page 79 but repeated here for you:

```
class apb_master_driver extends uvm_driver;
   virtual apb_if vif;       // Virtual interface declaration
   // UVM macros
   // Constructor
   // user methods
endclass : apb_master_driver
```

The `drive_transfer` task then accesses the DUT signals through this virtual interface:

```
1   task apb_master_driver::drive_transfer(apb_transfer trans);
2     int slave_indx;
```

```
3    if (trans.transmit_delay > 0)
4       repeat(trans.transmit_delay) @(posedge vif.pclock);

5   // Drive the address phase of the transfer
6     slave_indx = cfg.get_slave_psel_by_addr(trans.addr);
7     vif.paddr <= trans.addr;
8     vif.psel <= (1<<slave_indx);
9     vif.penable <= 0;
10    if (trans.direction == APB_READ)
11       vif.prwd <= 0;
12    else begin //APB_WRITE
13      vif.prwd <= 1'b1;
14      vif.pwdata <= trans.data;
15    end

16    // Data phase - Grab data if executing an APB_READ
17    @(posedge vif.pclock)
18      vif.penable <= 1;
19    @(posedge vif.pclock);
20    if (trans.direction == APB_READ)
21       trans.data = vif.prdata;
22    vif.penable <= 0;
23    vif.psel     <= 0;
24 endtask : drive_transfer
```

The connection between the virtual interface and actual interface is done in the testbench. More details about assigning the virtual interface is discussed later in this chapter. A simple example of this assignment is shown below:

```
apb0.master.driver.vif = my_top.apb_if0;
```

5.3   Creating the Sequencer

A sequencer is an advanced generator that returns data items to the driver upon request. To understand the sequencer and its implementation, let's walk through some typical randomization requirements and implement a simple non-UVM generator.

5.3.1   Key Randomization Requirements

Consistent stimuli control—In a typical testbench, the integrator needs to assemble reusable verification IP created by multiple individuals and for quite different protocols. After initial configuration of UVCs, the main verification activities are creating and debugging tests. It is important that the stimuli control of the different reusable environments will be as consistent as possible. Specifically, the solution should have a proven solution for various scenarios such as: interrupt modeling, looking at previous generated data, protocol layering, latency and timing control, and much more.

Infinity minus—Randomness has proven as an efficient tool for uncovering unanticipated bugs. As you implement your testbench it is a good practice to use all random values. The infinity minus flow means that a wide variety of values are randomized by default (infinity). Individual tests use constraints to trim the possible legal values to test-specific values. The opposite for infinity-minus is to start with directed tests or a structured stimuli and finish with randomness at the end.

Reactive generation—Data items should be generated as close as possible to when they are needed. This permits techniques like reactive generation where the contents of the data items can be influenced by the state of the DUT. In some cases, you randomize the traffic regardless of the DUT state but may want to coordinate the traffic to a simulation event in a specific test.

Pre-generation—In some environments, the stimuli must be created before the run phase. A classic example can be a program that needs to be created in advance and placed in memory. An ideal verification engine should support both reactive and pre-generation.

Ordered and individual transaction generation—In some cases, generation of individual data items is enough to create all legal stimuli or to fill coverage holes. In others, a specific sequence of data items is needed. For example, generating random register accesses is unlikely to properly initialize your DUT. In many environments, both ordered and semi-ordered transaction randomization is needed. An optimal solution will allow randomizing both individual data items and sequences of data items.

Enable horizontal and vertical reuse—Many of the transactions generated can be leveraged for different devices or as you integrate a device into a larger system. It is helpful to create a list of reusable data item sequences that have random parameters which can be further constrained for particular project needs.

5.3.2   A Non-UVM Generator

The example below illustrates a generator and a driver. The driver requests an item from the generator by calling a function directly in the generator. The generator "wakes up" and creates a new item when required. When the generator hits a maximum number of items, it stops creating new items.

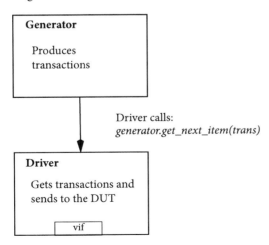

Figure 5-1   Non-UVM Generator and Driver

Example 5–6   Non-UVM Generator Code

```
1  class generator;
2    rand int max_cnt;
3    int count;
4    apb_transfer transfer;
5    task get_next_item(apb_transfer trans);
6      if (count <= max_cnt) begin
7        transfer = apb_transfer::type_id::create("transfer");
8        if (!transfer.randomize())
9          `uvm_fatal("RANDFAIL", "Failure to randomize transfer")
10       trans = transfer;
11       count++;
12     end
13   endtask : get_next_item
14 endclass : generator
```

In the generator above, you can change `max_cnt` and use constraint layering, but this generator does not provide the control that is frequently needed for verification. For example:

- It is not easy to express order or timing without a major code rewrite.

- Since the `get_next_item` function is called by a specific driver, there is no easy way for a single generator to coordinate the traffic on multiple drivers.

- We need a way to generate stimulus related to previous generated values or to the result it produced in the same task.

- Tasks do not provide the encapsulation needed to capture parameter dependencies that can be constrained from outside the task.

- Because the randomization call is `transfer.randomize()`, different transactions cannot have different constraints. All must have the same constraints.

- Similarly, the delay between transactions will be the same.

- Another generator implementation which randomizes the item and only then forwards it to the driver might be problematic because the driver may not be ready to inject the data (for example, needs to arbitrate for the DUT). Thus, it is challenging to react to the state of the DUT as the generated values grow stale by the time they are injected.

There are ways to modify the simple generator implementation above to support these requirements, but you will end up restructuring your code to address each requirement as it is introduced. The UVM sequencer and sequences mechanism was built with these considerations in mind and will prevent the user from needing to perform constant maintenance on their code generator as the project progresses.

The UVM sequencer provides these capabilities and much more. In the following section we discuss how to instantiate and connect this advanced generator. See Chapter 7 "Simple Testbench Integration" for more information on some of the built-in capabilities that this component and the sequences provide.

5.3.3   The UVM Sequencer

The sequencer generates stimulus data and passes it to a driver for execution. In typical operation, the sequencer waits for a `get_next_item()` call from a driver, randomizes the data item, and then sends the data item to the driver. The SystemVerilog UVM Class Library provides the `uvm_sequencer` base class, which, like the `uvm_driver` class, is parameterized by the `req` and `resp` item types. The `uvm_sequencer` is much more capable than the simple loop sequencer described above. Deriving your sequencer from `uvm_sequencer` allows you to leverage these built-in capabilities.

To create a sequencer:

1. Derive a sequencer from the `uvm_sequencer` base class and specify the `req` and `resp` (request and response) type parameters.

2. Use `` `uvm_sequencer_utils `` and `` `uvm_update_sequence_lib_and_item `` to indicate the generated data item type and field desired automation.

This is all that is required to define the baseline behavior for a sequencer. The rest of the sequencer's behavior is built in, and we explore the details later. The default behavior of the sequencer is to be a random stimulus generator. Refer to "Configuring the Sequencer's Default Sequence" on page 116 for a description of how a sequencer, driver, and sequences synchronize with each other to generate constrained-random data.

The class `apb_master_sequencer` in Example 5–7 on page 85 defines a sequencer class. The example derives it from `uvm_sequencer` and parameterizes it to use the `apb_transfer` type.

Example 5–7   APB Master Sequencer

```
1   class apb_master_sequencer extends uvm_sequencer #(apb_transfer);

2     // UVM automation macro for sequencers
3     `uvm_sequencer_utils(apb_master_sequencer)

4     // Constructor - required UVM Syntax
5     function new (string name, uvm_component parent);
6       super.new(name, parent);
7       `uvm_update_sequence_lib_and_item(apb_transfer)
8     endfunction : new

9   endclass : apb_master_sequencer
```

Notes

*   In the class definition, by default, the response type is the same as the request type. If a different response type is desired, the optional second parameter must be specified for the uvm_sequencer base type:

    ```
    class apb_master_sequencer extends uvm_sequencer #(apb_transfer, apb_rsp);
    ```

*   Use the `` `uvm_sequencer_utils `` macro instead of the `` `uvm_component_utils `` macro. The `` `uvm_sequencer_utils `` macro provides additional functionality for sequences. When using the

`uvm_seqeuencer_utils` macro, you should still use the normal UVM field registration macros (`uvm_field_int`, and so on). Refer to "UVM Macros" in the *UVM Class Reference* for more information.

- Call the `uvm_update_sequence_lib_and_item` macro from the constructor of your sequencer class. This macro registers all of the sequence types associated with the current sequencer, and indicates the sequencer's generated transaction type as a parameter. Refer to "UVM Macros" in the *UVM Class Reference* for more information.

- Never instantiate the `uvm_sequencer` class directly. A user may need to extend this class to add their own attributes. For example, the user may decide to raise an end-of-test object from all AHB masters or add a channel number to all the APB slaves.

To better understand the sequencer and the recommended way to generate stimuli in UVM, we review the sequences and their capabilities in Chapter 8 "Stimulus Generation Topics".

5.4   Connecting the Driver and Sequencer

The driver and the sequencer are connected via TLM, with the driver's `seq_item_port` connected to the sequencer's `seq_item_export` (see Figure 5-2, below). The sequencer produces data items to provide via the export. The driver consumes data items through its `seq_item_port`, and optionally provides responses back. The component that contains the instances of the driver and sequencer makes the connection between them. See Figure 5-2, Sequencer-Driver Interaction, below.

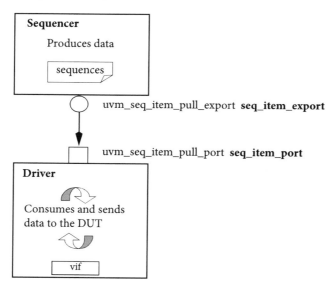

Figure 5-2   Sequencer-Driver Interaction

The `seq_item_port` in `uvm_driver` defines the set of methods used by the driver to obtain the next item in the sequence. An important part of this interaction is the driver's ability to synchronize to the bus, and to interact with the sequencer to generate data items at the appropriate time. The sequencer implements the set of methods that allows flexible and modular interaction between the driver and the sequencer.

5.4.1 Basic Sequencer and Driver Interaction

Basic handshake between the driver and the sequencer is done using the tasks `get_next_item()` and `item_done()`. As demonstrated in the example in "Creating the Driver" on page 78, the driver uses the task to request a randomized item from the sequencer. The driver will block waiting for the sequencer to have an item available. When the sequencer has an item available, it will provide it and the `get_next_item()` task will return this item. After sending it to the DUT, the driver signals the sequencer that the item was processed using `item_done()`. Typically, the main loop within a driver resembles the following pseudo-code.

```
seq_item_port.get_next_item(req);
// Send item following the protocol.
send_to_dut(req);
seq_item_port.item_done();
```

Note `get_next_item()` is blocking.

5.4.2 Querying for the Randomized Item

In some protocols, the driver can simply block and do nothing until an item is available to be sent. The `get_next_item()` is blocking and will serve this need. In some protocols, the driver may be required to send idle transactions while waiting for a meaningful one. For this purpose, the `uvm_seq_item_pull_port` class provides another task: `try_next_item()`. This task will return immediately, even if no data items are available for execution. Your driver code can use this task to test if there are valid items ready to be sent. If there are no items available, your driver can send idle transactions. The following example shows a revised implementation of the `get_and_drive()` task in the previous example (in "Creating the Driver" on page 78)—this time using `try_next_item()` to drive idle transactions as long, as there is no real data item to execute:

```
1  task apb_master_driver::get_and_drive();
2    forever begin
3      // Try the next data item from sequencer (does not block).
4      seq_item_port.try_next_item(transfer);
5      if (transfer == null) begin
6        // No data item to execute, send a simple idle transaction.
7        ...
8      end
9      else begin
10       // Got a valid item from the sequencer, execute it.
11       ...
12       // Signal the sequencer; we are done.
13       seq_item_port.item_done();
14     end
15   end
16 endtask: get_and_drive
```

5.4.3   Supporting Pipeline Protocols

In some protocols, such as pipelined protocols, the driver begins multiple data items before the earlier items are completely processed. In these cases, the driver calls `item_done()` without providing the response to the sequencer. In this scenario, the driver logic may look like the code example below.

Example 5–8   Simple Driver for Pipeline Protocol

```
class simple_driver extends uvm_driver #(simple_transfer);
  simple_transfer req_list [$];
  int max_pipeline_depth=4;
  // Component utils, constructor
  ...
  task run();
    fork
      get_and_drive();
      drive_transfers();
    join
  endtask : run

  // Fetch items from the sequencer to fill the pipeline
  task get_and_drive();
    while (req_list.size() < max_pipeline_depth) begin
      seq_item_port.get_next_item(req);
      $cast(rsp, req.clone());
      rsp.set_id_info(req);
      req_list.push_front(rsp);
      seq_item_port.item_done();
    end
  endtask : get_and_drive

  //Process items in req_list and execute according to the protocol
  task drive_transfers();
    simple_transfer cur_req;
    while (1) begin
      wait (req_list.size()>0);
      cur_req = req_list.pop_back();
      send_to_dut(cur_req);
      rsp_port.write(cur_req);
    end
  endtask : drive_transfers

  task send_to_dut(simple_transfer trans);
    // Logic to handle sending multiple data items
  endtask : send_to_dut
endclass : simple_driver
```

Note   The `send_to_dut()` task may require forked processes to execute multiple items in parallel to fill the pipeline.

5.4.4 Sending Processed Data Back to the Sequencer

In some sequences, a generated value depends on the response to previously generated data. By default, the data items between the driver and the sequencer are copied by reference, which means that changes made to the driver data item will be visible inside the sequencer. At times, a reference between the sequencer and the driver cannot be maintained. In such scenarios—for example, across different languages or between simulated and accelerated components—the user needs to return the processed response back to the sequencer. Do this using the optional argument to item_done().

```
task apb_master_driver::get_and_drive();
  forever begin
    seq_item_port.get_next_item(req);
    $cast(rsp, req.clone());
    rsp.set_id_info(req);
    drive_transfer(rsp);
    seq_item_port.item_done(rsp);
  end
endtask : get_and_drive
```

Note   Before providing the response, the response's sequence and transaction id must be set to correspond to the request transaction using rsp.set_id_info(req).

5.5 Creating the Collector and Monitor

In Chapter 2 "UVM Overview", we discuss a split-monitor approach to passively capture transactions on an interface and do checking and coverage. Here, we will use this alternate approach, using a collector and monitor component.

The collector is responsible for extracting signal information from the bus and translating it into transactions. This component essentially reverse engineers transactions sent on a SystemVerilog interface. We recommend using a SystemVerilog interface with SystemVerilog assertions for protocol-specific checking, but you can also add signal-level checking and coverage to the collector when appropriate. The monitor is responsible for doing transaction-level checking and coverage. Once the monitor has decoded the transaction, it sends the transaction to other components (that is, UVCs, scoreboards, or TLM models) via standard TLM connections. The monitor and collector should never rely on state information collected by other components, such as a driver. Checking and coverage should be configurable and configuration control information should be included in both components. An analysis port allows communication between the collector and monitor components.

Example 5–9   APB Collector

The following example shows a simple collector with the following functions:

- The collector captures bus information through a virtual interface (vif).

- The collected data is exported to the monitor on a TLM analysis port (item_collected_port).

Detailed code for the collector is not shown in this simplified example. A complete example can be found in the APB example in `apb_collector.sv`.

```
1   class apb_collector extends uvm_component;
2     virtual apb_if vif; // SystemVerilog virtual interface
3     bit checks_enable = 1;   // Controls checking in collector and interface.
4     bit coverage_enable = 1; // Controls coverage in collector and interface.
5     // TLM port for sending the collected transfer to the monitor
6     uvm_analysis_port #(apb_transfer) item_collected_port;

7     // UVM automation and utility macros

8     function new (string name, uvm_component parent);
9       super.new(name, parent);
10      item_collected_port = new("item_collected_port", this);
11    endfunction : new

12    extern virtual task run();
13    extern virtual function void perform_coverage();
14    extern virtual function void perform_checks();
15  endclass : apb_collector

16  task apb_collector::run();
17    apb_transfer trans_collected;
18    trans_collected = new("trans_collected");
19    forever begin
20      @(posedge vif.sig_clock);
21      ...// Capture signal data from the bus into trans_collected.
22      if (checks_enable) perform_checks();
23      if (coverage_enable) perform_coverage();
24      item_collected_port.write(trans_collected);
25    end
26    endtask : run
27  ...
```

The `run()` task executes a forever loop and collects the data as soon as the signals indicate that the data is available on the bus.

As soon as the data is available, it is sent via the analysis port (`item_collected_port`) to the monitor.

Example 5–10   APB Monitor

The following example shows a simple monitor which has the following functions:

- The monitor has a coverage group that captures interesting functional coverage information.

- The transaction is exported via a TLM analysis port (`item_collected_port`).

In complex protocols such PCI Express, the monitor contains transaction checkers such as transaction-level state machines and monitoring.

Detailed code for the monitor is not shown in this example. A complete example can be found in the APB example in apb_monitor.sv.

```
1   class apb_monitor extends uvm_monitor;
2   // flags used to control whether checks and coverage are executed.
3     bit checks_enable = 1;
4     bit coverage_enable = 1;
5   // TLM port for sending transactions OUT to the scoreboard, reg db, etc
6     uvm_analysis_port #(apb_transfer) item_collected_port;
7   // TLM port connection to the collector
8     uvm_analysis_imp #(apb_transfer, apb_monitor) coll_mon_port;
9   // Current APB transfer
10    apb_transfer trans_collected;

11  // UVM automation and utility macros

12  // Functional coverage groups declarations
13    covergroup apb_transfer_cg;
14      TRANS_ADDR: coverpoint trans_collected.addr {
15        bins ZERO = {0};
16        bins NON_ZERO = {[1:8'h7f]}; }
17      TRANS_DIRECTION : coverpoint trans_collected.direction;
18      TRANS_ADDR_X_TRANS_DIRECTION : cross TRANS_ADDR, TRANS_DIRECTION;
19    endgroup

20  // Constructor - UVM Required syntax
21    function new (string name, uvm_component parent);
22      super.new(name, parent);
23      apb_transfer_cg = new();
24      item_collected_port = new("item_collected_port", this);
25      coll_mon_port = new("coll_mon_port", this);
26    endfunction : new

27    // Additional class methods
28    extern virtual function void write(apb_transfer transfer);
29    extern virtual function void perform_checks();
30    extern virtual function void perform_coverage();
31  endclass : apb_monitor

32  // Transaction interface to the collector via TLM write()
33    function void apb_monitor::write(apb_transfer transfer);
34      trans_collected = transfer;
35      if (checks_enable) perform_checks();
36      if (coverage_enable) perform_coverage();
```

```
37      // Broadcast transaction to the rest of the environment
38      item_collected_port.write(trans_collected);
39    endfunction : write

40    function void apb_monitor::perform_checks();
41      // Add checks here
42    endfunction : perform_checks

43    function void apb_monitor::perform_coverage();
44      apb_transfer_cg.sample(); // Sample monitor covergroups
45    endfunction : perform_coverage
46 endclass : apb_monitor
```

Coverage collection and checking are conditional because they can affect simulation run-time performance. If not needed, they can be turned off by setting coverage_enable or checks_enable to 0, using the configuration mechanism. For example:

```
set_config_int("*.collector", "checks_enable", 0);
set_config_int("*.monitor", "checks_enable", 0);
```

If checking is enabled, the write task calls the perform_checks function, which performs the necessary checks on the collected data (trans_collected). If coverage collection is enabled, the write task calls the sample() method of the transaction coverage groups.

Section 5.12, "Implementing Protocol-Specific Coverage and Checks," on page 127 provides more details and examples of creating and controlling checks and coverage in an interface UVC.

5.5.1   Connecting the Collector and Monitor

The collector and the monitor are connected via TLM, with the collector's `uvm_analysis_port` connected to the monitor's `uvm_analysis_imp` (see Figure 5-3, below). The collector forms transactions from signal activity on the interface and delivers the transactions via the analysis port to the monitor.

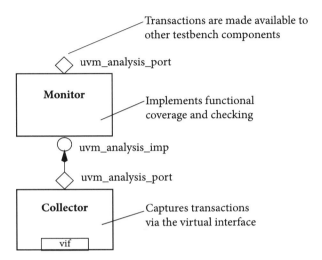

Figure 5-3   Collector-Monitor TLM Connections

The `uvm_analysis_port` in the `collector` is declared in the collector as:

```
uvm_analysis_port #(apb_transfer) item_collected_port;
```

The monitor has two TLM ports, a `uvm_analysis_imp` to connect to the collector, and a `uvm_analysis_port` which broadcasts transactions from the monitor:

```
uvm_analysis_imp #(apb_transfer) coll_mon_port;
uvm_analysis_port #(apb_transfer) item_collected_port;
```

A connection is made from the monitor to the collector in the UVM `connect()` phase:

```
collector.item_collected_port.connect(monitor.coll_mon_port);
```

This connection, and the mechanism for connecting to the monitor's analysis port are described later in this chapter.

5.6   Modeling Topology with UVM

So far, we have discussed four components:

- A sequencer to create streams of transaction-level traffic to the DUT
- A driver to convert these transactions to signal-level stimulus on the DUT interface

- A collector to recognize signal-level activity on the DUT interface and convert it into transactions

- A monitor to perform coverage and checking for transactions

A simplified testbench using these components is shown in Figure 5-4, Simplified Non-Recommended Transaction-Level Testbench. This simple testbench has a single interface for a single interface DUT (for example, a memory device).

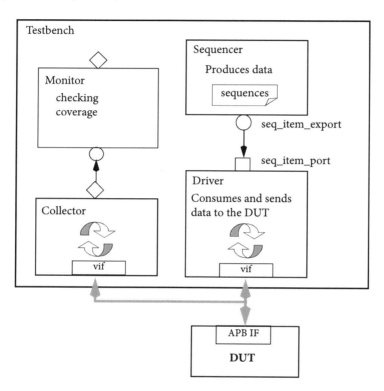

Figure 5-4   Simplified Non-Recommended Transaction-Level Testbench

The four components above collaborate to generate stimulus, check bus activity, and collect coverage for a desired standard protocol. All are indirectly derived from a UVM component class (uvm_component) and inherit needed services such as phases, message facilities, factory, and more. We highly recommend using the methodology classes and not the generic uvm_component class directly. The motivation for using the methodology classes are:

- Additional automation and consistency that come with some of these. For example, a sequencer allows generating sequences of transactions. A driver is parameterized with the request and response.

- The ability to extend all components of a specific role. For example, you can extend all the monitors to have an item_transmitted event.

- Role-specific processing and settings. For example, UVM allows creating a handle array to all drivers in the system, and analyzing or setting these in a loop.

- Visualizers and compliance checking enablers. The UVM already has multiple technologies that allow analyzing and visualizing environments and testbenches. These technologies rely on the ability to identify the role of each of the components. Using the methodology classes enables such capabilities. TLM interfaces in UVM provide a consistent set of communication methods for sending and receiving transactions between components. In this example, the components are instantiated, configured, and connected in the testbench, to perform the different operations required to verify a design.

In such a simplified testbench, users can reuse the monitor, driver, collector, and sequencer, but the instantiation, hook-up, and configuration of these interface-specific components is left to the integrator. A typical DUT would require many quartets (monitor, driver, collector, and sequencer sets) that need to be analyzed, configured, instantiated, and connected by the integrator. In fact, in most cases, these four components are always instantiated together for a specific interface. In order to leverage an interface-specific cluster of components, we introduce the concept of agents, below.

Figure 5-5, Highly Reusable UVC Agent, shows the recommended grouping of individual components into a reusable interface-level UVC agent. Instead of reusing the low-level classes individually, the developer creates a component that encapsulates its sub-classes in a consistent way. Promoting a consistent architecture makes these components easier to learn, adopt, and configure.

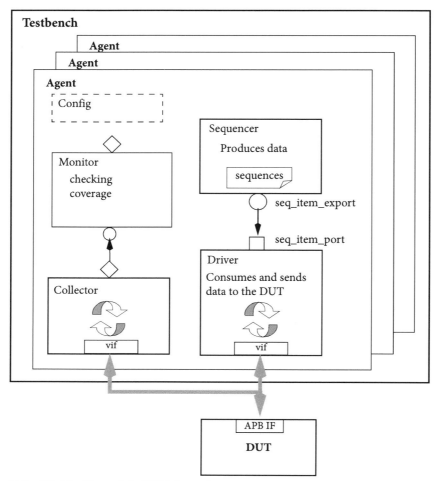

Figure 5-5   Highly Reusable UVC Agent

5.7   Creating the Agent

The agent (Figure 5-6 on page 97) instantiates and connects together a driver, collector, monitor, and sequencer using TLM connections as described in the preceding sections. To provide greater flexibility, the agent also contains configuration information and other parameters. A UVM-compliant agent will provide protocol-specific stimuli creation, checking, and coverage for a device. In a bus-based environment, an agent typically models either a master or a slave component. An agent has two basic operating modes:

- **Active mode**—The agent emulates a device in the system and drives DUT signals. This mode requires that the agent instantiate a driver and sequencer. A collector and monitor are also instantiated for checking and coverage.

- **Passive mode**—The agent does not instantiate a driver or sequencer and operates passively. Only the collector and monitor are instantiated and configured. Use this mode when only checking and coverage collection is desired.

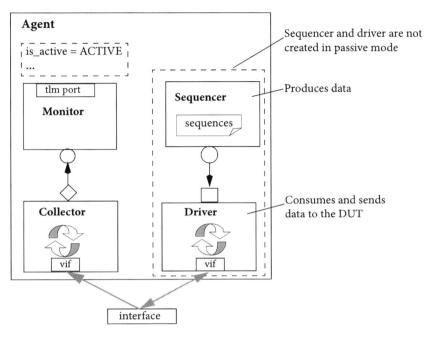

Figure 5-6   Agent Architecture

Remember that the passive section should not rely on the active section. (If an agent is placed in passive mode and the active logic is not present, the agent will stop working.) This means that it is okay for the sequencer to accept information from the monitor but not vice versa, as we may want to perform coverage and checking on interface buses driven by some other logic.

Note   Even if you do not have immediate plans for using passive mode, it is often easy to add this support during agent implementation. Retrofitting it is much more difficult later in the project when coding has finished.

The class `apb_master_agent` in the example below instantiates a sequencer, a driver, collector, and a monitor in the recommended way. Instead of using the constructor, the UVM `build()` method is used to configure and construct the subcomponents of the agent. Unlike constructors, this function can be overridden without any limitations. Also, instead of hard-coding the allocation, `type_id::create()` is used to instantiate the sub-components. The second part of Example 4–14 on page 62 illustrates how you can override existing behavior using `extends`.

Example 5–11   APB Master Agent

```
1   class apb_master_agent extends uvm_agent;
2     //Agent configuration information
```

```
 3    uvm_active_passive_enum is_active = UVM_ACTIVE;
 4    // Agent components
 5    apb_monitor monitor;
 6    apb_collector collector;
 7    apb_master_sequencer sequencer;
 8    apb_master_driver driver;

 9    // UVM utilities and automation macros
10    `uvm_component_utils_begin(apb_master_agent)
11       `uvm_field_enum(uvm_active_passive_enum, is_active, UVM_DEFAULT)
12    `uvm_component_utils_end
13    // Constructor - Required UVM Syntax
14    function new(string name, uvm_component parent);
15      super.new(name, parent);
16    endfunction : new

17    // Additional class methods
18    extern virtual function void build();
19    extern virtual function void connect();
20 endclass : apb_master_agent

21 // Use build() method to create agents's subcomponents.
22 function void apb_master_agent::build();
23   super.build()
24   monitor = apb_monitor::type_id::create("monitor",this);
25   collector =apb_collector::type_id::create("collector",this);
26   if (is_active == UVM_ACTIVE) begin
27     sequencer=apb_master_sequencer::type_id::create("sequencer",this);
28     driver = apb_master_driver::type_id::create("driver",this);
29   end
30 endfunction : build

31 // Use connect() method to connect the component TLM ports
32 function void apb_master_agent::connect();
33   super.connect();
34   collector.item_collected_port.connect(monitor.coll_mon_port);
35   if(is_active == UVM_ACTIVE)
36     driver.seq_item_port.connect(sequencer.seq_item_export);
37 endfunction : connect
```

Note   You should always call `super.build()` (see Line 23) to update the given component's configuration overrides. This is crucial to providing the capability for an enclosing component to be able to override settings of an instance of this component.

Lines 24-25: The collector and monitor are created using `create()`.

Lines 26-29: The `if` condition tests the `is_active` property to determine whether the driver and sequencer are created in this agent. If the agent is set to active (`is_active == UVM_ACTIVE`), the driver and sequencer are created using additional `create()` calls.

Both the sequencer and the driver follow the same creation pattern as the monitor.

This example shows the `is_active` flag as a configuration property for the agent. You can define any control flags that determine the component's topology.

Calling `create()` from the `build()` method is the recommended way to create any hierarchical component.

Line 34: The connection between the monitor and collector is made using `connect()`.

Lines 35-36: The `if` condition should be checked to see if the agent is active, and if so, the connection between the sequencer and driver is made using `connect()`.

5.7.1   Using connect() to Connect Components

The agent above uses a `connect()` phase to connect the driver to the sequencer and the monitor to the collector. Using the phases ensure that the components creation that took place in the `build()` phase is done. UVM simulation phases are further explained in Chapter 4 "UVM Library Basics".

5.7.2   Agent Configuration

The agent sub-components can share the same configuration options. Some agent configuration attributes are recommended by UVM (that is, `is_active`) while others are user-defined (for example, bus speed or a sub-protocol such as GMII versus SGMII Ethernet). The UVM configuration mechanism allows users to define configuration attributes and provides a mechanism to change them in a testbench or test without modifying individual components. The details of the configuration mechanism are discussed later in this chapter.

5.8   Creating the UVM Verification Component

In multi-drop bus interfaces such as APB, AHB, or a multi-layer verification component such as PCI-Express, multiple agents need to share common resources and settings and need to instantiate and connect in an environment-specific way. Examples could be common configuration options, similar virtual interface, joint sparse memory, and more.

A UVC is a reusable environment for a specific protocol. The idea here is similar to agents but involves a complete interface encapsulation level—we ask the UVC developer to instantiate and configure the multiple agents and other resources together as needed. In addition to agents, the verification component may contain a bus-level monitor and/or arbiter. Figure 5-7, Typical UVM Interface UVC Architecture, below, shows an example of a typical UVM bus-based verification component. The UVC users receive this highly encapsulated environment, configures and instantiates it using the configuration mechanism. The following sections describe how to create and connect environment sub-components. By following these guidelines, users can ensure that their environment will be architecturally correct, consistent with other UVCs, and reusable.

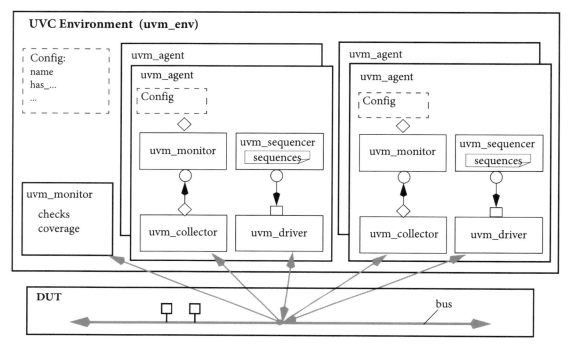

Figure 5-7   Typical UVM Interface UVC Architecture

5.8.1   The Environment Class

The environment class is the top container of reusable UVCs. It instantiates and configures all of its sub-components (agents, bus monitors, and so on). Most verification reuse occurs at the environment level, where the user instantiates an environment class and configures it and its agents for specific verification tasks. For example, a user might want to change the number of slaves in an APB bus environment as shown below.

```
1    class apb_env extends uvm_env;
2      apb_config cfg; // configuration class for this environment
3      apb_master_agent master;      // APB master (Bridge)
4      apb_slave_agent slaves[];     // APB can have multiple slave agents
5      apb_bus_monitor bus_monitor; // Shared bus monitor

6      `uvm_component_utils_begin(apb_env)
7        `uvm_field_object(cfg, UVM_DEFAULT)
8      `uvm_component_utils_end

9      function new(string name, uvm_component parent);
10       super.new(name, parent);
```

```
11   endfunction : new

12   // Additional class methods
13   extern virtual function void build();
14   extern virtual function void assign_vi (virtual apb_if vif);
15 endclass : apb_env

16 function void apb_env::build
17   uvm_object config_obj;
18   super.build();
19   if (cfg == null)begin
20     `uvm_info(get_type_name(),"Using default_apb_config", UVM_MEDIUM)
21     $cast(cfg,factory.create_object_by_name("default_apb_config","cfg"));
22   end
23   if (cfg.has_bus_monitor) begin
24     bus_monitor = apb_bus_monitor::type_id::create("bus_monitor", this);
25     bus_monitor.cfg = cfg;
26   end
27   master = ahb_master_agent::type_id::create("master",this);
28   master.cfg = cfg;
29   // Build slaves
30   slaves = new[cfg.slave_configs.size()];
31   // Create multiple slaves and give each a unique name
32   foreach slaves[i] begin
33     slaves[i] = ahb_slave_agent::type_id::create(
34               $psprintf("slaves[%0d]",i) ,this);
35     slaves[i].cfg = cfg.slave_configs[i];
36   endfunction : build

37 function void apb_env::assign_vi(virtual apb_if vif);
38     // Based on the configuration, assign master, slave and bus monitor
39     // signals.
40 endfunction : assign_vi
```

Note   Similarly to the agent, create is used to allocate the environment sub-components. This allows introducing derivations of the sub-components later. For the APB protocol, there is a single master and a variable number of slaves.

The user is not required to call build() explicitly. The SystemVerilog UVM Class Library will do this for all created components. When all of the components' build() functions are complete, the UVM will call each component's connect() function. Any connections between child components should be made in the connect() function of the parent component. This ensures that all components have been created before they are connected.

5.8.2   Point-to-Point Environments

In point-to-point protocols, such as transmit-receive communication protocols or buses that define a single master and slave interaction, we need a reusable environment class. Beyond consistency (an integrator always uses environments and their standard attributes), the agents in such environment may share a single monitor.

Block diagrams of point-to-point environments are illustrated in Figure 5-8, Point-to-Point UVC Configured to Verify a Master or a Slave Device. A point-to-point UVC needs to support verifying both master and slave agents for check and coverage. This is achieved by using the agent is_active attribute. To verify a slave, you instantiate the environment with an active master agent and a passive slave agent to check and collect coverage on the agent. To verify a master, the slave will be active and the master will be passive. If you want to collect coverage or check an internal bus, both the master and slave should be set to passive mode.

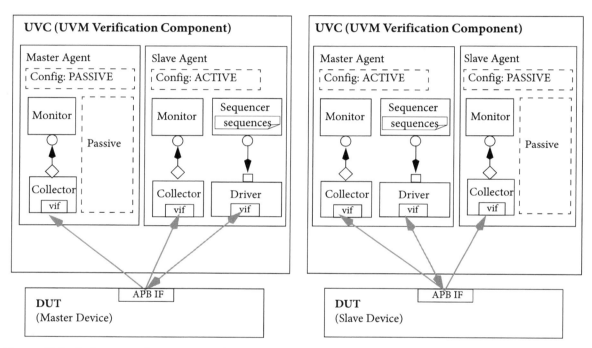

Figure 5-8   Point-to-Point UVC Configured to Verify a Master or a Slave Device

Note   In the development process, users may want to create both the agents and co-develop them against each other. The interesting part in a point-to-point environment is the monitor. This is highly protocol-dependent, but if the same signals are being used for both master and slave, then one collector and monitor are enough. This means that the bus monitor is both the slave and master monitor. For consistency, and keeping the same use model, we recommend adding a pointer from both the master and slave to this joint monitor. Figure 5-9, Interface UVC with Shared Monitor and Collector depicts this configuration.

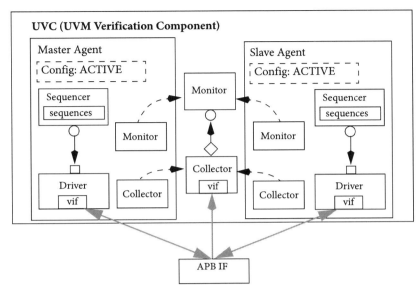

Figure 5-9   Interface UVC with Shared Monitor and Collector

5.8.3   The UVM Configuration Mechanism

A UVC is developed on a per-protocol basis for general purpose, protocol-related use. It may support various features or operation modes that are not required for a particular project. The UVM provides a standard configuration mechanism which allows you to define the UVC's configuration to suit the current project's requirements. The UVC can get this configuration information during the build phase or run phase, and within the constructor. The UVM configuration mechanism is tailored to enable reuse, but additional guidelines should be followed to achieve reusability.

5.8.3.1   Making the UVC Reusable

There are times when the developer knows the context in which the developing UVC will be used. In such cases, developers should take care to separate the requirements of the UVC's protocol from those of the project and avoid hard-coding configuration parameters with project specific values. We strongly recommend using only the interface-protocol documentation in developing the UVC. Later, developers can consult their project's documentation to see if there are some generic features which might be useful to implement. For example, they should be able to configure slave devices to reside at various locations within an address space, instead of hard-coding the address to a specific location used in the project.

As another example, if within a protocol frame a few bits are defined as reserved, they should stay reserved within the UVC. The verification logic that understands how a specific implementation uses these bits should be kept outside the global generic code.

As a developer, it is critical to identify these generic parameters and document them for the environment users.

5.8.3.2 Configuration Requirements

There are many verification component configuration requirements. The configuration mechanism is used by the testbench integrator and the test writer who wishes to modify the default configuration for a specific test case. The verification component should check the validity of the configuration, to make sure proper settings are applied before simulation run time. A user should be able to randomize the configuration and collect coverage on the randomized values. It should also be possible to use configuration of a subsystem in a larger system, set the system default configuration and leave it up to the user to further control the configuration. Configuration should be extensible, as some users may want to add a new project-specific configuration attribute or constraints. While project specifics and modification are always possible, the following sections describe the recommend configuration flow.

5.8.3.3 UVC Configuration Object

The UVM allows users to specify configuration objects for components either as separate fields or as a group contained within a configuration object. Using the configuration attribute for scalar settings is simpler than allocating a configuration class. However, for most real-world applications, users find a configuration object to be more practical. The number of attributes in real-world UVCs quickly grows beyond the one or two planned attributes. Creating a configuration object allows for a place to capture dependencies between individual attributes in constraints. Users can easily print the attributes, pass them by value or by reference to a different object (even in a different language), wrap existing sub-environments configuration within a larger class, and much more.

Both agents and environments should have their own configuration class. For example, agents have a configuration class that holds the standard and protocol-specific attributes. The environment class will have a configuration class that contains the agent config classes (may be an array in the case of a multi-drop BUS). Testbench configuration classes should wrap the multiple environment configuration classes. Each layer can impose constraints on its field configuration classes or between siblings. An example of an interface environment configuration class is illustrated below.

Example 5–12 APB Configuration Classes (slave, master and env config)

```
1   class apb_slave_config extends uvm_object;
2     string name;
3     uvm_active_passive_enum is_active = UVM_ACTIVE;
4     rand int start_address;
5     rand int end_address;
6     rand int psel_index;
7     constraint c_addr { start_address <= end_address; }
8     constraint c_psel { psel_index inside {[0:15]}; }
9     // UVM object_utils, field macros and constructor
10    extern virtual function bit (check_address_range(int unsigned addr);
11  endclass : apb_slave_config

12  class apb_master_config extends uvm_object;
13    string name;
14    rand uvm_active_passive_enum is_active = UVM_ACTIVE;
```

```
15  // UVM object utils, field macros and constructor syntax
16  endclass : apb_master_config

17  class apb_config extends uvm_object;
18    // APB has one master and N slaves
19    rand apb_master_config master_config;
20    rand apb_slave_config slave_configs[];
21    rand bit has_bus_monitor = 1;
22    // constraints on the composite configuration
23    //UVM object_utils, field macros and constructor
24    extern virtual function void add_slave(string name, int start_addr,
25             int psel_indx, uvm_active_passive_enum is_active=UVM_ACTIVE);
26    extern virtual function int get_slave_psel_by_addr(int addr);
27  endclass : apb_config
```

The nature of the configuration mechanism allows a testbench to define default constraints and, for specific tests, to override these for corner-case purposes. Each layer, by calling the get config_object, can receive its configuration object, check its validity, and use the set_config_object mechanism to configure its sub-components.

Note   The config object is automatically retrieved in the build() method if it is set in the test or testbench. It is up to the developer to check the configuration object, and in the case of a null object, to randomize a default config. The example below illustrates how a UVC checks the validity of a the configuration object, using randomize(null), and sets its agents to behave accordingly.

Example 5–13   Configuring the APB UVC in the build() Method

```
1   function void apb_env::build();
2     super.build();
3     if (cfg == null) begin
4       cfg = apb_config::type_id::create("cfg");
5       // Randomize here OR specify a default configuration for the env
6       if (!cfg.randomize()) `uvm_fatal("RNDFAIL", "APB config rand failed")
7     end
8     master = apb_master_agent::type_id::create(cfg.master_config.name,
    this);
9     master.cfg = cfg;
10    slaves = new[cfg.slave_configs.size()];
11    foreach(slaves[i]) begin
12      slaves[i] =
    apb_slave_agent::type_id::create(cfg.slave_configs[i].name, this);
13      slaves[i].cfg = cfg.slave_configs[i];
14    end
15  endfunction : build
```

Extensions are an important aspect of any configuration strategy. New system dependencies are typically layered from a system to its sub-components. We highly recommend using the factory in the testbench or tests to allocate configuration classes.

Example 5–14   Extending the Default APB Configuration

```
class demo_config extends apb_config;
  `uvm_object_utils(demo_config)
  function new(string name="demo_config");
    add_slave("slave[0]", 32'h0000_0000, 32'h7FFF_FFFF, 0, UVM_ACTIVE);
    add_slave("slave[1]", 32'h8000_0000, 32'hFFFF_FFFF, 1, UVM_PASSIVE);
    add_master("master", UVM_ACTIVE);
  endfunction : new
endclass : demo_config
```

Example 5–15   Testbench build() Method Overrides the Default APB Configuration

```
function void demo_tb::build();
  super.build();
  demo_cfg = demo_config::type_id::create("demo_cfg");
  set_config_object("*.apb0", "cfg", demo_cfg);
  apb0 = apb_env::type_id::create("apb0", this);
  ...
endfuntion : build
```

In this simple case, the testbench only shows the creation of the apb_cfg. In a real test environment the apb_cfg class is just one sub-class of a complete testbench configuration class. Within the testbench, users can randomize the configuration class or build it procedurally. Using randomization is more powerful than using procedural settings, as users can re-randomize with a different seed and get a different configuration that follows the requirements. An example of a testbench config class is described in "Testbench Configuration" on page 153.

5.8.3.4   Reconfiguring a Device

In some cases, after initial configuration, devices can be reconfigured to different operation modes. Regardless of whether this is initiated by the testbench or by another component, these modifications need to be reflected in the testbench. Some of the device states should remain the same and should not be configured to their default values. Whether you can deploy reconfiguration randomly or procedurally, using an encapsulated configuration object helps. You can re-randomize a configuration class while maintaining the existing values of some of the configuration attributes by using the SystemVerilog rand_mode() construct.

When a new configuration is generated or detected, components need to be notified to fetch a new configuration object and update their attributes or behavior accordingly. This is done via a recursive call of the user-defined update_config(uvm_object cfg) function. In the update_config() that is defined in every level of the hierarchy, the component typically:

- Checks the validity of the configuration. In specific the function checks that no topology parameters were modified (for example, the number of slaves was changed), and that a legal configuration was provided.

- Apply the desired configuration on its own attributes. In some cases, variables and queues need to be reset and threads need to be killed and resumed (for example, if a transaction is being sent when reconfig appears).

- Calls its sub-component update_config() method.

5.8.4   Setting the Agent Virtual Interface

The driver and the collector access the DUT signals via a virtual interface which is a reference to a physical interface. When setting the virtual interfaces, users may want to separate the DUT hierarchy from the testbench hierarchy. This allows, for example, swapping the DUT or a subsystem with a different one that uses the same interfaces. To set the virtual interface, a user can use two schemes, use an `assign_vi` on agents and the environment, or encapsulate the virtual interface in a generic parameterized container class. While `assign_vi` is simpler, we recommend using the containers that decouple the hierarchy between the two. Both techniques are described below.

Using assign_vi() for virtual interface connections

```
1   // ENV: assign the virtual interface for all components in the env
2   function void apb_env::assign_vi(virtual apb_if vif);
3     master.assign_vi(vif);
4     foreach(slaves[i]) slaves[i].assign_vi(vif);
5   endfunction : assign_vi
6
7   // AGENT: assign the virtual interfaces of the agent's children
8   function void apb_master_agent::assign_vi(virtual apb_if vif);
9     this.vif = vif;
10    collector.vif = vif;
11    if (is_active == UVM_ACTIVE) driver.vif = vif;
12  endfunction : assign_vi
13
14  function void my_tb::connect();   // TESTBENCH: Connect method
15    // Assign interface for apb0
16    apb0.assign_vi(my_top.apb_if0);
17  endfunction : connect
18
19  module my_top; // TOP MODULE
20    ...
21    apb_if apb_if0 (clock, reset);  //interface instance
22    ...
23  endmodule : my_top
```

Note   `assign_vi` is simple. The disadvantage of `assign_vi()` is that in line 14 above, we hard-code the hierarchical path of the testbench. The `assign_vi()` also does not use the `set_config` which is the standard way to configure reusable components.

Using a Generic Container for Virtual Interface Assignments

The configuration mechanism API allows passing strings, integers and objects types. Virtual interfaces cannot be set via the configuration mechanism. However, wrapping the virtual interface in a class allows passing the virtual interface within an object. The following utility allows wrapping any type within a class.

```
1   package uvm_config_prop_pkg;
```

```
 2   import uvm_pkg::*;
 3   class uvm_config_prop #(type T=int) extends uvm_object;
 4       T value;
 5       function new(T value);
 6         this.value = value;
 7       endfunction
 8       static function void set_config (string target, string field, T value,
 9                                 uvm_component cntxt=null);
10         uvm_config_prop#(T) wrapper = new(value);
11         if(cntxt == null) cntxt = uvm_root::get();
12   cntxt.set_config_object(target, field, wrapper, 0);
13       endfunction: set_config

14       static function bit get_config (uvm_component cntxt, string field,
     output T value);
15         uvm_config_prop#(T) wrapper;
16         uvm_object obj;
17         if(cntxt == null) cntxt = uvm_root::get();
18         if(!cntxt.get_config_object(field,obj,0)) return 0;
19         if(!$cast(wrapper,obj)) return 0;
20         value = wrapper.value;
21         return 1;
22       endfunction

23       static function bit get_config_object (uvm_component cntxt, string
                   field, inout T value, bit clone=0);
24         uvm_object obj;
25         T tmp;
26         if(cntxt == null) cntxt = uvm_root::get();
27         if(!cntxt.get_config_object(field,obj,clone)) return 0;
28         if(!$cast(tmp,obj)) return 0;
29         value = tmp;
30         return 1;
31       endfunction
32     endclass
33   endpackage
```

Line 3: Wrapper class for configuring a single standalone object. The object can be any type that can be passed as an input to and output from a function. This allows things like virtual interfaces, dynamic arrays, and so on to be used as configuration properties. The setter and the getter must agree on the type being passed, and the type must match exactly. There are two static functions.

Line 8: The set_config() function has the same signature as the various set_config_* functions (an option context is available if the method is being used from inside of a component context). This is needed to enable a higher level component to override a sub-component settings.

Line 14: The get_config() function has a similar signature to the get_config_* functions, but requires that a context be provided. The context is the component fetching the value from the configuration table.

Line 23: The wrapper also provides a simplified get_config_object interface so that the user doesn't have to create a temporary object and do a cast in order to get a configuration object.

The following code shows the usage of the wrapper in the APB UVC:

```
1   module my_top; // TOP MODULE
2     import uvm_config_prop_pkg::*;
3     ...
4     apb_if apb_if0 (clock, reset);  //interface instance
5     ...
6     initial begin
7       uvm_config_prop#(virtual apb_if)::
                          set_config("uvm_test_top.my_tb.apb0", "vif", apb_if0);
8       run_test();
9     end
10  endmodule : my_top

11  // ENV: build() method
12  function void apb_env::build();
13    super.build();
14    void'(uvm_config_prop#(virtual apb_if)::get_config(this, "vif", vif));
15    if (vif != null)
         uvm_config_prop#(virtual apb_if)::set_config("*", "vif", vif, this);
16  endfunction : build
17  // ENV: run() task   (OPTIONAL)
18  task apb_env::run();
19    if (vif == null) `uvm_fatal("NOVIF", "Virtual interface has not been set")
20  endtask : run

21  // AGENT: build() method
22  function void apb_master_agent::build();
23    super.build();
24    void'(uvm_config_prop#(virtual apb_if)::get_config(this, "vif", vif));
25    if (vif != null)
         uvm_config_prop#(virtual apb_if)::set_config("*", "vif", vif, this);
    ...
26  endfunction : build

27  // DRIVER: build() method
28  function void apb_master_agent::build();
29    super.build();
30    void'(uvm_config_prop#(virtual apb_if)::get_config(this, "vif", vif));
31  endfunction : build
```

Line 4: The top module holds the interface instance.

Line 7: The wrapper util is used to configure the APB UVC. The static function call creates a wrapper class and set_config that class to uvm_test_top.my_tb.apb0.

Line 14: The APB environment `build()` method, calls the `get_config()` that unwraps the container, and assigns the `vif` to the environment `vif` field.

Line 15: Sets the virtual interface to all of the APB environment children.

Lines 24-25: Similar to the UVC, the agent gets the configuration from above and sets its sub-components.

Line 28: The driver gets its virtual interface within the `build()` method.

Note   You can use wildcards here, as in any `set_config` call.

This `set_config` technique is cleaner but requires more understanding. Cadence introduced this technique in the URM methodology and not all users appreciated the complexity nor needed the flexibility. This utility may eventually before part of the methodology. We recommend users to take the extra step and use the wrapper utility.

We do *not* recommend putting the virtual interface within a configuration class. The virtual interfaces are set from the top module of from the testbench and are a physical connection that has little to do with the randomization or reconfiguration.

5.9   Creating UVM Sequences

In most cases, randomizing transactions in a loop cannot capture the high-level intention of a test and an ordered stream of stimulus is required. For example, you might want to configure a device before sending "random" traffic. Or you might want to generate related back-to-back transactions.

The UVM sequencer controls the generation of random stimulus by controlling and executing **sequences**. Most of the intelligence of UVM traffic generation is in the sequences (and the sequence item) and their capabilities, not in the sequencer. Some sequences are predefined and pre-registered to a sequencer. For example, every sequencer has a "random" sequence that generates other registered sequences in a loop. Users can define other interesting scenarios by creating user-defined sequences. Defining a sequence is always preferred over creating a new test because a sequence is tagged with a name and later can be reused in multiple tests or to build new sequences.

Each sequence produces a stream of data items or can leverage other sequences to create more abstract sequences. The leaves of the sequence tree are always data items that are sent to the driver and eventually to the DUT. Figure 5-10 below illustrates an example of how sequenceA combines both data items and sequenceB. SequenceA starts by doing data1, followed by sequenceB, and finishing with data4. SequenceB does data2 and data3. Eventually, as the sequences unfold, what is sent to the DUT is an ordered stream of data1, data2, data3, and data4.

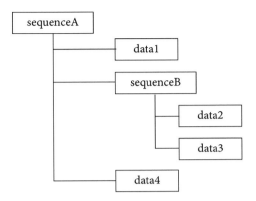

Figure 5-10   Sequences and Sub-Sequences

Some sequences are provided as part of a reusable component and others are created to test a specific DUT. For example, a bus-based protocol UVC may include predefined sequences for a single write, a single read, a burst write, and a burst read. The reusable component developer can also include a library of protocol-specific interesting sequences that examine certain protocol scenarios. Other sequences may include a sequence to write random data to a DUT-specific address range and then read it back.

The test writer controls the environment-generated patterns by configuring its sequencers. The test writer can:

- Add a user-defined sequence of transactions to a sequencer
- Override the sequencer's default starting sequence to start with a user-defined sequence

5.9.1   User-Defined Sequences

In this section, we describe how to create a library of reusable sequences that later can be leveraged and enhanced by the environment users.

Verification components can include a library of basic sequences, which test writers can leverage. This approach enhances reuse of common stimulus patterns and reduces the length of tests. In addition, a sequence can call upon other sequences, thereby creating more complex scenarios.

The UVM class library provides the `uvm_sequence` base class. You should derive all sequence classes directly or indirectly from this class. Sequences allow reactive generation (reaction to the current state of the DUT), have many built-in capabilities like interrupt support, prioritization schemes and automatic factory support. Sequences can be called by other sequences and are reusable at higher levels of design integration.

To create a user-defined sequence:

1. Derive a sequence from the `uvm_sequence` base class and specify the request and response item type parameters. In the example below, only the request type is specified, `apb_transfer`. This will result in the response type also being of type `apb_transfer`.

2. Use the `uvm_sequence_utils` macro to associate the sequence with the relevant sequencer type and to provide the various automation utilities. This macro also adds a p_sequencer variable that is a pointer to the specific sequencer invoking that sequence. Static sequencer properties such as hierarchical path, channel number (if there are multiple channels), end-of-test control and more are accessible through the p_sequencer variable. The macro provides a downcasted version of this variable using the second argument of this macro.

3. Implement the sequence's body() task with the specific scenario you want the sequence to execute. In the body task, you can execute data items and other sequences using "`uvm_do" on page 114 and "`uvm_do_with" on page 115.

A simple APB transfer sequence declaration is shown below. The body() of the sequence creates, randomizes and sends a single data item of type apb_transfer.

```
 1  class apb_transfer_seq extends uvm_sequence #(apb_transfer);
 2    // Constructor and UVM automation macros - note the second ARG
 3    `uvm_sequence_utils(apb_transfer_seq, apb_master_sequencer)
 4    function new(string name="apb_transfer_seq");
 5      super.new(name);
 6    endfunction : new

 7    virtual task body();
 8      `uvm_do(req)
 9    endtask : body
10  endclass : apb_transfer_seq
```

Line 1: Defines a sequence called apb_transfer_seq, with apb_transfer data items. A sequence variable **req** of type **apb_transfer** is built into the base uvm_sequence class.

Line 3: The `uvm_sequence_utils macro registers the sequence to be executed with a specific sequencer type. This allows only the intended sequencer type to execute this sequence. This macro is similar to the `uvm_object_utils macro (and its variations) except that it takes a second argument, which is the sequencer type name this sequence is associated with.

Note   Do not use the `uvm_object_utils macro when using the `uvm_sequence_utils macro. The functionality of `uvm_object_utils is included in `uvm_sequence_utils.

Line 8: The body() task is the main behavior of the sequence. It leverages parameters (if any) and does data items or other sequences. In this simple example, the body calls a `uvm_do macro to execute a single random data item.

Note   Timing, flow control, looping and forking are allowed in the body() task.

This second sequence example creates a higher-level sequence by executing multiple apb_transfer_seq sequences.

```
 1  class multi_apb_transfer_seq extends uvm_sequence #(apb_transfer);
 2    rand int num_seq;
 3    constraint c_num_seq (num_seq inside {[1:10]}; }
 4    // Constructor and UVM automation macros
```

```
5      `uvm_sequence_utils(multi_apb_transfer_seq, apb_master_sequencer)
6      function new(string name= "multi_apb_transfer_seq");
7        super.new(name);
8      endfunction : new

9      task body();
10       apb_transfer_seq apb_seq; // Instance of another sequence type
11       repeat (num_seq)
12         `uvm_do(apb_seq)
13     endtask : body
14 endclass : multi_apb_transfer_seq
```

Line 1: This sequence also extends from uvm_sequence and is parameterized by the apb_transfer type.

Lines 2–3: Sequences can optionally contain random fields with constraints. These fields are randomized when the sequence is created and executed. In this example, the sequence will execute the apb_transfer sequence num_seq times, and num_seq is a random integer between 1 and 10.

Line 5: All sequences should use the `uvm_sequence_utils macro to register the sequence to the appropriate sequencer.

Line 10: An instance of the apb_transfer_seq. This sequence is executed in the uvm_do call.

Lines 9–13: The body() task uses a repeat loop, and the `uvm_do macro will execute an apb_transfer_seq sequence num_seq times.

In many cases, users will want to generate sequences that are a bit more complex and have more built-in control. The class apb_write_read_word_seq in the following example defines another APB sequence to write a transaction and read it back from the same address. This sequence includes a field constraint (start_addr) and inline constraints.

```
1  class apb_write_read_word_seq extends uvm_sequence #(apb_transfer);
2    rand bit [31:0] start_addr;
3    constraint c_addr { start_addr[1:0] == 2'b00; }
4    // Constructor and uvm_automation macros for sequences
5    `uvm_sequence_utils(apb_write_read_word_seq, apb_master_sequencer)

6    // The body() task executes 2 APB transfers with the same address.
7    task body();
8      `uvm_do_with(req, {req.addr == start_addr;
                          req.direction == APB_WRITE;)
9      `uvm_do_with(req, {req.addr == start_addr;
                          req.direction == APB_READ;)
10   endtask : body
11 endclass : apb_write_read_word_seq
```

Line 2: This sequence has a random start_addr field. The address is randomized once and is used for both the write and read operations.

Line 3: The field constraint ensures that the randomized addresses are byte-aligned.

Line 8: In this example, the body uses a `uvm_do_with` macro to execute a req (apb_transfer) and to specify inline constraints to be used when the item is randomized. The syntax for the constraint block is the same syntax used for an inline constraint. The first transaction processed is an APB_WRITE transaction with start_addr as the address.

Line 9: The second `uvm_do_with` macro executes an APB_READ transfer from the same address.

The next sequence example shows how a user can invoke the previous two sequences and set constraints on the sequence parameters:

```
1   class apb_traffic_seq extends uvm_sequence #(apb_transfer);
2     multi_apb_transfer_seq multi_seq; // rand param is num_seq
3     apb_write_read_word_seq wr_rd_seq; // rand param: start_addr
4     // Constructor and uvm_automation macros for sequences
5     `uvm_sequence_utils(apb_write_read_word_seq, apb_master_sequencer)

6     // The body executes two pre-defined sequences with constraints.
7     task body();
8       repeat (5)
9         `uvm_do_with(wr_rd_seq, {start_addr inside {['h0000:'h1fff]};})
10        `uvm_do_with(multi_seq, {num_seq == 5;)
11      repeat (5)
12        `uvm_do_with(wr_rd_seq, {start_addr inside {['h2000:'hffff]};})
13    endtask : body
14 endclass : apb_traffic_seq
```

Lines 2-3: Declarations of previously defined sequences. The multi_apb_transfer_seq has a random parameter for num_seq. When we "do" this sequence on line 10, we specify the value of the num_seq parameter to be 5. The apb_write_read_word_seq has a random parameter for start_addr.

Lines 9 and 12: The sequence is called with a constraint specified on start_addr. This constraint will be solved in conjunction with the apb_write_read_seq constraint (start_addr[1:0] ==0).

5.9.1.1   Sequence and Sequence Item Macros

So far, we have introduced two macros. But what do they do? Let's take a look at each.

`uvm_do

This macro takes as an argument either a variable of type uvm_sequence_item or of type uvm_sequence. An object is created using the factory and assigned to the specified variable. When the driver requests an item from the sequencer, the item is randomized and provided to the driver.

The do operation translates into a number of steps:

1.   The sequence waits until an item is requested from the driver.

2.   The transaction (or sequence) is allocated using the factory.

3. The transaction (or sequence) is randomized with built-in data item or sequence field constraints.

4. If you are *doi*ng a transaction, it is sent via TLM to the driver for execution. In the case of a sequence, it starts executing the `body()` task of the sequence (repeating steps 1–3, above).

5. Block code execution until the item was sent. The driver indicates via TLM that the item is done.

Explicit calls to execute each of the steps above results in more code to maintain and can yield human errors. For example, if you forget to use the factory to allocate a data item, you may get unexpected results when a test overrides the default data item to address a coverage hole. UVM introduces one-line macros to simplify this.

`uvm_do_with

This macro is similar to "`uvm_do" on page 114. The first argument is a variable of a type derived from `uvm_sequence_item`, which includes items and sequences. The second argument can be any valid inline constraints that would be legal if used in `arg1.randomize()` with inline constraints. This enables adding different inline constraints, while still using the same item or sequence variable.

```
`uvm_do_with(req, {req.addr == start_addr;
                   req.direction == APB_WRITE;)
```

More options exist for creating and executing data items and sequences. For more information, see Chapter 8 "Stimulus Generation Topics".

5.9.2   Predefined Sequences

There are three built-in sequences: `uvm_random_sequence`, `uvm_exhaustive_sequence`, and `uvm_simple_sequence`.

5.9.2.1   uvm_random_sequence

This built-in sequence is the default sequence to be executed by the sequencer. This sequence randomly selects and executes one or more sequences from the sequencer's queue of registered sequences (excluding `uvm_random_sequence` and `uvm_exhaustive_sequence`). The number of sequences executed depends on the *count* field of the sequencer. If *count* is set to –1, the random sequence will randomize a number between 0 and `uvm_sequencer::max_random_count`. If *count* is not –1, then *count* sequences will be executed by `uvm_random_sequence`.

Note   For a sequencer to not execute any items, set the default sequence to `uvm_random_sequence` and its count to 0. Users often do this in conjunction with a virtual sequencer (see "Controlling Other Sequencers" on page 170 for more information).

5.9.2.2   uvm_exhaustive_sequence

This built-in sequence is also predefined in the sequencer. This sequence will exhaustively execute all user-defined sequences for the current sequencer. The predefined `uvm_simple_sequence` will also be executed, but the other two predefined sequence types (uvm_random_sequence and uvm_exhaustive_sequence) will not. The sequences are executed exactly once and in a random order.

The example below shows the body for the uvm_exhaustive_sequence.

```
task uvm_exhaustive_sequence::body();
  l_count = m_sequencer.sequences.size() - 2;
  max_kind = m_sequencer.sequences.size();
  l_exhaustive_seq_kind =
     m_sequencer.get_seq_kind("uvm_exhaustive_sequence");
  repeat (l_count) begin
    assert(randomize(l_kind) with {
      l_kind > l_exhaustive_seq_kind &&l_kind < max_kind; });
    // l_kind is randc.
    do_sequence_kind(l_kind);
  end
endtask
```

Note   The l_kind variable is declared as randc in order to randomize without replacement.

5.9.2.3   uvm_simple_sequence

This is the third built-in sequence which is predefined in the sequencer. This sequence is provided to allow default execution of the UVC without any user-defined sequences.

```
task uvm_simple_sequence::body();
  `uvm_do(item)
endtask
```

5.10   Configuring the Sequencer's Default Sequence

By default, all sequencers execute their uvm_random_sequence object that, in a loop, selects a sequence from its sequence library and executes it. The sequencer has a string property named default_sequence which can be set to any sequence listed in a sequencer's queue. This sequence is used as the default sequence for that instance of the sequencer.

To change the default sequence:

1. Declare a user-defined sequence class which derives directly or indirectly from uvm_sequence.

2. Configure the default_sequence property for a specific sequencer or a group of sequencers. Typically, this is done inside the test or testbench class before creating the component that includes the relevant sequencer(s). For example,

    ```
    set_config_string("*.master.sequencer","default_sequence","apb_traffic_seq");
    ```

    The first argument uses a wildcard mechanism. Here, any instance name containing .master.sequencer will have its default_sequence property (if it exists) set to the value apb_traffic_seq.

More information about how to configure the sequencer is provided in Chapter 7 "Simple Testbench Integration".

5.10.1 Controlling the Sequencer and Generated Sequences

Libraries of sequences are compiled as part of UVM testbench. The `uvm_sequence_utils` associates each sequence with a sequencer. When the testbench is created, the sequencer builds an array of sequences to be executed in its constructor using the `uvm_update_sequence_lib_and_item()` macro. Figure 5-11 on page 117 shows the Sequencer/Driver/Sequences Array interaction.

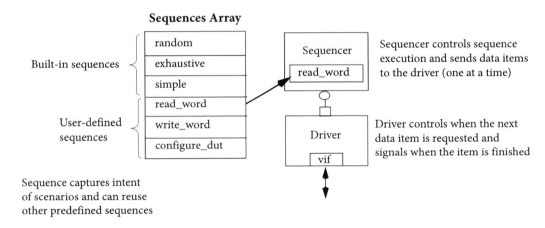

Figure 5-11 Interaction of Sequencer, Driver, and Sequences Array

Here is the general flow of interaction when the driver/sequencer are executing in pull mode:

1. The driver calls seq_item_port.get_next_item(req) to indicate that it is ready for a data item. Inside the TLM code, the seq_item_port.get_next_item(req) function calls sequencer.get_next_item(req).

2. The sequencer chooses which sequence it will allow to execute and acknowledges a sequence to generate a data item.

3. The sequence is randomized and created and then the body() of the sequence is started. A data item is generated and it lets the sequencer know that an item is available.

4. The sequencer delivers the data item to the driver and waits for item_done() from the driver.

5. The driver sends the item to the DUT and calls seq_item_port.item_done() to indicate it is finished.

This flow is repeated with the driver requesting another item via the seq_item_port.get_next_item(req) call. The sequencer acknowledges the sequence to deliver its next data item and the item is sent.

Note   Sequences can create other sequences, called nested sequences.

5.10.2 Overriding Sequence Items and Sequences

In a user-defined uvm_test—for example, apb_base_test (discussed in "Creating the Base Test" on page 156)—users can configure the simulation environment to use a modified version of an existing sequence or sequence item by using the common factory to create instances of sequence and sequence-item classes. See "UVM Factory" on page 62 for more information.

To override any reference to a specific sequence or sequence-item type:

1. Declare a user-defined sequence and/or sequence item class. The example in the next step assumes the declaration of a basic sequence item of type apb_transfer, and a derived item of type word_aligned_transfer.

2. Invoke the appropriate uvm_factory override method, depending on whether you are doing a global or instance-specific override. For example, assume the apb_write_read_word_seq sequence is executed by a sequencer of type apb_master_sequencer (both defined in "User-Defined Sequences" on page 111). You can choose to replace all usage of apb_transfer types with word_aligned_transfer types. This can be selected for all requests for apb_transfer types from the factory, or for specific instances of apb_transfer. From within an UVM component, a user can execute the following:

    ```
    // Affect all factory requests for type apb_transfer.
    set_type_override_by_type(apb_transfer::get_type(),
       word_aligned_transfer::get_type());

    // Affect requests for type apb_transfer on only a given sequencer.
    set_inst_override_by_type("env0.master.sequencer.*",
       apb_transfer::get_type(), world_aligned_transfer::get_type());

    // Alternatively, affect requests for type apb_transfer for all
    // sequencers of a specific env.
    set_inst_override_by_type("env0.*.sequencer.*",
      apb_transfer::get_type(),word_aligned_transfer::get_type());
    ```

3. Use any of the sequence macros that allocate an object (as defined in "Sequence and Sequence Item Macros" on page 114); for example, the `uvm_do macro.

Because the sequence macros call the common factory to create the data item object, existing override requests will take effect and a word_aligned_item will be created instead of an apb_transfer.

5.10.3 Building a Reusable Sequence Library

A reusable sequence library is a set of user-defined sequences. Creating a UVC reusable sequence library is an efficient way to facilitate reuse. The environment developer can create a meaningful set of sequences to be leveraged by the test writer. Such sequence libraries avoid code duplication in tests, making them more maintainable, readable, and concise.

Tips

- Try to think of interesting protocol scenarios that many test writers can use.

- As some users may not want to use the reusable sequence library (because the sequences may not match the design requirements of the user), do not `include a reusable sequence library within the UVC package file list. Leave it to the user to decide whether to use them.

5.11 Coordinating End-of-Test

UVM provides an objection mechanism to allow hierarchical status coordination between components. The built-in objection, `uvm_test_done`, provides a way for components and sequences to synchronize their activity and indicate when it is safe to end the test.

5.11.1 UVM Objection Mechanism

In general, the process is for a component or object in the component's context (for example, a sequence) to raise a `uvm_test_done` objection at the beginning of an activity that must be completed before the simulation stops, and to drop the objection at the end of the activity. When all the raised objections are dropped, the simulation terminates. The end of test API includes `raise_objection`, `drop_objection`, and `all_dropped` calls that are described below:

raise_objection

The syntax of `raise_objection` is as follows:

```
function void raise_objection (uvm_object obj = null,
        string description = "", int count = 1 )
```

Raises the number of objections for the source object by count, which defaults to 1. The object is usually the handle of the caller. If object is not specified or is null, the implicit top-level component, `uvm_top`, is chosen. The description parameter allows users to specify a user message that typically provides the reason for raising the objection. Rasing an objection causes the following:

- The source and total objection counts for object are increased by count.

- The raised objection's virtual method is called, which calls the `uvm_component:raised` method for all of the components up the hierarchy.

- A trace message including the description may be issued if the trace bit is set.

drop_objection

The syntax for dropping an objection is as follows:

```
function void drop_objection (uvm_object obj = null,
                string description = "", int count = 1 )
```

The `drop_objection` drops the number of objections for the source object by count, which defaults to 1. The object is usually the handle of the caller. If object is not specified or is null, the implicit top-level component, `uvm_top`, is chosen.

The description parameter allows users to specify a user message that typically provides the reason for dropping the objection. Dropping an objection causes the following:

- The source and total objection counts for object are decreased by count. It is an error to drop the objection count for object below zero.

- A trace message including the description string might be issued.

- If the total count is non-zero at for a hierarchical level, the drop is propagated up the hierarchy immediately.

- If the total count is zero, the drain time is initiated. If the drain time completes and the count is still zero, the drop is propagate up the hierarchy.

5.11.2   End-of-Test Objection Mechanism Usage

Proactive agents may have a meaningful agenda to be achieved before the test goals can be declared as done. For example, a master agent may need to complete all its read and write operations before the run phase should be allowed to stop. A re-active slave agent may not object end-of-test as it is merely serving requests as they appear without a well-defined agenda.

A typical use is for a sequence to raise an objection when it is started as a root sequence (a sequence that has no parent sequence), and to drop the objection when it is finished as a root sequence.

```
1  class apb_read_block_seq extends uvm_sequence#(apb_transfer);
2      task pre_body();
3          // raise objection if started as a root sequence
4          uvm_test_done.raise_objection(this, "APB read block");
5      endtask

6      task body();
7        //read block activity
8        ...
9      endtask
10     task post_body();
11         // drop objection if started as a root sequence
12         uvm_test_done.drop_objection(this,
13                     "APB read block");
14     endtask
15 endclass
```

To avoid re-implementing the raise and drop, you might want to create a parent sequence that implements the pre_body() and post_body() for its derivatives. Keep in mind that the pre_body() and post_body() are called only when the sequence is started. So if the sequence is started as the default sequence, the raise and drop will be activated; but if it is a sub-sequence of a more abstract sequence, then, as desired, no raises and drops occur.

Note   It is beneficial to associate the raise description string with the associated string for drop. We recommend using the same string for both. In the future, UVM might leverage this information to produce more descriptive log files to determine why a simulation stopped or did not stop as intended.

In some contexts or tests, a master could be part of the main simulation agenda or some supporting logic for a different high-level desired. In such contexts the user may want to configure the sequencer to object or avoid objecting end of test. We recommend adding a switch to the sequencer to enable and disable end-of-test objection. This allows the user to use this kind of style:

```
// in a test
   set_config_string("tb.env0.master.sequencer", "default_sequence",
            "uvm_exhaustive_sequence");
 set_config_int  ("tb.env0.master.sequencer", "object_test_done", 1);
```

The best way to implement this technique is by deriving a new sequencer that takes the configuration attribute into account and changes the behavior as needed.

```
1   class apb_sequencer extends uvm_sequencer #(apb_transfer);
2      bit object_test_done;
3   // UVM automation macro for sequencers
4     `uvm_sequencer_utils_begin(apb_sequencer)
5         `uvm_field_int(objecting_test_done, UVM_ALL_ON)
6     `uvm_sequencer_utils_end
7     // Constructor - required UVM Syntax
8     function new (string name, uvm_component parent);
9       super.new(name, parent);
10      `uvm_update_sequence_lib_and_item(apb_transfer)
11    endfunction : new
12    // a test-done objection
13    task start_default_sequence();
14      if (object_test_done)
15        uvm_test_done.raise_objection(this);
16      super.start_default_sequence();
17      if (object_test_done)
18        uvm_test_done.drop_objection(this);
19    endtask
20  endclass : apb_sequencer
```

Lines 3-5: Adding a configurable attribute to enable objection raising/dropping including UVM automation.

Lines 13-19: Raising and dropping the uvm_test_done objection before and after the default.

5.11.3 Tracing Objection Information

Debugging the raise and drop of objections is a critical part of the objection mechanism. For debug, a user can query the components about objection status and also get run-time trace information about objections activity.

5.11.3.1 Querying the Objection Status

Users can query the objection mechanism using:

- `function int get_objection_count(uvm_object obj)`

  Returns an object's number of raised objections.

- `function int get_objection_total(uvm_object obj=null)`

  Returns an object and its descendants number of raised objections.

- `function string m_display_objections(uvm_object obj = null, bit show_header = 1 )`

  Displays objection information for a given object. If an object was not specified or null was used, the entire system objections information starting from the top is shown.

5.11.3.2 Trace Objection Information

A user might want to analyze trace information of objections that are raised or dropped. This is achieved using the `set_trace` function:

```
uvm_objection::set_trace(bit trace_objection)
```

Setting the `trace_objection` to 1 will issue trace information to the screen. Trace information is displayed using the standard reporting structure. Each specific type of trace information has its own tag so that users can control the specific type of information they are concerned about.

5.11.4 Setting Drain Time

Vertical reuse allows building larger systems out of existing ones. Often, when all the subsystem objections are dropped, there is still some outstanding activity that must complete before the simulation stops (for example, internal propagation of data within the device). The UVM objection mechanism allows subsystem environment developers to define a drain time per subsystem. The full system testbench integrator does not need to worry about the drain-time of sub-environments and can add full system requirements on top.

The reusable nature of objections is achieved by having objection information propagated up the hierarchy. This allows components to get a notification any time one of their children raise or drop an objection, or when all of the objections at a current level have been dropped. A typical usage example is to set a drain time on `all_objections` dropped when the `uvm_test_done.set_drain_time()` is insufficient; for example, when the maximum time through the DUT is 15 clock cycles, the all objections dropped task can be used in the environment to perform the drain calculation like:

```
class myenv extends uvm_env;

  ...
  task all_dropped (uvm_objection objection, uvm_object source_obj,
      int count);
    if(objection == uvm_test_done)
      repeat(15) @(posedge vif.clk);
```

A Practical Guide to Adopting the Universal Verification Methodology (UVM)

```
    endtask

  endclass: myenv
```

Note UVM components have a drain-time built-in property. We recommend extending `all_dropped` and not using the drain-time attribute of a component and not using the component drain-time. Using clocks or other user-defined events provides much more control and are scalable in vertical reuse as clocks or time scales change.

5.11.5 Identifying Lack of Progress

The heartbeat capability is useful to determine when objects are no longer functioning properly. For example, a testbench may wish to define a heartbeat that detects when a deadlock condition occurs and the simulation cannot advance. The mechanism works by registering components that need to indicate viability within a window of two-event occurrences. The objection mechanism provides built-in support for heartbeats.

There are three modes that a heartbeat can have:

- `UVM_ALL_ACTIVE`—All registered components must emit a heartbeat during the heartbeat window.
- `UVM_ANY_ACTIVE`—One or more of the registered components must emit the heartbeat during the window.
- `UVM_ONE_ACTIVE`—Exactly one of the components must emit the heartbeat during the window.

5.11.5.1 Using the Heartbeat Mechanism

The steps to define a heartbeat are shown below.

Step 1: Defining the Heartbeat Objection

The first step is to define the heartbeat objection itself.

```
  uvm_objection hb_obj=new("hb_obj");
```

This definition should be visible by any objects responsible for producing the heartbeat objection.

Step 2: Defining the Heartbeat Event and Heartbeat

The next step is to define the heartbeat event, which determines the heartbeat window. The heartbeat window means that the heartbeat objection must be raised at least once in between two consecutive heartbeat events (which components can raise an objection within the window depends on the mode). A fatal error is produced if the heartbeat criteria is not met. An `uvm_event` is used for the heartbeat event and should be triggered by whatever object is responsible for determining the heartbeat window. A basic example is shown here:

```
  uvm_event hb_e;
  uvm_heartbeat my_heartbeat;
  ...<other test code>...
```

```
hb_e = new("hb_e"); // in the constructor or build() if in a component
my_heartbeat=new("my_heartbeat",this,hb_obj);
...<other test code>...
virtual task run;
    repeat(10) #100 hb_e.trigger;
endtask
```

Here, the `run()` task simply triggers the heartbeat window every 100 time units.

Step 3: Setting the Heartbeat Event and Component List

The heartbeat list is the list of components that must provide the heartbeat objection within the heartbeat window based on the operation mode. The heartbeat list is a SystemVerilog queue of UVM objects that is populated by the user. First define a list:

```
uvm_component hb_l[$];
```

When the heartbeat objection and heartbeat list are defined, the user assigns the event and list to the heartbeat. This can be done as follows:

```
my_heartbeat.set_heartbeat(hb_e, hb_l);
```

Step 4: Setting the Heartbeat

Then, each component is added to the heartbeat list. For example,

```
my_heartbeat.add (parent.child_component);
```

5.11.5.2 Heartbeat Example

This is an example of the heartbeat usage of the objection mechanism. In this scenario we have:

1. A `child_component` that:

    - Can be configured to emit *N* number of heartbeat objections

    - Can be configured with the delay between the heartbeat objections

2. A `parent_component` that:

    - Uses the event specified in #4 as the event for the heartbeat objection

    - Contains three `child_component` objects

3. A #100 clock

4. A `uvm_event` that is triggered every posedge of #3

5. A test that:

    - Configures `child_0` of `parent_component` to emit 3 heartbeats #90 apart

- Configures child_1 of parent_component to emit 5 heartbeats #90 apart

- Configures child_2 of parent_component to emit 2 heartbeats #90 apart. This child will cause the heartbeat timeout.

Example 5–16   Heartbeat

```
1   module test;

2   import uvm_pkg::*;
3   `include "uvm_macros.svh"

4   // Declare an objection for the heartbeat mechanism
5   uvm_objection hb_obj = new("hb_obj");

6   class child_component extends uvm_component;
7     int num_hb = 0;

8     function new(string name, uvm_component parent);
9       super.new(name, parent);
10    endfunction : new

11    `uvm_component_utils_begin(child_component)
12      `uvm_field_int(num_hb, UVM_DEFAULT)
13    `uvm_component_utils_end

14    virtual task run();
15      `uvm_info("HBS", $psprintf("####: NUM HB: %0d", num_hb), UVM_LOW);
16      for (int i=0; i<num_hb; i++)
17        #90 hb_obj.raise_objection(this);
18    endtask : run
19  endclass : child_component

20  class parent_component extends uvm_agent;
21    child_component child_0, child_1, child_2;
22
23    function new(string name, uvm_component parent);
24      super.new(name, parent);
25    endfunction : new

26    `uvm_component_utils(parent_component)

27    function void build();
28      super.build();
29      child_0 = child_component::type_id::create("child_0", this);
30      child_1 = child_component::type_id::create("child_1", this);
31      child_2 = child_component::type_id::create("child_2", this);
32    endfunction : build
```

```
33  endclass : parent_component

34  class simple_test extends uvm_test;
35    parent_component parent_0;
36    // Declare the heartbeat event and component
37    uvm_event hb_e;
38    uvm_heartbeat my_heartbeat;

39    function new(string name, uvm_component parent);
40      super.new(name, parent);
41    endfunction : new

42    `uvm_component_utils(simple_test)

43    function void build();
44      super.build();
45      set_config_int("parent_0.child_0", "num_hb", 3);
46      set_config_int("parent_0.child_1", "num_hb", 5);
47      set_config_int("parent_0.child_2", "num_hb", 2);
48      parent_0 = parent_component::type_id::create("parent_0", this);
49      my_heartbeat = new("my_heartbeat", this, hb_obj);
50      hb_e = new("hb_e");
51    endfunction : build

52    function void connect();
53      uvm_component hb_l[$];
54      void'( my_heartbeat.hb_mode(UVM_ANY_ACTIVE));
55      // Set the heartbeat event and component list
56      my_heartbeat.set_heartbeat(hb_e, hb_l);
57      // Add each component to the heartbeat component list
58      my_heartbeat.add(parent_0.child_0);
59      my_heartbeat.add(parent_0.child_1);
60      my_heartbeat.add(parent_0.child_2);
61    endfunction : connect

62    function void start_of_simulation();
63      this.print();
64    endfunction  : start_of_simulation

65    virtual task run;
66      repeat (10)  #100 hb_e.trigger;
67    endtask : run
68  endclass : simple_test

69  initial
70    run_test("simple_test");
71  endmodule : test
```

Note The heartbeat mechanism should be set by the reusable environment development, but its activation should be left to the testbench integrator. Only the integrator knows the what activity is mandatory for each project, and it is not desirable to end a long simulation just because a heartbeat mechanism was active but improperly configured.

5.12 Implementing Protocol-Specific Coverage and Checks

Checks and coverage are crucial in a coverage-driven verification flow. As the traffic is randomized and not explicitly called for, it is critical to use a metric to ensure that the verification goals were achieved and no area was overlooked. Functional coverage is user-defined and should represent precisely (no more and no less) the coverage goals. If a user thinks of a scenario that was not sufficiently exercised, they can add a coverage attribute to their testbench.

Interface UVCs are focused on protocol-specific coverage. The coverage groups are implemented by the UVC developer, who knows the protocol and what kind of interesting scenarios need to be observed. An interface UVC coverage model includes signal and assertion-level coverage and transaction-level coverages, such as the type and nature of data items that are injected, interesting transition of these and more.

Some of the questions related to coverage collection are:

- *Where do I place the coverage items?*
- *When and how to sample coverage?*
- *How do I enable and disable coverage items?*
- *How do I collect instance versus type coverage?*
- *How do I know how many coverage items I need?*

The following section discusses such coverage-related concerns.

5.12.1 Placing Coverage Groups

Coverage and checking are done in the monitor and collector. Coverage is collected on injected or observed transactions (passive mode). After sampling the observed transaction values, the monitor adds these to the coverage database. Sampling the generated data directly in the driver is not recommended. Sampling coverage that was collected from the bus ensures that the data reached the bus and did not get dropped between the randomization and the final injection. It also allows for better reuse of coverage code. Placing coverage in a driver allows you to collect coverage only when creating transactions, while placing coverage in a collector and monitor allows you to capture coverage in every simulation.

Note SystemVerilog allows sampling the coverage via event or by calling the `sample()` attribute. For many reasons, using the event can be tricky; it is quite possible that between the time the event was emitted and the actual sampling, the values of the transaction properties have changed. We highly recommend using the `sample()` call.

5.12.1.1 Transaction Coverage

Transaction coverage involves a transaction's physical properties, information abstracted from these properties (such as ranges of values) and crosses between the properties. Some of the transaction attributes are added for coverage purposes. (For example, a transaction may collect start_time and end_time to capture the processing start and end time). You may want to collect instance-based or type-based transaction coverage. Instance coverage creates a different coverage result for each instance of a monitor or collector. For example, for a router with multiple ports, you may want to collect coverage of packet types that were sent to port1, as opposed to the type of packets that were sent to all ports. Transition coverage is often more meaningful on instance coverage. For example, type-based coverage may indicate a good distribution of reads on writes on multiple ports, but—when used in conjunction with instance-based coverage—transition coverage will indicate an important requirement that you execute a read on a specific port directly following a write to that port.

Transaction coverage groups can be placed either in the data item class or in the monitor. If you follow the object-oriented principle of loose coupling between classes you may believe the best place for transaction coverage groups is in the transaction itself. If the same transaction is used by multiple components, each component can sample the transaction attributes without duplicating the properties or spreading its attributes across multiple components. Coverage groups added to items are more difficult to manage and often cause additional performance penalties. We recommend that you declare and instantiate coverage groups within the monitor and collector.

The example below illustrates the APB monitor coverage group:

```
1   //From: class apb_bus_monitor extends uvm_monitor;

2   covergroup apb_transfer_cg;
3       TRANS_ADDR : coverpoint trans_collected.addr {
4         bins ZERO = {0};
5         bins NON_ZERO = {[1:8'h7f]};
6       }
7       TRANS_DIRECTION : coverpoint trans_collected.direction ;
8       TRANS_DATA : coverpoint trans_collected.data {
9         bins ZERO     = {0};
10        bins NON_ZERO = {[1:8'hfe]};
11        bins ALL_ONES = {8'hff};
12      }
13      TRANS_ADDR_X_TRANS_DIRECTION: cross TRANS_ADDR, TRANS_DIRECTION;
14   endgroup
```

Placing a single coverage group in the monitor allows a single instance of the coverage group to be used for all data items that the monitor collects. The SystemVerilog language requires that coverage groups must be created in the class constructor, so you cannot use the build() method. For performance reasons, you may want to disable creation of the coverage group when coverage_enable is set to 0. Thus, we recommend:

- Instantiating the desired covergroup in the monitor constructor by calling get_config_int and only creating the covergroup if coverage_enable is set to 1.

- Setting the instance name of the coverage group to be the monitor hierarchical path

The example below illustrates construction of the APB monitor coverage group:

```
// apb_master_monitor constructor
function new (string name, uvm_component parent);
    super.new(name, parent);
    // Create covergroup only if coverage is enabled
    void'(get_config_int("coverage_enable", coverage_enable));
    if (coverage_enable) begin
        apb_transfer_cg = new();
        apb_transfer_cg.set_inst_name({get_full_name(), ".apb_transfer_cg"});
    end
...
endfunction : new
```

Note   While some attributes in the transaction are needed only for coverage, it is typically not recommended to create a base transaction and derive from it a coverage_transaction and a sequencer_transaction. While this could be the right modeling and might have positive memory and run-time impacts, it prevents the user from further extending the definition of both the monitor and the sequencer sub-types.

The embedded covergroup uses the sample() method as its sampling trigger. The sampling of the covergroup is done in a perform_coverage function which is called after a transfer has been collected.

```
function void apb_bus_monitor::perform_coverage();
    cov_apb_transfer.sample();
endfunction : perform_coverage
```

This function covers several properties of the transfer. The perform_coverage() function is called procedurally after the item has been collected by the monitor.

```
if (coverage_enable)
    perform_coverage();
```

5.12.1.2 Timing-Related Coverage

Timing-related coverage such as inter-packet gap, should be done by the collector. In order to allow transaction-level and even untimed execution mode, the monitor should not contain the concept of time.

5.12.2 Implementing Checks

Class checks should be implemented in the classes derived from uvm_monitor and uvm_collector. The derived classes of uvm_monitor and uvm_collector are always present in the agent, and thus always contain the necessary checks. The bus monitor is created by default in an env, and if the checks are enabled, the bus monitor will perform these functions. The remainder of this section uses the master monitor as an example of how to implement class checks, but they apply to the bus monitor as well.

You can write class checks as procedural code or SystemVerilog immediate assertions.

Tip   Use immediate assertions for simple checks that can be written in a few lines of code, and use functions for complex checks that require many lines of code. The reason is that as the check becomes more complicated, so does the debug of that check.

Note   Concurrent assertions are not allowed in SystemVerilog classes per the IEEE1800 LRM. These are allowed only within an interface.

Following is a simple example of an assertion check. This assertion verifies that the least-significant bits of the address are 2'b00 for word addressing. Otherwise, the assertion fails.

```
function void bus_monitor::check_address();
   check_address : assert(trans_collected.addr[1:0] == 2'b00) else
        `uvm_error("ADDRERR", "Invalid transfer address!")
     end
endfunction : check_address
```

Following is a simple example of a function check for a bus transfer of variable size (not part of the APB protocol). This function verifies that the size field value matches the size of the data dynamic array. While this example is not complex, it illustrates a procedural code example of a check.

```
function void bus_monitor::check_transfer_data_size();
   if (trans_collected.size != trans_collected.data.size())
     // Call DUT error: Transfer size field / data size mismatch.
endfunction : check_transfer_data_size
```

The proper time to execute these checks depends on the implementation. You should determine when to make the call to the check functions shown above. For the above example, both checks should be executed after the transfer is collected by the monitor. Since these checks happen at the same instance in time, a wrapper function can be created so that only one call has to be made. This wrapper function follows.

```
function void bus_monitor::perform_checks();
   check_address();
   check_transfer_data_size();
endfunction : perform_checks
```

The `perform_checks()` function is called procedurally after the item has been collected by the monitor.

5.12.3 Enabling and Disabling Coverage and Checks

The monitor and the collector should have `coverage_enable` and `checks_enable` configuration fields. Yet, sometimes these flags are not enough, as you may wish to have a finer granularity of control over which coverage and checks are enabled. Some of the requirements on enabling and disabling coverage include:

- Enabling and disabling coverage and checking for agents

- For performance reasons you may want to avoid collecting the coverage (as opposed to post simulation filtering).

- Supporting fine granularity of control for specific checks and coverage groups (see "Fine Granularity for Enabling and Disabling" on page 131)

- Disabling coverage and checks from the command line without recompilation or re-elaboration

5.12.3.1 Using the checks_enable and coverage_enable Flags

To address coverage and checking filtering at the component level, you should provide a means to control whether the checks are enforced and the coverage is collected. Use the coverage_enable and checks_enable fields for this purpose or provide this information as part of an agent configuration class. The field can be controlled using the uvm_component set_config* interface. The following is an example of using the checks_enable bit to control the checks.

```
if (checks_enable)
  perform_checks();
```

If checks_enable is set to 0, the function that performs the checks is not called, thus disabling the checks. The following example shows how to turn off the checks for all master.monitor components:

```
set_config_int("*.master.monitor", "checks_enable", 0);
```

The same capabilities exist for the coverage_enable field in the APB agent monitors and bus monitor.

5.12.3.2 Fine Granularity for Enabling and Disabling

The developer can provide an additional flag for each coverage group to prevent or enable its instantiation. Once this is provided, the user can enable and disable these separately.

A protocol may have multiple operation modes. As well as separate flags, coverage groups and checks can be relevant or irrelevant for these. For example, if we configure a UVC to have a single master, some coverages and checks of the arbitration may not be necessary. The UVC developer should capture these configuration dependency modes in their UVC. For example, the UVC environment may accept parameters, and based on that data, determine which checkers and coverage attributes should be enabled and configure the agents or monitors accordingly.

In a UVC, checks and coverage are defined in multiple locations depending on the category of functionality being analyzed. In Figure 5-7 on page 100, checks and coverage are depicted in the uvm_monitor, uvm_collector, and SystemVerilog interface. The following sections describe how the cover, covergroup, and assert constructs are used in the UVM APB UVC example.

5.12.4 Implementing Checks and Coverage in Interfaces

Interface checks are implemented as assertions. Assertions are added to check the signal activity for a protocol. The assertions related to the physical interface are placed in the env's interface. For example, an assertion might check that an address is never X or Y during a valid transfer. Use assert as well as assume properties to express these interface checks.

An assert directive is used when the property expresses the behavior of the device under test. An assume directive is used when the property expresses the behavior of the environment that generates the stimulus to the DUT.

The mechanism to enable or disable the physical checks works by mirroring the coverage and checks settings in the physical interfaces and propagating the data into the interfaces. This initial configuration values are copied in the run() phase and their changes are propagated to the interface within a forever loop.

5.13 Handling Reset

Resets are typically done for a system or a subsystem level. When a reset appears, each testbench component should return itself to its initial state. Because multiple resets can occur in a single simulation, ensure that the DUT can handle multiple reset conditions. Primary UVC reset requirements are:

- Graceful shutdown and reinvocation of assertions, threads and checkers.

- Smooth resetting of variables, scoreboard and other data structures. Not all values need to be reset (for example, memories may retain their existing values).

- No false coverage information, no missed DUT errors, no coverage errors.

- Easy/flexible hooks for users to do what they want upon reset (for example, drive chosen reset values into signals during reset).

Note   The testbench should be able to react to the DUT reset or trigger a reset on its own; but this is a system UVC responsibility and not an interface UVC.

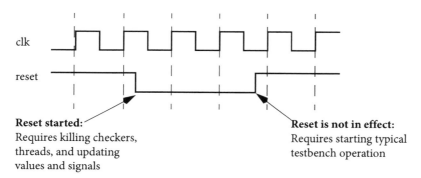

Figure 5-12   Reset Started and Reset Ended Events

5.13.1 Reset Methodology for Interface UVCs

Note   The current UVM reset methodology will be updated once the run-time phases features will be added to UVM. At the same time, the main concepts of multiple resets in a single simulation remain the same, and much of the logic recommended here will stay valid.

5.13.1.1 Propagating a Reset to the Interface UVC

Resetting Signal-Level Components

Though a reset signal is not part of the protocol signals, the interface UVC virtual interface should hold the reset signal. This is needed for terminating assertions upon reset and avoiding false negative errors. This means that the signal-level components (that is, the driver, the collector, and if a single monitor topology was used, then also the monitor), can sense the assertion and de-assertion of the reset signal and respond as needed. The are many ways to implement the desired reset logic within the driver. The code below demonstrates the reset implementation of the APB master driver.

- The `run()` method initiates the driver main activity.

```
1   // Declaration of the UVM run() phase method.
2   task apb_master_driver::run();
3     ...
4     get_and_drive();
5   endtask : run
```

- Every sub-component should have a reset task that resets signals and testbench variable to their default reset values. The reset can optionally invoke sub-components of the current component.

```
1   task apb_master_driver::reset();
2     // If the reset is not active, then wait for it to become active before
3     // resetting the interface.
4     wait(!vif.preset);
5     vif.paddr    <= 'h0;
6     vif.pwdata   <= 'h0;
7     vif.prwd     <= 'b0;
8     vif.psel     <= 'b0;
9     vif.penable  <= 'b0;
10  endtask : reset
```

- The driver's main `get_and_drive` loop forks reset and regular activity in an endless loop. If reset appears, the driver is stopped, `reset()` is called, and another iteration of the while loop is executed.

```
11  // This task manages the interaction between the sequencer and driver
12  task apb_master_driver::get_and_drive();
13    while (1) begin
14      reset();
15      fork
16        @(negedge vif.preset)
17          `uvm_info(get_type_name(), "get_and_drive: Reset Asserted",
                              UVM_MEDIUM)
18        begin
19          // This thread will be killed on reset
20          forever begin
21            @(posedge vif.pclock iff (vif.preset))
22              seq_item_port.get_next_item(req);
```

```
23              drive_transfer(req);
24              seq_item_port.item_done(req);
25          end
26        end
27        join_any
28        disable fork;
29        //If we are in the middle of a transfer, need to end the tx. Also,
30        //do any reset cleanup here. The only way we got to this point is via
31        //a reset.
32        if(req.is_active()) this.end_tr(req);
33    end
34 endtask : get_and_drive
```

Guidelines about reset:

- In some examples, soft, hard or other user-defined resets need to be implemented. You can implement different styles of reset as an input parameter to the `reset()` task.

- Many times, a reset needs to be triggered by the testbench. However, this is not the task of the interface UVC and is discussed in Chapter 10 "System UVCs and Testbench Integration".

Resets and Assertions

Concurrent assertions reside within the SystemVerilog interface. You might want to kill running assertions when a reset appears or `has_checks` is dropped within the simulation. This could be achieved using the following:

```
1  interface yapp_if (input clock, input reset );
2    // SVA default reset
3    default disable iff (reset && !has_checks);
4    ...
5  endinterface
```

Resetting the Transaction-Level Components

The transaction-level components do not have access to the virtual interface and cannot use the reset signal to reset themselves. The solution for the transaction-level component is:

- For every agent, define a `reset()` function that resets the agent and calls the sub-components reset. As needed, each sub-component can have a default reset function. Remember that the signal-level components trigger their own reset.

- Define a reset analysis port in the monitor. Upon a reset event, the agent reset function is called.

The reset function can be called by the monitor or can be invoked from above by a higher-level component.

Reset of the sequencer might require one of the following behaviors:

- Discard the current item, but continue the current sequences.

- Reset the sequencer by calling the `stop_sequences()` function. After this function is called, the default sequence or any other sequence that was started at time zero needs to be restarted. Use the `get_config` to get the `default_sequence` that needs to be executed.

Note There is no need to modify the seed on a `reset()`, as the random stability rules in SystemVerilog cause the randomized value to be different than the previous sequences execution.

5.14 Packaging Interface UVCs

As a user adopts a new package they may want to find the docs, examples, and other files. They may also want to run a quick test to make sure that the package is complete and no files are missing. UVM recommends a standard directory structure that addresses many users requirements. Directory structure and filename consistency may seem trivial, but as you integrate and share verification components, the standard directory structure becomes a big factor in reducing the support effort within and between teams. The packaging guidelines of UVM include:

- Standard directory structure
- File organization and naming conventions
- Package and name space recommendations

5.14.1 Interface UVC Directory Structure

Each interface UVC resides within a top root directory that is named for its interface protocol. The following figure illustrates the standard directory structure for the APB UVC:

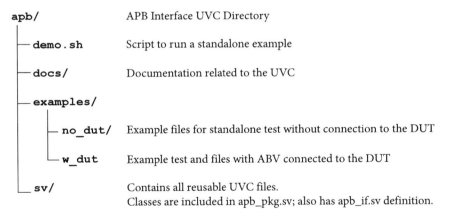

Figure 5-13   APB Interface UVC Directory Structure

Notes

- All reusable code resides within the `sv` sub-directory. The bulk of the UVC files are placed here, with the SystemVerilog interface file(s) for the UVC. The `sv` directory may optionally contain subdirectories for coverage, checking, or sequences.

- The docs directory contains the UVC documentation.

- The examples directory contains one or more usage examples. This may include a connection to a dummy DUT and/or examples to demonstrate different UVC configurations.

- A `demo.sh` scripts allows standalone checking of the completeness of the UVC by running one of the provided examples.

- Other optional directories may also be included. You may include a SystemC, or *e* directory for UVCs that contain components written in those languages. You may also include a data directory to store memory data for sequences, ROMs and other memory requirements in a UVC.

5.14.2 File Naming Conventions

Using a standard file naming convention makes it easy to identify and find files during UVC development and debug. Each component should be specified in its own file, and the filename should match the class name, which in turn should include the name of the component. For example, the APB master driver class will be found in the `apb_master_driver.sv` file. Figure 5-14 on page 136 shows an example from the AMBA APB sv directory:

```
apb_collector.sv          apb_master_seq_lib.sv       apb_slave_seq_lib.sv
apb_config.sv             apb_master_sequencer.sv     apb_slave_sequencer.sv
apb_env.sv                apb_monitor.sv              apb_transfer.sv
apb_if.sv                 apb_pkg.sv                  apb_types.sv
apb_master_agent.sv       apb_slave_agent.sv
apb_master_driver.sv      apb_slave_driver.sv
```

Figure 5-14   APB Interface UVC Reusable Files

5.14.3 UVC Packages

Finally, we recommend capturing all of the reusable data declarations in a SystemVerilog package and importing the package into a testbench that uses it. The package file should contain only definitions and class declarations that will be included as part of a reusable component. These files are included in the package file (`apb_pkg.sv`) as shown below:

```
package apb_pkg;
    // Import the UVM package and include the UVM macro definitions
    import uvm_pkg::*;
    `include "uvm_macros.svh"
    // Data types and data item declaration
    `include "apb_types.sv"
    `include "apb_transfer.sv"
    //Shared files
    `include "apb_collector.sv"
    `include "apb_monitor.sv"
    // APB master files
    `include "apb_master_driver.sv"
    `include "apb_master_sequencer.sv"
```

```
`include "apb_master_agent.sv"
// APB slave files
`include "apb_slave_driver.sv"
`include "apb_slave_sequencer.sv"
`include "apb_slave_agent.sv"

`include "apb_env.sv"
endpackage : apb_pkg
```

This package is compiled and imported into any test or testbench that uses the component.

Note   In previous sections we recommended that you do not include the sequence library files in the UVC package. If you have standard sequences that will be used in many applications it makes sense to capture these sequences in a `seq_lib` file and include these files in the package. For example the APB interface may have: `apb_read_byte_seq` and `apb_read_word_seq` as standard UVC sequences. Otherwise, the sequence files will be included into the testbench.

Summary

This chapter covers the details of developing interface UVCs, which are key building blocks of a verification testbench. Each UVC follows a consistent architecture and contains a complete set of elements for generating stimulus, as well as checking correctness and collecting coverage information for a specific design protocol. Following this recommended architecture will lead to increased productivity because UVCs can be reused for verification at the block level, cluster level and system level, and can also be reused for follow-on projects with the same interface protocols.

6   Automating UVC Creation

The following are common reactions most verification engineers have to the encapsulation and hook-up recommendations of the UVM reuse methodology:

- *Creating reusable UVCs introduces a lot of overhead.*

- *How many rules do you need to memorize?*

- *We don't need all that extra encapsulation—it just introduces the opportunity for syntax errors.*

Our experience has shown that users who follow the UVM methodology recommendations experience a speed improvement in their first project and a more significant improvement in follow-up integrations. In addition, the standard hierarchy and commonality allows further automation. Code generators can leverage the canonical structure and produce bug-free, well-commented code, with more consistency between components. A compliance checklist and methodology-level linters can ensure seamless integration and eliminate expensive support or code modifications. This chapter discusses a technology and development flow that expedites UVC development and usage.

6.1   UVC Development Flow

Before we discuss automation, we need to look at the development flow. Protocols specify the handshake requirements of components. For example, to interact with slave devices you need to implement master component logic. In PCI Express, to communicate with a downstream device you need an upstream testbench component.

Two approaches can be taken in building verification IP:

- Build the verification component against the DUT.

- Build the verification IP in isolation and connect it to the DUT once it has been developed.

Developing the UVC in isolation requires implementation of both the device and the testbench logic (master/slave, Tx/Rx, and so on).

The advantage of building the verification IP against the DUT is that the DUT IP might already be implemented and only the counter logic needs to be developed. However, usually it is more efficient to use distributed VIP development. In this development flow, an individual or a team owns developing a UVC for a given protocol. Even though only a master agent may be needed for the project, both the slave and master agents are developed, checked against each other, verified that the waveform follows the protocols, and only later is the UVC configured to verify the project DUT. Figure 6-1 shows this flow.

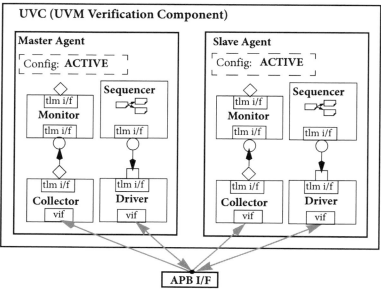

Figure 6-1   Active Master and Active Slave Development Mode

Figure 6-2 shows the same verification component connected to a slave device with the slave agent in passive mode.

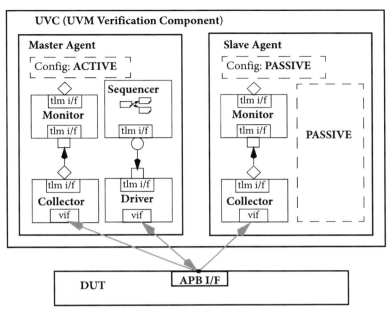

Figure 6-2   UVC Verifying a Slave Device

The advantages of this flow are:

- No dependency on device availability or maturity

- Easy development of the protocol logic as you focus on a single interface

- No interpretation and implementation bugs to leak from the device to the testbench. This prevents UVC developers from introducing design errors into their testbench as they try to bring up the device.

- Easy to distribute the work between multiple individuals or teams

- A complete UVC is developed that can emulate other components. In our example, the result can emulate both master and slave as needed.

- No complex scripts required or performance penalty incurred due to a system-level activation

For these reasons, we recommend following the distributed development mode whenever possible.

6.2   Code Generators

As noted in the introduction to this book, the commonality and the generality of the methodology allow code generators to produce a lot of initial skeleton code and infrastructure code. The key in using code generators is to ensure that they generate compliant and agreed-upon code, and support an acceptable level of customization before the unavoidable manual typing begins.

One example of a good code generator is the Cadence® Incisive® Verification Builder. The Builder is a *wizard* technology that produces UVM standard environments. The user provides initial information about the desired verification IP environment. Based on the initial input, more queries are asked until the system is ready to produce a verification environment skeleton. A set of finalization action items is provided to guide users on how to complete the protocol specific UVC environment. The Builder technology benefits both novice users (there is no need to know all the guidelines and rules) and experts alike (as a productivity tool that answers the question "*Why should I start from scratch?*"). The actual code produced by the Builder is readable and well-commented, and the implementation is constantly updated as new methodology features and implementation techniques are introduced. The figures below illustrate the Builder input forms and the generated result.

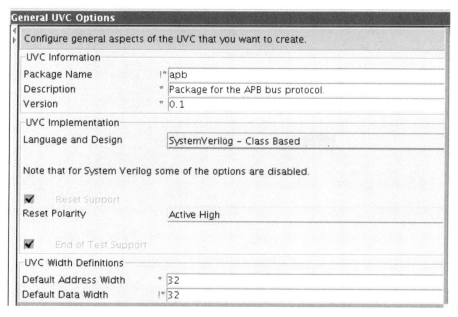

Figure 6-3   Incisive Verification Builder Initial Form for Creating an Interface UVC

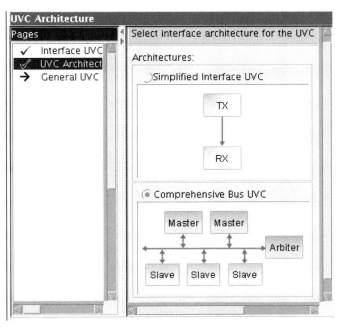

Figure 6-4   Interface UVC Architecture Form

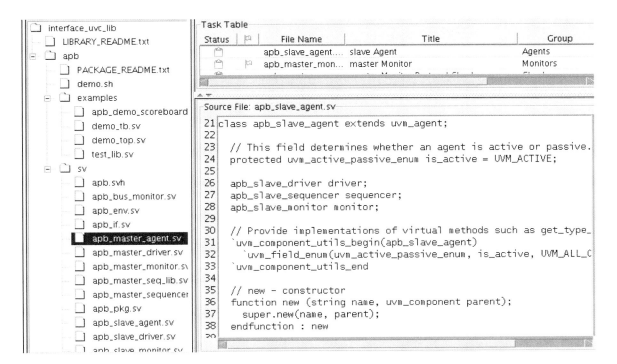

Figure 6-5   Incisive Verification Builder Post-Generation Form

The figures above illustrate a few of the Builder forms. The Builder uses a graphical user interface to lead you through the UVC creation process. After UVC code generation, you are presented with a finalization task list that points to the files and functions that need to be updated to finalize the UVC creation.

The Builder also generates an isolated development environment for the desired UVC, which allows you to enhance the master and the slave agent in a symmetric manner until the UVC implementation is complete.

6.3   Compliance Checklist

Code generators are efficient productivity tools. But if you did not purchase commercial VIP, you still need to go through the protocol specifications and implement the desired UVC. While template-driven solutions can start a verification engineer on the right path, it is still easy to stray from the methodology. It is the UVM compliance checklist and associated automatic checkers that ensure the developer builds, and the integrator receives, UVCs compliant to the methodology, which leads to reuse without rework.

A compliance checklist is also efficient if commercial VIPs are used. A compliance checklist is needed by an integrator to qualify commercial VIP and by VIP vendors who want a way to measure and prove to potential users the level of their methodology compliance.

A UVM compliance checklist is provided by Cadence and is also provided on **www.uvmworld.org**. These requirements were collected and tuned over years by many customers on many projects. If the reasoning for a check is not clear, or if you have an enhancement suggestion, it is best to follow the checklist and in parallel, express your concerns to the UVM development team.

The UVM compliance checklist contains the following categories:

- Packaging and Name Space—Provides guidelines on how to package environments in a consistent way for easy shipping and delivery

- Architecture—Includes checks to ensure similar high-level topology for UVM environments. This is critical for understanding a new UVC, its configuration, and class hierarchy.

- Reset and Clock—Has various reset and clocking topics

- Checking—Touches the self checking aspects of reusable UVC

- Sequences—Provides good practices on creating a reusable sequence library

- Messaging—Defines message methodology to allow for an efficient debug environment and reduces support requirements

- Documentation—Satisfies the requirement for complete documentation

- General Deliverable—Includes more delivery requirements

- End of Tests—Gives minimal end-of-test requirements

- UVM SystemVerilog specific compliance checks—Supplies checks that are specific to UVM SystemVerilog implementation

Each check has a unique identification code, which is used for documentation, queries that supply more detail, and cross-tool consistency.

6.4   Automated Compliance Checking

Many users of the *e*RM/OVM/UVM who apply the compliance checklist have requested an automated tool for checking verification IP (VIP) against the checklist. This allows them to use qualifying third-party VIP or internally developed IP. These tools exist today in the industry.

For example, AMIQ, an EDA company that is part of the growing UVM ecosystem, provides a tool called DVT, which automates UVM compliance checking. DVT is an Eclipse-based integrated development environment (IDE) targeted at increasing productivity for SystemVerilog and *e* developers. In addition to UVM compliance checking, users can also benefit from UVM-dedicated wizards, UVM-simulation log recognition, code and project templates, and in-line documentation. For more information on DVT, refer to **www.dvteclipse.com**.

Summary

In this chapter, we introduce options for automating the task of UVC creation. We discuss the benefits of implementing both the master and slave testbench logic so that UVCs can be developed independently of the DUT and configured for project-specific requirements. Then, we show an example of a code generator that produces the standard infrastructure and connections for a reusable UVC. The generated code follows the consistent UVC architecture, and can be a productivity tool for both new users to UVM and experienced developers who want to quickly get started. Finally, we introduce a compliance checklist and compliance-checking tools that allow verification IP developers and project teams to qualify their code against methodology guidelines.

7   Simple Testbench Integration

Chapters 5 and 6 covered the process of creating interface UVM-compliant UVCs. The UVM views a testbench as a collection of reusable components with additional glue logic. An advanced verification environment contains more than interface UVCs. For example, we recommend adding the DUT verification logic (scoreboard and coverage) in a reusable module UVC. To gradually introduce the integration tasks, we start in this chapter with simple testbenches that do not use a module UVC. In Chapter 10 "System UVCs and Testbench Integration" we expand on the concepts covered here and integrate DUT-related components into a module UVC. In this chapter, a distinction is made between the UVC integrator and the test writer, who might have less knowledge about verification and wants to create tests on top of an already existing testbench.

7.1   Testbenches and Tests

As illustrated in Figure 7-1, A Simple Integrated Testbench Example, the UVC integrator instantiates and configures reusable components to build a testbench infrastructure. Then tests are created to steer the stimulus generation to visit interesting areas. In UVM, a test creates the testbench infrastructure, and using the configuration mechanism, can customize the testbench operation and stimulus generation.

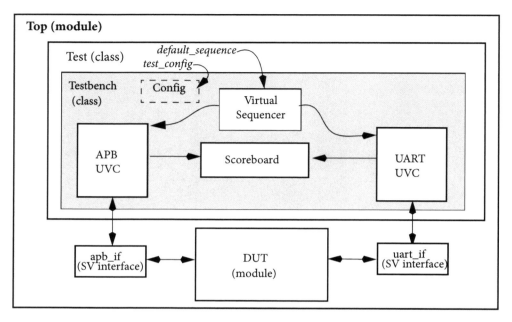

Figure 7-1   A Simple Integrated Testbench Example

7.1.1   The Testbench Class

The testbench defines the verification environment topology. It instantiates the reusable verification IP and defines the configuration of that IP as required by the application. Why do we need a testbench class instead of creating everything in a test? Instantiating the reusable components directly inside each test has several drawbacks:

- The test writer must know how to instantiate, configure and connect the environment.

- Changes to the topology require updating multiple test files, which can become a huge task.

- The tests are not reusable because they incorporate a specific environment structure.

Separating the instantiation and hook-up of the environment from the stimulus generation control allows a single testbench to be used by multiple tests, and allows multiple tests to be used with different testbenches and configurations.

7.1.2   The Test Classes

A UVM test enables configuration of the testbench and interface UVCs, and defines the default scenario for the testbench to execute. Although the testbench class provides default configuration values for the interface UVCs, a test can modify both topological and run-time configuration properties as needed. Configuration customization is done via the advanced UVM configuration mechanism provided in the UVM library. Note that UVM tests are relatively small in content. Much of the reuse is achieved via a collection of sequences developed as part of the reusable interface components and the testbench. The test writer uses these sequences as building blocks for each test scenario. The UVC developer can provide user-defined sequences in a file or package, which is included or imported by the test class. A test provides data and sequence generation and inline constraints. Test files are typically associated with a single configuration; however, because the testbench class can be extended and type-overridden by the factory, the same test can be used with different though similar configurations.

For usage examples of test classes, refer to "Creating a Test" on page 156.

7.1.2.1   Where Is My Test?

If you search your top-level module, you will not be able find the test class instantiation. This is because the test is instantiated through the top module in a simple call to a global function called `run_test()`. The name of the test class is provided as an argument to the `run_test()` function or can be specified as a simulator command-line argument. This way, you can use the command-line selection and the fact that tests are classes, to compile the entire test suite for a regression run without the need to re-elaborate the testbench or DUT for every test. This global function is described in "Test Selection" on page 157.

7.1.2.2   Why Not Use Program Blocks?

We do not recommend using program blocks in testbenches, as they provide little value in UVM environments. The semantics of package threads activated within a program block was unclear and resolved only in the SystemVerilog 2009 LRM. At this point, the correct behavior was not implemented on all simulators and will result different behavior on different simulators.

7.2   Creating a Simple Testbench

The steps you need to perform to create a simple testbench using reusable UVCs are:

1.   Identify the UVCs you will need for your testbench and review their configuration parameters and built-in sequence libraries.

2.   Create a testbench class and instantiate reusable UVCs along with other control and checking logic.

3.   Configure, create, and hook up the testbench components.

4.   Create additional reusable sequences for interface UVCs (optional).

5.   Add a virtual sequencer and create virtual sequences (optional).

6.   Add checking (scoreboard) and functional coverage extensions.

When your testbench is complete, create tests to exercise the sequence sets and achieve coverage goals.

7.2.1   Instantiating UVCs in a Testbench

Figure 7-2, Simple UVM Testbench for a UART Controller Device, shows a typical verification environment for a UART Controller device. It also includes the test class containing the uart_ctrl testbench class.

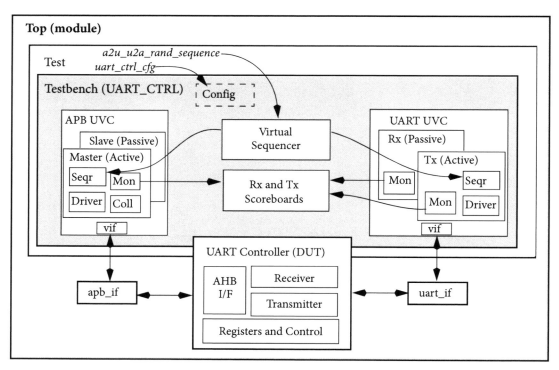

Figure 7-2   Simple UVM Testbench for a UART Controller Device

Referring to Figure 7-2, let's look at how we develop the testbench. The UART Controller design pictured has an APB bus interface and a UART serial interface. Assuming we have developed a UVC for each interface, we instantiate these in a testbench along with a scoreboard and a virtual sequencer. The scoreboard and virtual sequencer will be discussed later in this chapter. The testbench class is derived from the uvm_env class. It instantiates and configures the reusable components for the design being tested. Multiple tests can instantiate this testbench class and determine the nature of traffic to generate and send for the selected configuration.

Example 7–1   UART Controller Testbench

```
1   class uart_ctrl_tb extends uvm_env;
2     // UVC Components
3     apb_env   apb0;     // APB UVC
4     uart_env uart0;     // UART UVC

5     // Scoreboard
6     uart_ctrl_tx_scbd tx_scbd;
```

```
7      uart_ctrl_rx_scbd rx_scbd;

8      // Virtual sequencer
9      uart_ctrl_virtual_sequencer virtual_sequencer;

10     // UVC Configuration Classes
11     apb_config  apb_cfg;
12     uart_config uart_cfg;

13     // UVM component automation
14     `uvm_component_utils(uart_ctrl_tb)

15     // Constructor - required UVM syntax
16     function new(input string name, input uvm_component parent=null);
17       super.new(name,parent);
18     endfunction

19     // Additional class methods
20     extern virtual function void build();
21     extern virtual function void connect();
22   endclass : uart_ctrl_tb
```

Line 1: Extend the testbench class from uvm_env.

Lines 3-4: Place instances of the APB and UART reusable UVCs.

Lines 6-7: Place instances of the scoreboards for checking. This design has two scoreboard components.

Line 9: Place an instance of a Virtual Sequencer.

Lines 11-12: Instances of the APB and UART config classes. These can also optionally be combined into a uart_ctrl_config class, which contains instances of these two classes.

Lines 20-22: Declarations of additional testbench class methods (UVM phases). The testbench configuration and creation are performed in the build() method. The connect() method is used to make connections between the UVC monitors and the scoreboard. The connect() method is also where the virtual interface connections are made.

Use the UVM build() method to create and configure the testbench components. First the UVC configuration classes are created (and optionally randomized). Then the configuration mechanism is used to set the configuration object for each UVC before it is created. This is shown in the build() code below:

```
1    function void uart_ctrl_tb::build();
2      super.build();
3      // Create the UVC configurations if they have not already been set
4      if (apb_cfg == null) begin
5        apb_cfg = apb_config::type_id::create("apb_cfg", this);
6        apb_cfg.add_master("master", UVM_ACTIVE);
7        apb_cfg.add_slave("slave0", 32'h000000, 32'h81FFFF, 0, UVM_PASSIVE);
```

```
8    end
9    if (uart_cfg == null)
10     uart_cfg= uart_config::type_id::create("uart_cfg",this);

11   set_config_object("apb0", "cfg", apb_cfg);
12   set_config_object("uart0", "cfg", uart_cfg);

13   apb0 = apb_env::type_id::create("apb0",this);
14   uart0 = uart_env::type_id::create("uart0",this);
15   virtual_sequencer =
   uart_ctrl_virtual_sequencer::type_id::create("virtual_sequencer",this);
16   tx_scbd = uart_ctrl_tx_scbd::type_id::create("tx_scbd", this);
17   rx_scbd = uart_ctrl_rx_scbd::type_id::create("rx_scbd", this);
18 endfunction : build
```

There are three things to remember when implementing the build() method:

1. Call super.build() first to update the configuration fields of the testbench.

2. Use create() instead of new() to allocate objects so you can override sub-components with derivative versions using the UVM factory.

3. We recommended that you set configuration parameters before you create the components. This allows the component to fetch configuration values in their constructors (for example, to control coverage group instantiation).

Now use the UVM connect() method to hook up the testbench components after they have been built. The connect phase includes connecting the UVC TLM monitor ports to the scoreboard, connecting the virtual sequencer to the UVC sequencers and setting the virtual interface connections. This is shown in the connect() code below:

```
1   function void uart_ctrl_tb::connect();
2     super.connect();
3     // Connect TLM ports from the monitors to the scoreboards
4     uart0.Rx.monitor.frame_collected_port.connect(rx_scbd.uart_match);
5     apb0.bus_monitor.item_collected_port.connect(rx_scbd.apb_add);
6     uart0.Tx.monitor.frame_collected_port.connect(tx_scbd.uart_add);
7     apb0.bus_monitor.item_collected_port.connect(tx_scbd.apb_match);

8     //  Hook up virtual sequencer to interface sequencers
9     virtual_sequencer.apb_seqr =  apb0.master.sequencer;
10    if (uart0.Tx.is_active == UVM_ACTIVE)
11      virtual_sequencer.uart_seqr =  uart0.Tx.sequencer;

12    // Set the virtual interfaces
13    apb0.assign_vi(uart_tb_top.apb_if0);
14    uart0.assign_vi(uart_tb_top.uart_if0);

15 endfunction : connect
```

When the testbench infrastructure is captured in a testbench class, many test classes may instantiate the testbench class above, so test writers do not need to understand all the details of how it is created and configured.

7.3   Testbench Configuration

The build method described above configures both the APB UVC and UART UVC before they are created. Reusable testbench components have built-in configuration information that can be controlled using the UVM configuration mechanism.

7.3.1   UVC Configurable Parameters

Based on the protocols used in a device, the integrator instantiates the needed environment classes and configures them for a desired operation mode. Some standard configuration parameters are recommended to address common verification needs. Other parameters are protocol- and implementation-specific.

Chapter 5 "Interface UVCs" introduces examples of standard UVC component configuration parameters:

- A monitor, collector and `env` component have two standard configuration fields: `checks_enable` and `coverage_enable`.

- An agent has an `is_active` field to configure that component as active or passive. In active mode, the agent drives traffic to the DUT. In passive mode, the agent passively checks and collects coverage for a device. A rule of thumb to follow is to use an active agent per device that needs to be emulated, and a passive agent for every RTL device that needs to be verified.

Examples of user-defined parameters:

- The `env` (UVC) may have configuration fields to indicate the number of masters (`num_masters`), number of slaves (`num_slaves`) and if a `bus_monitor` is present (`has_bus_monitor`).

- A driver, sequencer, monitor and collector may need DUT-specific configuration information to generate and/or capture transactions. For example, the operation mode of a device, the maximum payload size or the speed of a bus.

A UVM UVC should support the standard configuration parameters and provide user-defined configuration parameters as needed.

7.3.2   UVC Configuration Mechanism

Figure 7-3, Standard Configuration Fields and Locations, shows some of the configuration fields for a typical bus-based UVM verification component. UVM provides a configuration mechanism to allow integrators to configure an environment without needing to know the UVC implementation and hook-up scheme. Following are some examples.

- Do not collect coverage for `slaves[0]` agent:
    ```
    set_config_int("apb0.slaves[0].monitor", "coverage_enable", 0);
    ```

- Set all APB slaves (using a wildcard) to be passive:

      set_config_int("apb0.slaves*", "is_active", UVM_PASSIVE);

- Specify the default config class for the APB:

      set_config_object("apb0", "apb_config", default_apb_config);

The order of configuration is that the container component always takes precedence (and thus overrides) the contained component settings. This allows the testbench to override the UVC configuration and allows the tests to override the testbench settings. Using a configuration class for UVCs is recommended, but this decision is made by the UVC developer.

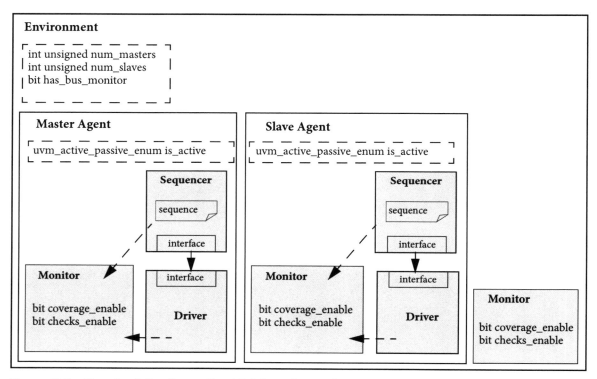

Figure 7-3 Standard Configuration Fields and Locations

7.3.3 Using a Configuration Class

We recommend that UVCs randomize configuration attributes inside a configuration class. Dependencies between these attributes are captured using constraints within the configuration object. In such cases, users can extend the configuration class to add new constraints, or layer additional constraints on the class using inline constraints. Once the configuration is randomized, the test writer can use set_config_object() to assign the configuration object to one or more environments within the testbench. Similar to set_config_int(), set_config_object() allows you to set the configuration to multiple environments in the testbench, regardless of their location, and impact the build process of the testbench.

Configuration classes are also important for vertical reuse. A system configuration class may include two subsystem configuration classes, with a few extra system-level attributes and constraints. Chapter 5 "Interface UVCs" introduced a config class for an APB UVC. That code is repeated here for your reference:

Example 7–2   APB Configuration Classes (slave_config, master_config and config)

```
1   class apb_slave_config extends uvm_object;
2     string name;
3     uvm_active_passive_enum is_active = UVM_ACTIVE;
4     rand int start_address;
5     rand int end_address;
6     rand int psel_index;
7     constraint addr_cst { start_address <= end_address; }
8     constraint psel_cst { psel_index inside {[0:15]}; }
9     // UVM object_utils, field macros and constructor
10    extern virtual function bitcheck_address_range(int unsigned addr);
11  endclass : apb_slave_config

12  class apb_master_config extends uvm_object;
13    string name;
14    uvm_active_passive_enum is_active = UVM_ACTIVE;
15  // UVM object utils, field macros and constructor syntax
16  endclass : apb_master_config

17  class apb_config extends uvm_object;
18    // APB has one master and N slaves
19    rand apb_master_config master_config;
20    rand apb_slave_config slave_configs[$];
21    // constraints on the composite configuration
22    //UVM object_utils, field macros and constructor
23    extern function void add_slave(string name, int start_addr,
24           int psel_indx, uvm_active_passive_enum is_active=UVM_ACTIVE);
25    extern function int get_slave_psel_by_addr(int addr);
26  endclass : apb_config
```

The next example shows a subset of the config class for a UART interface UVC which also is used to configure the UART controller device:

Example 7–3   UART Configuration Class

```
1   class uart_config extends uvm_object;
2     //UART topology parameters
3     uvm_active_passive_enum  is_tx_active = UVM_ACTIVE;
4     uvm_active_passive_enum  is_rx_active = UVM_PASSIVE;

5     // UART device parameters
6     rand bit [7:0] baud_rate_gen; // Baud Rate Generator Register
```

```
7    rand bit [1:0] nbstop;       // Number stop bits (mode_reg[7:6])
8    rand bit [1:0] ua_chmode;    // Channel mode     (mode_reg[9:8])
9    rand bit       parity_en ;   // Parity Enable (control_reg[3])
10   rand bit       parity_even ; // Parity Even(control_reg[4])

11   // Constraints
12   constraint c_num_stop_bits { nbstop inside {[0:2]};}

13   // Constructor, uvm_object_utils and uvm_field_* macros

14 endclass : uart_config
```

7.4   Creating a Test

In UVM, a test is a class that encapsulates test-specific instructions written by the test writer. This section describes how to create and select a test. It also describes how to create a test family base class to verify a topology configuration.

Tests in UVM are classes that are derived from an uvm_test base class. Using classes, instead of modules or program blocks, allows inheritance and reuse of tests.

7.4.1   Creating the Base Test

The following example shows a base test that uses the uart_ctrl_tb defined in "UART Controller Testbench" on page 150. This base test is a starting point for all derivative tests that will use the uart_ctrl_tb. The complete test class is shown here:

```
1   class uart_ctrl_base_test extends uvm_test;

2     uart_ctrl_tb uart_ctrl_tb0; //Testbench Instance

3     `uvm_component_utils(uart_ctrl_base_test)

4       // Update this component's properties and create the testbench.
5     virtual function void build();
6       super.build();
7       uart_ctrl_tb0 = uart_ctrl_tb::type_id::create("uart_ctrl_tb0", this);
8     endfunction

9       // Constructor
10    function new (input string name, uvm_component parent = null);
11      super.new(name, parent);
12    endfunction
13  endclass : uart_ctrl_base_test
```

The build() function of the base test creates the uart_ctrl_tb. The SystemVerilog UVM Class Library will execute the build() function of the uart_ctrl_base_test for the user when cycling through the simulation phases of the components. This creates the testbench environment because each sub-component will create components that will create more components in their build() functions.

All of the definitions in the base test will be inherited by any test that derives from uart_ctrl_base_test. This means that any derivative test will not have to build the testbench if the test calls super.build(). Likewise, the run() task behavior can be inherited. If the current implementation does not meet the needs of a specific test, you can redefine both the build() and run() methods because they are both virtual.

7.4.2   Creating a Test Library Using a Base Test

You can derive from the base test defined in "Creating the Base Test" on page 156 to create tests that reuse the same topology. Because the testbench is created by the base test's build() function and the run() task defines the run phase, the derivative tests can make minor adjustments. (For example, changing the default sequence executed by the agents in the environment.) Below is an example of a simple test that inherits from uart_ctrl_base_test.

```
1   class u2a_a2u_rand_test extends uart_ctrl_base_test;
2     `uvm_component_utils(u2a_a2u_rand_test)

3     virtual function void build();
4       super.build();
5       // Substitute the default sequences for the APB and UART UVCs.
6       set_config_string("uart_ctrl_tb0.apb0.master.sequencer",
7          "default_sequence", "apb_write_to_uart_seq");
8       set_config_string("uart_ctrl_tb0.uart0.Tx.sequencer",
9          "default_sequence", "uart_write_to_apb_seq");
10    endfunction
11    //Constructor ...
12  endclass : u2a_a2u_rand_test
```

This test changes the default sequence executed by the APB master agent and the UART Tx agent. It is important that the settings for the default_sequence be set after calling super.build(), which allows the set_config directives of this class to override the base_test set_config directives. When super.build() is called, the uart_ctrl_tb0 and all of its sub-components are created. if you need to set configuration items for the testbench, these set_config_* calls must be placed before the super.buid() call.

7.4.3   Test Selection

After you have declared a user-defined test (described in "Creating a Test Library Using a Base Test" on page 157), invoke the global UVM run_test() task in the top-level module to select a test to be simulated. Its prototype is:

```
task run_test(string test_name="");
```

When a test name is provided to the run_test() task, the factory is called to create an instance of the test with that type name. Simulation then starts and cycles through the simulation phases.

A test name is provided to `run_test()` via a simulator command-line argument. If the top module calls `run_test()` without an argument, the `+UVM_TESTNAME=`*test_name* simulator command-line argument is checked. If present, `run_test()` will use *test_name*. Using the simulator command-line argument avoids having to hard-code the test name in the `run_test()` task. For example, in the top-level module, call the `run_test()` as follows:

```
module uart_ctrl_top;
  // DUT, interfaces, and all non-testbench code
  initial
    run_test();
endmodule
```

To select a test of type `u2a_a2u_rand_test` (described in "Creating a Test Library Using a Base Test" on page 157) using simulator command-line option, use the following command:

```
% simulator-command other-options +UVM_TESTNAME=u2a_a2u_rand_test
```

If the test name provided to `run_test()` does not exist, the simulation will exit immediately via a call to `$fatal`. If this occurs, it is likely the name was typed incorrectly or the `uvm_component_utils` macro was not used.

By using this method and only changing the `+UVM_TESTNAME` argument, you can run multiple tests without having to recompile or re-elaborate the design or testbench.

7.5   Creating Meaningful Tests

The previous sections show how test classes are put together. At this point, random traffic is created and sent to the DUT. The user can change the randomization seed to achieve new test patterns. To achieve verification goals in a systematic way, the user will need to control test creation to cover specific areas.

Users can control test creation as follows:

- Add constraints to control individual data items. This method provides basic functionality. It is described in "Constraining Data Items" on page 158.

- Use UVM sequences to control the order of multiple data items. This method provides more flexibility and control. It is described in "Sequences and Sequencer Control" on page 161.

- Use the configuration mechanism to override a configuration attribute that changes a UVC or testbench configuration.

- Use a UVM callback to modify the code.

7.5.1   Constraining Data Items

By default, sequencers repeatedly generate random data items. At this level, the test writer can control the number of generated data items and add constraints to data items to control their generated values.

To constrain data items:

1. Identify the data item classes and their generated fields in the UVC.

2. Create a derivation of the data item class that adds or overrides default constraints.

3. In a test, adjust the environment (or a subset of it) to use the newly-defined data items.

4. Run the simulation using a command-line option to specify the test name.

The following example, `uart_frame,` is created by the UART UVC developer.

Example 7–4   UART Frame Data Item

```
1   typedef enum bit {BAD_PARITY, GOOD_PARITY} parity_e;
2   class uart_frame extends uvm_sequence_item;
3     rand bit start_bit;
4     rand bit [7:0] payload;
5     rand bit [1:0] stop_bits;
6     rand bit [3:0] error_bits;
7     bit parity;
8     // Control fields
9     rand int unsigned transmit_delay;
10    rand parity_e parity_type;
11    // Constructor and uvm_object_utils macro
12    // Specification section 1.2: the error bits value should be
13    // different than zero.
14    constraint c_error_bits {error_bits != 4'h0;}
15    // Default distribution constraints
16    constraint c_default_parity_type {parity_type dist {
17      GOOD_PARITY:=90, BAD_PARITY:=10};}
18    // Utility functions
19    extern function bit calc_parity ( );
20    ...
21  endclass: uart_frame
```

A few fields in the class come from the device specification. For example, a frame should have a payload that is sent to the DUT. Other fields are there to assist the test writer in controlling the generation. For example, the field `parity_type` is not being sent to the DUT, but it allows you to easily specify and control the parity distribution. Such control fields are called *knobs*. The UVC documentation should list the data item's knobs, their roles, and legal range.

Data items have specification constraints. These constraints can come from the DUT specification to create legal data items. For example, a legal frame must have `error_bits` not equal to 0. A different type of constraint in the data items controls the traffic generation. For example, in the constraint block `c_default_parity_type` (in the example above), the parity bit is constrained to be 90-percent legal (good parity) and 10-percent illegal (bad parity).

7.5.1.1   Creating a Test-Specific Frame

In tests, the user may want to change the way data items are generated. For example, the test writer may want to have short delays. This can be achieved by deriving a new data item class and adding constraints or other class members as needed.

```
1   // A derived data item example
2   class short_delay_frame extends uart_frame;
3     // This constraint further limits the delay values.
4     constraint c_test1_txmit_delay {transmit_delay  < 10;}
5     // Constructor and uvm_object_utils macro
6   endclass: short_delay_frame
```

Deriving the new class is not enough to get the desired effect. You also need to have the environment use the new class (`short_delay_frame`) rather than the UVC frame. The UVM factory mechanism allows you to introduce the derived class to the environment without the need to rewrite or change anything in it.

```
1   class short_delay_test extends uvm_test;

2     uart_ctrl_tb uart_ctrl_tb0;
3     // Constructor and uvm_object_utils macro
4     virtual function void build();
5       super.build();
6       // Use short_delay_frame throughout the environment.
7       factory.set_type_override_by_type(uart_frame::get_type(),
8         short_delay_frame::get_type());
9       uart_ctrl_tb0 = uart_ctrl_tb::type_id::create("uart_ctrl_tb0", this);
10    endfunction
11    virtual task run();
12      uvm_top.print_topology();
13    endtask
14  endclass: short_delay_test
```

Calling the factory function `set_type_override_by_type()` (in bold above) instructs the environment to use short-delay frames.

At times, a user may want to send special traffic to one interface but keep sending the regular traffic to other interfaces. This can be achieved by using `set_inst_override_by_type()` inside an UVM component.

```
set_inst_override_by_type("uart0.Tx.sequencer.*",
  uart_frame::get_type(), short_delay_frame::get_type());
```

You can also use wildcards to override the instantiation of a few components.

```
set_isnt_override_by_type("uart*.Tx.sequencer.*",
  uart_frame::get_type(), short_delay_frame::get_type());
```

7.5.2   Sequences and Sequencer Control

Constraint layering is an efficient way of uncovering bugs in your DUT. Having the constraint solver randomly select values ensures a non-biased sampling of the legal input space. However, constraint layering does not allow a user to control the order between consecutive data items. Many high-level scenarios can only be captured using a stream of ordered transactions.

User-defined sequences can be added to the sequencer's sequence library and randomly executed. If no user-defined sequences are added, then the only executed sequence is the built-in sequence called `uvm_random_sequence`. The `uvm_random` sequence executes a random number of the `simple_sequence` that executes a single data item.

This section introduces ways to control the sequencer, including:

- Controlling the number of sequences created by `uvm_random_sequence`

- Creating and adding a new sequence to be executed

- Adjusting the sequencer to start from a sequence other than the predefined random sequence

7.5.2.1   Controlling the Number of Sequences Created by uvm_random_sequence

The default number of generated sequences is a random number between 0 and `uvm_sequencer::max_random_count`. The user can modify the number of generated sequences (*count*). Use the configuration mechanism to change the value of *count*. For example, to generate and send 10 sequences, use:

```
set_config_int("*.cpu_seqr", "count", 10);
```

You can disable a sequencer from generating any sequences by setting the *count* to 0.

```
set_config_int("*.cpu_seqr", "count", 0);
```

Note   Having more data items than *count* is not necessarily a bug. The sequencer does not generate data items directly. By default, it generates *count* number of simple sequences that translate into *count* number of items. If user-defined sequences are registered to the sequencer, they are executed by the `uvm_random_sequence` and can result in many more data items than the sequencer count. The sequencer has more built-in capabilities, which are described in the next section.

The three built-in sequences were introduced in "Predefined Sequences" on page 115.

7.5.2.2   Creating and Adding a New Sequence

In "User-Defined Sequences" on page 111, we described how to create sequences. Some sequences are created by the UVC developer and provided as part of the reusable UVC package.

The testbench developer can create additional sequences for specific tests, or for random selection and execution by the `uvm_random` built-in sequence.

The class `retry_seq` in the example below defines a new sequence. It is derived from `uvm_sequence` and uses the `` `uvm_sequence_utils `` macro to associate this sequence with `uart_tx_sequencer` and to declare the various utilities `` `uvm_object_utils `` provides.

Example 7–5   UART Retry Sequence

```
1   // Send one BAD_PARITY frame followed by a GOOD_PARITY
2   // frame with the same payload.
3   class retry_seq extends uvm_sequence #(uart_frame);
4     rand bit [7:0] pload; // Randomizable sequence parameter
5     ...
6     // UVM automation for sequences
7     `uvm_sequence_utils_begin(retry_seq, uart_tx_sequencer)
8       `uvm_field_int(pload, UVM_DEFAULT)
9     `uvm_sequence_utils_end
10    // Constructor
11    function new(string name="retry_seq");
12      super.new(name);
13    endfunction
14    virtual task body ( ); // Sequence behavior
15      `uvm_do_with(req, {payload == pload; parity == BAD_PARITY;} )
16      `uvm_do_with(req, {payload == pload; parity == GOOD_PARITY;} )
17    endtask : body
18  endclass: retry_seq
```

Sequences can have parameters that can be randomized (for example, `pload` in this example) using constraints. The randomized parameters can then be used within the `body()` task to guide the sequencer's behavior.

The `body` task defines the main behavior of a sequence. Since it is a task, you can use any procedural code, loops, fork and join, wait for events, and so on.

The `` `uvm_do_with `` macro randomizes and executes an item with inline constraints. The `` `uvm_do_with `` also sends the data item to the driver, which sends it to the DUT. The execution of the `body` task is blocked until the driver has sent the item to the DUT. Use the `` `uvm_do `` macro to randomize the item without inline constraints.

In the example above, when the retry sequence is executed, it will randomize the payload, send a frame with the generated payload having illegal parity, and follow it with a frame with a similar payload but with legal parity.

A sequencer type is provided as the second parameter to the `` `uvm_sequence_utils `` macro, which means that this sequence is added to the sequencer pool and could be randomly executed by the default random sequence. Since the sequencer type is provided, the `p_sequencer` variable can be declared with the appropriate type and initialized to be used by the sequence.

7.5.2.3   Creating Nested Sequences

You can define more abstract sequences using existing sequences. Doing so provides additional reuse and makes it easier to maintain the test suite. For example, after defining the configuration sequence per device in a block-level testbench, the user may define a system-level configuration sequence which is a combination of the already-defined sequences.

Example 7–6   UART Nested Retry Sequence

Executing (*do*ing) a sequence is similar to doing a data item. For example:

```
1   // Call retry sequence wrapped with random frames.
2   class rand_retry_seq extends uvm_sequence #(uart_frame);
3     // Constructor, and so on
4     ...
5     `uvm_sequence_utils(rand_retry_rand_seq, uart_tx_sequencer)
6     retry_seq retry_sequence; // Variable of a previously declared sequence
7     task body (); // Sequence behavior
8       `uvm_do (req)
9       `uvm_do_with(retry_sequence, {pload inside {[0:31]};})
10      `uvm_do(req)
11    endtask
12  endclass
```

The `rand_retry_seq` has a field called `retry_sequence`. `retry_seq` is a user-predefined sequence.

The `body()` task is *do*ing this sequence and layering inline constraints from above.

7.5.2.4   Setting the Default Sequence

As was described in Chapter 5 "Interface UVCs", the sequencer has a string property named `default_sequence` which can be set to a user-defined sequence type. This sequence type is used as the default sequence for the current instance of the sequencer (Figure 7-4, Sequencer with a Sequence Library). The sequencer starts the default sequence during the run phase, and allows it to finish, after which the sequencer is idle. By setting the default sequence, you control the root of the sequence tree that will be generated by that sequencer through the entire test.

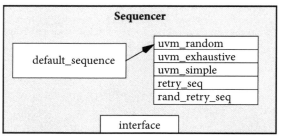

In default mode, the sequencer executes the random sequence, which randomly selects sequences and executes them.

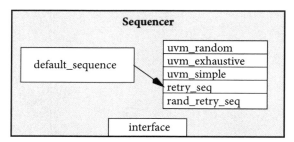

Setting default_sequence to "retry_seq" using
set_config_string("*Tx.sequencer", "default_sequence", "retry_seq");
causes the sequencer to execute the "retry_seq" sequence.

Figure 7-4   Sequencer with a Sequence Library

To override the default sequence, configure the `default_sequence` property for a specific sequencer or a group of sequencers. This is typically done inside the test class, before creating the component that includes the relevant sequencer(s). For example,

```
set_config_string("*.Tx.sequencer", "default_sequence","retry_seq");
```

The first argument uses a wildcard to match any instance name containing `.master0.sequencer` to set the `default_sequence` property (if it exists) to the value `retry_seq`.

7.5.2.5   Sequence Libraries and Reuse

Use of sequences is an important part of UVC reuse. The environment developer who knows and understands the UVC protocol specifications can create interesting parameterized reusable sequences. This library of sequences enables the environment user to leverage interesting scenarios to achieve coverage goals more quickly. Check to see if your UVCs sequencer comes with a library of sequences. The example below shows the output of a `sequencer.print()` statement.

```
-------------------------------------------------------------
Name                 Type                 Size    Value
-------------------------------------------------------------
sequencer            uart_tx_sequencer-           @1011
default_sequence     string                 19    uvm_random_sequence
sequences            da(string)              4    -
   [0]               string                 19    uvm_random_sequence
   [1]               string                 23    uvm_exhaustive_sequence
   [2]               string                 19    uvm_simple_sequence
   [3]               string                  9    retry_seq
   [4]               string                 14    rand_retry_seq
count                integral               32    -1
max_random_count     integral               32    'd10
max_random_depth     integral               32    'd4
```

The default sequence of this sequencer is `uvm_random_sequence`, which means that sequences will be randomly generated in a loop.

This sequencer has five sequences associated with it. Three sequences are built-in sequences (`uvm_random_sequence`, `uvm_exhaustive_sequence`, and `uvm_simple_sequence`), and two are user-defined (`retry_seq` and `rand_retry_seq`).

The built-in exhaustive sequence is similar to random sequence. It randomly selects and executes once each sequence from the sequencer's library, excluding `uvm_random_sequence` and `uvm_exhaustive_sequence`. If *count* equals 0, the sequencer start the random or exhaustive sequence but will not automatically execute any sub-sequences. If desired, the user may start a sequence manually. This operation typically is used for virtual sequencers.

The exhaustive sequence does not use the *count* variable. However, the sub-sequences started by the exhaustive sequence may use *count*.

The value of *count* in this sequencer is -1, which means that the number of generated sequences will be between 0 and `max_random_count` (10, the default value, in this example).

For more information about sequences, refer to "Stimulus Modeling and Generation" on page 73.

7.5.2.6   Disabling a Sequencer

In some cases, you may need to disable a sequencer. This may be required for reset purposes or for virtual sequence operation in which a system-level sequence controls the sequencer. The safest way to deactivate a sequencer is by calling the `stop_sequences()` function of the sequencer. This function kills the active sequences and child sequences, and removes all requests, locks, and responses that are currently queued.

To disable a sequencer for the entire simulation, we recommend:

- Deriving from `uvm_sequencer` and adding an `enable_default_sequence` configurable bit field

- Overriding the `start_default_sequence()` task to do:
  ```
  virtual start_default_sequence();
      if (enable_default_sequence) super.start_default_sequence();
  ```

```
        endtask
```

If you want to disable a sequencer for the entire simulation, and the `start_default_sequence` was not extended, you need to call the `stop_sequences()` after it was started. For example, if a specific testbench calls for an idle sequencer in one of the interfaces, it can call the `stop_sequences()` function in the `run` phase.

```
1   class uart_ctrl_tb extends uvm_env;
2     // UVC Components
3     apb_env   apb0;      // APB UVC
4     uart_env uart0;      // UART UVC

5     ...
6     virtual task run();
7       #0;
8         apb0.master.sequencer.stop_sequences();
9     endtask: run
10  endclass : uart_ctrl_tb
```

Line 7: We add a #0 delay to make sure that the sequencer started before we disable it.

Note We recommend stopping the sequencer using `stop_sequences()` and not using the count, since user-defined sequences may ignore the count or may start other sub-sequences.

7.5.2.7 Directed-Test Style Interface

The sequence style discussed in "Sequences and Sequencer Control" on page 161 is the recommended way to create and execute tests. Focus is placed on creating reusable sequences that you can use across many tests, instead of placing stimulus scenarios directly inside the test. Each sequencer is pre-loaded with the default traffic that will be generated at run time and sent to the DUT. Inside the tests, the test writer needs to touch only the sequencers that need to be modified.

Some test writers, however, are accustomed to writing directed tests. In directed tests, you write procedural code in which you explicitly request each interface to generate and send items. While directed tests are not the recommended method of test creation, the UVM does support it, using the sequencer's `execute_item()` task. Before using directed tests, consider the following:

- Directed tests require more code to write and maintain. This becomes critical in system-level environments.

- In directed tests, the high-level intention of the code is not as clear or as easy to read and understand. In the recommended method, the code is focused on test-specific needs, and other system-related aspects are present by default. For example, the arbitration logic for slaves that service requests does not need to be coded in every test.

- Directed tests are less reusable because they contain specific and un-reusable information.

- In the recommended method, tests are random by default. All declared sequences are candidates for execution by default. You must explicitly exclude a sequence from being executed. This prevents the problem of missing sequences and creates a more random pattern that can expose more bugs.

- In the recommended method for many protocols, you should never have to touch the high-level sequence, which serves as a template for other sub-sequences to be executed in a certain order.

Example 7–7   Directed Test

```
1   class directed_test extends uart_ctrl_base_test;
2     `uvm_component_utils(directed_test)
3     uart_ctrl_tb uart_ctrl_tb0;
4     function new (string name = "directed_test",
5       uvm_component parent = null);
6       super.new(name, parent);
7     endfunction
8     virtual function void build();
9       super.build();
10      set_config_int("*.sequencer", "count", 0);
11      // Create the testbench.
12      uart_ctrl_tb0 = uart_ctrl_tb::type_id::create("uart_ctrl_tb0", this);
13    endfunction
14    virtual task run();
15      uart_frame frame;
16      #10;
17      frame = uart_frame::type_id::create("frame", this);
18      if !(frame.randomize()) `uvm_error("RANDFAIL", "Frame randomize
    failed")
19      uart_ctrl_tb0.uart0.Tx.sequencer.execute_item(frame);
20      if !(frame.randomize() with { addr < 32'h0123; })
21          `uvm_error("RANDFAIL", "Frame randomize with constraints failed")
22      uart_ctrl_tb0.uart0.Tx.sequencer.execute_item(frame);
23    endtask
24  endclass: directed_test
```

Notes

- The execute_item() task can execute a data item or a sequence. It blocks until the item or the sequence is executed by the sequencer. You can use regular SystemVerilog constructs such as fork/join to model concurrency.

- The default activity in the sequencers is disabled by setting the count parameters of all sequencers to 0. The execute_item() task is used to send traffic in a deterministic way.

- Using default random activity is a good practice. It is straightforward and a good investment. The use of execute_item() should be minimized and limited to specific scenarios.

7.6   Virtual Sequencers and Sequences

"Creating Meaningful Tests" on page 158 describes how to efficiently control a single-interface UVC generation pattern. However, in a system-level environment multiple components are generating stimuli in parallel. The user might want to coordinate timing and data between the multiple channels. Also, a user may want to define a reusable system-level scenario. Virtual sequences are associated with a virtual sequencer and are used to coordinate stimulus generation in a testbench hierarchy. In general, a virtual sequencer contains references to the testbench sub-sequencers, that is, sequencers or other virtual sequencers in which it will invoke sequences. Virtual sequences can invoke other virtual sequences associated with their sequencer, as well as sequences in each of the sub-sequencers. Virtual sequences can execute items on other sequencers that can execute items.

Virtual sequences enable centralized control over the activity of multiple verification components that are connected to the various interfaces of the DUT. By creating virtual sequences, you can easily reuse existing sequence libraries of the underlying interface components and block-level environments to create coordinated system-level scenarios.

In Figure 7-5, Virtual Sequencer Controlling Multiple UVCs, the virtual sequencer invokes sequences on the APB and UART UVCs. The configuration sequences are developed during block-level testing.

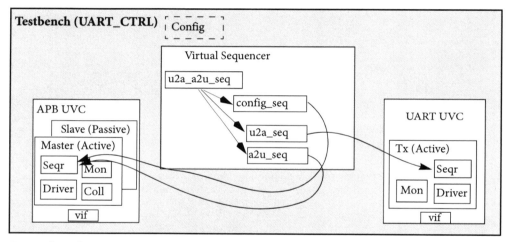

Figure 7-5   Virtual Sequencer Controlling Multiple UVCs

When using virtual sequences, most users disable the sub-sequencers and invoke sequences only from the virtual sequence. For more information, see "Controlling Other Sequencers" on page 170.

To invoke sequences, you can do one of the following:

- Use the appropriate do macro
- Use the sequence `start()` method.

7.6.1   The Virtual Sequencer

For high-level control of multiple sequencers from a single sequencer, use a sequencer that is not attached to a driver and does not process items itself. A sequencer acting in this role is referred to as a virtual sequencer.

To create a virtual sequencer that controls several sub-sequencers:

1. Derive a virtual sequencer class from the uvm_sequencer class.

2. Add references to the sequencers on which the virtual sequences will coordinate the activity. These references will be assigned by a higher-level component (typically the testbench).

The following example declares a virtual sequencer with two sub-sequencer references (apb_master_sequencer and uart_sequencer), which will be hooked up to the actual sub-sequencers.

Example 7–8   UART Controller Virtual Sequencer

```
class uart_ctrl_virtual_sequencer extends uvm_sequencer;
  apb_master_sequencer apb_seqr;
  uart_sequencer uart_seqr;
  // Constructor
  function new(input string name, uvm_component parent);
    super.new(name, parent);
    // Automation macro for virtual sequencer (no data item)
    `uvm_update_sequence_lib
  endfunction
  // UVM automation macros for sequencers
  `uvm_sequencer_utils(uart_ctrl_virtual_sequencer)
endclass: uart_ctrl_virtual_sequencer
```

Note   The `uvm_update_sequence_lib macro is used in the constructor when defining a virtual sequencer. This is different from (non-virtual) sequencers, which have an associated data item type. When this macro is used, the uvm_simple_sequence is not added to the sequencer's sequence library. This is important because the simple sequence only does items, and a virtual sequencer is not connected to a driver that can process the items. For regular sequencers, use the `uvm_update_sequence_lib_and_item macro. See "Creating the Sequencer" on page 82 for more information.

Sub-sequencers can be regular sequencers or other virtual sequencers. The connection of the actual sub-sequencer instances via reference shown in "Connecting a Virtual Sequencer to Sub-Sequencers" on page 171.

7.6.2   Creating a Virtual Sequence

Creating a virtual sequence is similar to creating an interface UVC sequence, with the following differences:

- A virtual sequence uses `uvm_do_on or `uvm_do_on_with to execute sequences on any of the sub-sequencers connected to the current virtual sequencer.

- A virtual sequence uses `uvm_do or `uvm_do_with to execute other virtual sequences of this virtual sequencer. A virtual sequence cannot use `uvm_do or `uvm_do_with to execute items. Virtual sequencers do not have items associated with them, only sequences.

To create a virtual sequence:

1. Declare a sequence class by deriving it from uvm_sequence, just like a regular sequence.

2. Define a `body()` method that implements the desired logic of the sequence.

3. Use the `uvm_do_on` (or `uvm_do_on_with`) macro to invoke sequences in the underlying sub-sequencers.

4. Use the `uvm_do` (or `uvm_do_with`) macro to invoke other virtual sequences in the current virtual sequencer.

The following example shows a UART controller virtual sequence controlling two sub-sequencers: an APB bus sequencer and an UART sequencer. Assume that the APB sequencer has a `config_seq` and an `a2u_seq` sequence in its library, and the UART sequencer provides a `u2a_seq` sequence in its library. The following sequence example invokes these three sequencers.

Example 7–9   UART Controller Virtual Sequence

```
1  class u2a_a2u_vseq extends uvm_sequence;
2    ... // Constructor and UVM automation macros
3    // Sequences from the APB sequence library
4    apb_config_seq config_seq;
5    apb_a2u_seq a2u_seq
6    // A sequence from the UART sequence library
7    uart_u2a_seq u2a_seq;

8    virtual task body();
9      // Invoke a sequence in the apb sub-sequencer.
10     `uvm_do_on(config_seq, p_sequencer.apb_seqr)
11     // Then execute the u2a and a2u sequences in parallel.
12     fork
13       `uvm_do_on(u2a_seq, p_sequencer.uart_seqr)
14       `uvm_do_on(a2u_seq, p_sequencer.apb_seqr)
15     join
16   endtask : body
17 endclass : simple_virt_seq
```

7.6.3   Controlling Other Sequencers

When using a virtual sequencer, you need to consider how you want the sub-sequencers to behave in relation to the virtual sequence behavior being defined. There are three basic possibilities:

- Business as usual—You want the virtual sequencer and the sub-sequencers to generate traffic at the same time, using the built-in capability of the original sub-sequencers. The data items resulting from the sub-sequencers' default behavior—along with those injected by sequences invoked by the virtual sequencer—will be inter-mixed and executed in an arbitrary order by the driver. This is the default behavior, so there is no need to do anything to achieve this.

- Disable the sub-sequencers—Using the `stop_sequences()` function of the sequencer as described in "Disabling a Sequencer" on page 165. The following code snippet disables the sub-sequencers in the example in "Connecting a Virtual Sequencer to Sub-Sequencers" on page 171.

- Use `grab()` and `ungrab()`—Using `grab()` and `ungrab()`, a virtual sequence can achieve full control over its sub-sequencers, for a limited time, and then let the original sequences continue working.

Note   Only (non-virtual) driver sequencers can be grabbed. Therefore, you should make sure that a given sub-sequencer is not a virtual sequencer before you attempt to grab it. The following example illustrates this using the functions `grab()` and `ungrab()` in the sequence consumer interface.

```
virtual task body();
  // Grab the apb sequencer if not virtual.
  if (p_sequencer.apb_seqr != null)
    p_sequencer.apb_seqr.grab(this);
  // Execute a sequence.
  `uvm_do_on(config_seq, p_sequencer.apb_seqr)
  // Ungrab.
  if (p_sequencer.apb_seqr != null)
    p_sequencer.apb_seqr.ungrab(this);
endtask
```

Note   When grabbing several sequencers, work conventionally to avoid deadlocks. For example, always grab in a standard order.

7.6.4   Connecting a Virtual Sequencer to Sub-Sequencers

To connect a virtual sequencer to its sub-sequencers, assign the sequencer references specified in the virtual sequencer to instances of the sequencers. This is a simple reference assignment and should be done only after all components are created. For example, this can be done with the testbench `connect()` method:

```
virtual_sequencer.apb_seqr = apb0.master.sequencer;
virtual_sequencer.uart_seqr = uart0.Tx.sequencer;
```

The following more-complete example shows a top-level testbench, which instantiates the UART and APB components and the virtual sequencer that controls the two. At the testbench level, the path to the sequencers inside the various components is known and that path is used to get a handle to them and connect them to the virtual sequencer.

Example 7–10   UART Controller Testbench with Virtual Sequencer

```
1   class uart_ctrl_tb extends uvm_env;
2     apb_env apb0;    // APB UVC
3     uart_env uart0; // UART UVC
4     uart_ctrl_virtual_sequencer virtual_sequencer;
5     ... // Constructor and UVM automation macros
6     virtual function void build();
7       super.build();
8       // Configuration: Disable subsequencer sequences.
9       set_config_int("apb0.master.sequencer", "count", 0);
10      set_config_int("uart0.Tx.sequencer", "count", 0);
11      // Build envs with subsequencers.
12      apb0 = apb_env::type_id::create("apb0", this);
```

```
13      uart0 = uart_env::type_id::create("uart0", this);
14      // Build the virtual sequencer.
15      virtual_sequencer =
    uart_ctrl_virtual_sequencer::type_id::create("virtual_sequencer", this);
16    endfunction : build
17    // UVM connect() phase.
18    function void connect();
19      virtual_sequencer.apb_seqr = apb0.master.sequencer;
20      virtual_sequencer.uart_seqr = uart0.Tx.sequencer;
21    endfunction : connect
22 endclass: uart_ctrl_tb
```

7.7   Checking for DUT Correctness

Getting the device into desired states is a significant part of verification. The environment should verify valid responses from the DUT before a feature is declared verified. Two types of auto-checking mechanisms can be used:

- Assertions—Derived from the specification or from the implementation and ensure correct timing behavior. Assertions typically focus on signal-level activity.

- Data checkers—Ensure overall device correctness.

As we mentioned in "Monitor" on page 11, checking and coverage should be done in the monitor regardless of the driving logic. Reusable assertions are part of reusable components. Designers can also place assertions in the DUT RTL. Refer to your ABV documentation for more information.

7.7.1   Scoreboards

A crucial element of a self-checking environment is the scoreboard. Typically, a scoreboard verifies the proper operation of your design at a functional level. The responsibility of a scoreboard varies greatly depending on the implementation. This section shows an example of a scoreboard that verifies the uart_ctrl transmit and receive paths. While the details of the scoreboard functionality are specific to the UART controller device, you should focus on the steps necessary to create and use a scoreboard in an environment so those steps can be repeated for any scoreboard application.

7.7.1.1   UART Controller Scoreboard Example

For the UART controller demo environment, two scoreboards are necessary to verify functionality. One verifies the transmit path and the other verifies the receive path. The desired topology is shown in Figure 7-6 on page 173.

In this example, the user has created a testbench containing one APB UVC that contains the bus monitor, and one UART UVC.

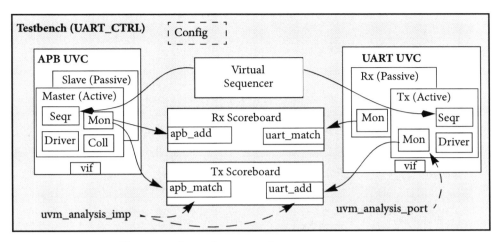

Figure 7-6   UART Controller Scoreboard Connections

7.7.1.2   Creating the Scoreboard

Before the scoreboard can be added to the uart_ctrl_tb, the scoreboard component must be defined.

To define the scoreboard:

1.   Add the TLM export necessary to communicate with the environment monitor(s).

2.   Implement the necessary functions and tasks required by the TLM export.

3.   Define the action taken when the export is called.

7.7.1.3   Adding TLM Ports to uvm_scoreboard

In the example shown in Figure 7-6 on page 173, each scoreboard requires two ports to communicate with the environment. Since the monitors in the environment have provided an analysis port write() interface via the TLM uvm_analysis_port(s), the scoreboard will provide the TLM uvm_analysis_imp.

The uart_ctrl_tx_scbd component derives from the uvm_scoreboard and declares and instantiates two analysis_imp ports. For more information on TLM interfaces, see "TLM Interfaces" in the *UVM Class Reference*. The declaration and creation is done inside the constructor.

```
1    // Declaration of TLM analysis imp ports
2    `uvm_analysis_imp_decl(_apb)
3    `uvm_analysis_imp_decl(_uart)
4    class uart_ctrl_tx_scbd extends uvm_scoreboard;
5      uvm_analysis_imp_apb #(apb_transfer, uart_ctrl_tx_scbd) apb_match;
6      uvm_analysis_imp_uart #(uart_frame, uart_ctrl_tx_scbd) uart_add;
7      ...
8      function new (string name, uvm_component parent);
```

```
9       super.new(name, parent);
10      apb_match = new("apb_match", this);
11      uart_add = new("uart_add", this);
12   endfunction : new
13   ...
```

Line 5 declares the `uvm_analysis_imp` for the APB connection. The parameter, `apb_transfer`, defines the `uvm_object` communicated via this TLM interface. The second parameter defines the type of this implementation's parent. This is required so that the parent's `write()` method can be called by the export.

Line 10 creates the implementation instance. The constructor arguments define the name of this implementation instance and its parent.

7.7.1.4   TLM Write Implementation

Because the scoreboard provides an `uvm_analysis_imp`, the scoreboard must implement all interfaces required by that export. This means you must define the implementation for the `write` virtual function. For the `uart_ctrl_tx_scbd`, you will need two `write()` functions, one for each imp declaration:

```
virtual function void write_uart(uart_frame frame);
  // frame.payload to the queue for checking;
endfunction : write_uart

virtual function void write_apb(apb_transfer transfer);
...// Retrieve frame data from the queue and compare against transfer.data
endfunction : write_uart
```

The implementation functions make the appropriate calls and comparisons needed to add and check the result. This information is DUT specific and is not crucial to the communication of the scoreboard with the rest of the environment and will not be discussed. The `uart_ctrl_scoreboard.sv` file shows the implementation.

7.7.1.5   Adding the Scoreboard to the Environment

Once the scoreboard is defined, the scoreboard can be added to the testbench. First, declare the TX and RX scoreboards inside the `uart_ctrl_tb` class.

```
uart_ctrl_tx_scbd tx_scbd
uart_ctrl_rx_scbd rx_scbd;
```

After the scoreboard is declared, you can construct the scoreboard inside the `build()` phase:

```
function void uart_ctrl_tb::build();
  ...
  tx_scbd = uart_ctrl_tx_scbd::type_id::create("tx_scbd", this);
  rx_scbd = uart_ctrl_rx_scbd::type_id::create("rx_scbd", this);
  ...
endfunction
```

Here, the `scoreboards` are created using the `create()` function and given the names `tx_scbd` and `rx_scbd`.

After the scoreboard is created, the `uart_ctrl_tb` can connect the ports in the testbench.

```
function void uart_ctrl_tb::connect();
  ...
  uart0.Rx.monitor.frame_collected_port.connect(rx_scbd.uart_match);
  apb0.bus_monitor.item_collected_port.connect(rx_scbd.apb_add);
  uart0.Tx.monitor.frame_collected_port.connect(tx_scbd.uart_add);
  apb0.bus_monitor.item_collected_port.connect(tx_scbd.apb_match);
  ...
endfunction
```

This `uart_ctrl_tb`'s `connect()` function code makes the connection, using the TLM ports `connect()` interface, between the port in the monitor of the APB and UART agents inside the 0 environment and the implementation in the scoreboards. For more information on the use of TLM ports, see "TLM Interfaces" in the *UVM Class Reference*.

7.8 Implementing a Coverage Model

To ensure thorough verification, you need observers to represent your verification goals. SystemVerilog provides a rich set of functional coverage features.

7.8.1 Selecting a Coverage Method

No single coverage metric ensures completeness. There are two categories of coverage:

- **Explicit coverage** is user-defined coverage. The user specifies the coverage goals, the needed values, and collection time. As such, analyzing these goals is straightforward. Achieving 100% of your coverage goals means that your verification has been completed. An example of such a metric is SystemVerilog functional coverage. The disadvantage of such metrics is that missing goals are not taken into account.

- **Implicit coverage** is done with automatic metrics that are derived from the RTL or other metrics already existing in the code. Typically, creating an implicit coverage report is straightforward and does not require a lot of effort. For example, code coverage, expression coverage, and FSM (finite-state machine) coverage are types of implicit coverage. The disadvantage of implicit coverage is that it is difficult to map the coverage requirements to the verification goals. It also is difficult to map coverage holes into unexecuted high-level features. In addition, implicit coverage is not complete, since it does not take into account high-level abstract events and does not create associations between parallel threads (that is, two or more events occurring simultaneously).

Starting with explicit coverage is recommended. You should build a coverage model that represents your high-level verification goals. Later, you can use implicit coverage as a "safety net" to check and balance the explicit coverage.

Note   Reaching 100% functional coverage with very low code-coverage typically means that the functional coverage needs to be refined and enhanced.

7.8.2   Implementing a Functional Coverage Model

A UVC should come with a protocol-specific functional-coverage model. You may want to disable some coverage aspects that are not important or do not need to be verified. For example, you might not need to test all types of bus transactions in your system, or you might want to remove that goal from the coverage logic that specifies all types of transactions as goals. You might also want to extend the functional coverage model and create associations between the UVC coverage and other attributes in the system or other interface UVCs. For example, you might want to ensure proper behavior when all types of transactions are sent and the FIFO in the system is full. This would translate into crossing the transaction type with the FIFO status variable. This type of functional coverage is discussed in Chapter 10 "System UVCs and Testbench Integration".

7.8.2.1   Enabling and Disabling Coverage

The verification IP developer should provide configuration properties that allow you to control the interesting aspects of the coverage (see "Enabling and Disabling Coverage and Checks" on page 130). The VIP documentation will tell you what properties can be set to affect coverage. The most basic of controls would determine whether coverage is collected at all. The APB monitors and collectors demonstrate this level of control. If the you want to disable coverage before the environment is created, use the `set_config_int()` interface.

```
set_config_int("apb0.master.monitor", "coverage_enable", 0);
set_config_int("apb0.master.collector", "coverage_enable", 0);
```

Once the environment is created, you can set this property directly.

```
apb0.master.monitor.coverage_enable = 0;
apb0.master.collector.coverage_enable = 0;
```

This is a simple Verilog assignment to a class property (or variable).

Summary

This chapter covers basic UVC integration concepts. The integration in this chapter is not reusable and is introduced here for educational purposes and phased introduction of the material. In Chapter 10 "System UVCs and Testbench Integration" we introduce a more appropriate integration component.

8   Stimulus Generation Topics

The UVM sequencer and sequences provide an efficient solution for many basic and advanced modeling needs. A subset of the sequences capability was introduced in Chapter 5 "Interface UVCs" and in Chapter 7 "Simple Testbench Integration". Much of the UVC reuse capability is due to the sequence feature, as many UVCs from different application domains use sequences for creating the required stimuli. This section discusses various techniques for sequence and randomization control.

8.1   Fine Control Sequence Generation

In "User-Defined Sequences" on page 111, we introduce two sequence macros: `uvm_do` and `uvm_do_with`. These macros perform several steps sequentially, including the allocation of an object (sequence or sequence item), synchronization with the driver (if needed), randomization, sending to the driver, and so on. In a typical testbench, the macros provide all of the required functionality and ensure that reactive generation, factory usage, and TLM are being used. Occasionally, you might need more control over the way sequences and items are created, randomized, and sent. The SystemVerilog UVM Class Library provides additional sequence macros to enable finer control of these steps. This set of macros enables important use cases such as:

- Randomizing a sequence item without committing to drive it
- Avoiding the re-allocation of a sequence item
- Allowing procedural assignments of sequence items, reading items from a file, and much more

The following sections describe these macros in detail.

`uvm_create

The `uvm_create` macro allocates an object using the common factory and initializes its properties. Its argument is a variable of type uvm_sequence_item or uvm_sequence. You can use this macro with the SystemVerilog constraint_mode() and rand_mode() functions in order to enable or disable constraints.

In the following example, apb_byte_seq is similar to sequences that have been discussed previously. The main difference involves the use of the `uvm_create(req) call.

After the macro call, the `rand_mode()` and `constraint_mode()` functions can be used, as well as some direct assignments to properties of `req`. The manipulation of the `req` object is possible since memory has been allocated for it, but randomization has not yet taken place. Subsequent sections review the possible options for sending this pre-generated item to the driver.

```
1   class apb_byte_seq extends uvm_sequence #(apb_transfer);
2     rand bit [31:0] start_addr;
3     ... // Constructor and UVM automation macros
4     virtual task body();
5       `uvm_create(req)
6       req.addr.rand_mode(0); // Disables randomization of addr
7       req.c_addr.constraint_mode(0); // Disables constraint c_addr
8       req.addr = start_addr;
9       ...// Additional sequence macros to follow
10    endtask : body
11  endclass: my_seq
```

You can also use a sequence variable as an argument to `uvm_create`.

Note   Sometimes you need to provide an object as a parameter to a sequence (for example, a user may want a configuration object to a certain sequence to affect its behavior). Specifying an object as a constraint value is not supported in SystemVerilog. Users can use `uvm_create`, assign the object to the sequence field, randomize the object, and send it.

`uvm_send

The `uvm_send` macro processes the `uvm_sequence_item` or `uvm_sequence` class handle argument without any allocation or randomization. Sequence items are placed in the sequencer's queue to await processing, while sequences are processed immediately. The parent sequence's `pre_do()`, `mid_do()`, and `post_do()` methods still occur.

In the following example, we show the use of `uvm_create()` to pre-allocate a sequence item along with `uvm_send`, which processes it without allocation or randomization.

```
1   class apb_write_byte_seq extends uvm_sequence #(apb_transfer);
2     rand bit [31:0] start_addr;
3     rand bit [7:0] byte_data;
4     ... // Constructor and UVM automation macros
5     virtual task body();
6       `uvm_create(req)
7       req.addr = start_addr;
8       req.data = byte_data;
9       req.direction == APB_WRITE;
10      // No randomization. Use a purely pre-generated item.
11      `uvm_send(req)
12    endtask : body
13  endclass: apb_write_byte_seq
```

Similarly, a sequence variable could be provided to the `uvm_create and the `uvm_send calls, above, in which case the sequence would be processed without allocation or randomization.

`uvm_rand_send and `uvm_rand_send_with

These macros are identical to the `uvm_send macro, with the single difference of randomizing the given class handle before processing it. This enables you to adjust an object as required while still using class constraints with late randomization; that is, randomization on the cycle for which the driver is requesting the item.

The `uvm_rand_send() macro takes just the object handle, while the `uvm_rand_send_with() macro takes an extra argument, which can be any valid inline constraint to be used for the randomization.

The following example shows the use of `uvm_create to pre-allocate a sequence item along with the `uvm_rand_send* macros. The `uvm_rand_send* macros process an item or a sequence previously allocated using `uvm_create. The rand_mode() and constraint_mode() constructs are used to show fine-grain control on the randomization of an object.

```
1   class apb_write_read_byte_seq extends uvm_sequence #(apb_transfer);  ...
    // Constructor and UVM automation macros
2     virtual task body();
3       `uvm_create(req)
4       req.direction.rand_mode(0); // don't randomize direction
5       req.addr_c.constraint_mode(0); //disables constraint on addr[1:0]
6       req.direction = APB_WRITE;
7       // Randomize and process the item.
8       `uvm_rand_send_with(req, {data[31:8] == 24'h000000;})
9       req.addr.rand_mode(0); // don't randomize addr
10      req.direction = APB_READ;
11      // Randomize and process again, this time with inline constraints.
12      `uvm_rand_send(req)
13    endtask : body
14  endclass: apb_write_read_byte_seq
```

Executing Sequences and Items on Other Sequencers: `uvm_do_on, `uvm_do_on_with, `uvm_do_on_pri, `uvm_do_on_pri_with

In the preceding sections, all uvm_do macros (and their variants) execute the specified item or sequence on the current p_sequencer. To allow sequences to execute items or other sequences on specific sequencers, additional macro variants, which are described in the following section, are included. These macros allow for the specification of a desired sequencer. All of these macros are exactly the same as their root versions, except that they all take an additional argument (always the second argument) which is a reference to a specific sequencer.

```
`uvm_do_on(s_seq, that_sequencer);
`uvm_do_on_with(s_seq, that_sequencer, {s_seq.foo == 32'h3;})
```

These macros are used in virtual sequences, as shown in Example 7–8 on page 169.

More details about the UVM sequence macros can be found in the *UVM SystemVerilog Reference Manual.*

8.2 Executing Multiple Sequences Concurrently

There are two ways you can create concurrently-executing sequences:

- Using the fork/join construct with `uvm_do in the body of a sequence
- Starting several sequences in parallel using the sequence start() method

The following sections show an example of each method and the differences between them.

8.2.1 Using fork/join and `uvm_do in the Body of a Sequence

Because the body() sequence is a task, it allows spawning and waiting for threads. In this example, the sequences are executed with fork/join. The simulator schedules the sequences that request interaction with the sequencer. The sequencer schedules the items that are provided to the driver and selects them one at a time, arbitrating between the sequences willing to provide an item for execution. The write_seq and read_seq sequences are sub-sequences of fork_join_do_seq.

```
1  class fork_join_do_seq extends uvm_sequence #(apb_transfer);
2    ... // Constructor and `uvm_sequence_utils macro go here.
3    rand_write_seq write_seq;
4    rand_read_seq read_seq;
5    virtual task body();
6      fork
7        `uvm_do(write_seq)
8        `uvm_do(read_seq)
9      join
10   endtask : body
11 endclass : fork_join_do_seq
```

8.2.2 Starting Several Sequences in Parallel

In this example, the concurrent_start_seq sequence activates two sequences in parallel. The process does not wait for the sequences to complete. Instead, it immediately finishes after activating the sequences. Also, the write_seq and read_seq sequences are started as root sequences because no parent sequence reference is passed to the start() task.

```
1  class concurrent_start_seq extends uvm_sequence #(apb_transfer);
2    ... // Constructor and `uvm_sequence_utils macro go here.
3    rand_write_seq write_seq;
4    rand_read_seq read_seq;
5    virtual task body();
```

```
6       // Create the sequences using the factory.
7       `uvm_create(write_seq)
8       `uvm_create(read_seq)
9       fork    // Start each subsequence as a new thread.
10        write_seq.start(p_sequencer);
11        read_seq.start(p_sequencer);
12      join
13    endtask : body
14  endclass : concurrent_start_seq
```

Note   The `sequence.start()` method allows the sequence to be started on any sequencer.

8.3   Using p_sequencer

We discuss `p_sequencer` in a few chapters of this book—using it in virtual sequences to access the interface UVC sequencers, and, in the previous section, to start a sequence.

The `p_sequencer` field is present in every sequence, pointing to its sequencer component. It is automatically initialized by the UVM library when a sequence is created by the user, which makes it a handy reference for test writers. This is useful for accessing objects residing elsewhere in the environment from the sequence, as well as sequencer fields and methods. In addition to those mentioned, some other useful applications of `p_sequencer` include using `get_config()` to fetch configuration properties set in a test or testbench, and using `find()` to search the component tree and look up information in other UVCs.

8.4   Using the pre_body() and post_body() Methods

The SystemVerilog UVM Class Library provides two additional sequence tasks, `pre_body()` and `post_body()`, which are invoked before and after the sequence's `body()` task, respectively. These methods are invoked only when a sequence is started by its sequencer's `start_sequence()` task or the sequence's `start()` task.

Examples for using the `pre_body()` and `post_body()` methods include:

- Synchronization to some event before the `body()` task starts.

- Calling a cleanup task when the `body()` task ends.

The following example declares a new sequence and implements its `pre_body` and `post_body` methods.

```
1   class revised_seq extends fork_join_do_seq;
2     ... // Constructor and `uvm_sequence_utils macro go here.
3     task pre_body();
4       super.pre_body();
5       @p_sequencer.init_done;   // Wait until initialization is done
6     endtask : pre_body
7     task post_body();
```

```
8       super.post_body();
9       do_cleanup();
10   endtask : post_body
11 endclass : revised_seq
```

Notes

- The `pre_body()` and `post_body()` methods are not invoked in a sequence that is executed by one of the `uvm_do` macros.

- The `init_done` event declared in the sequencer can be accessed directly by way of the `p_sequencer` variable. The `p_sequencer` variable is available, since the `uvm_sequence_utils` macro was used. This prevents the user from having to declare a variable of the appropriate type and initialize it using `$cast`.

8.5   Controlling the Arbitration of Items

At times, there may be several sequences processing items concurrently. However, the driver can handle only one item at a time. Therefore, the sequencer maintains a queue of do actions. When the driver requests an item, the sequencer chooses a single do action to perform from all of the do actions waiting in its queue. Therefore, when a sequence is *do*ing an item, the do action is blocked until the sequencer is ready to choose it.

The scheduling algorithm works on a first-come-first-served basis. In addition, the sequencer provides an arbitration mode that determines how a do action is selected among those pending. You can affect the algorithm using: `grab()`, `ungrab()`, `lock()`, `unlock()`, and `is_relevant()`.

If a sequence is *grabbing* the sequencer, then the sequencer chooses the first do action that satisfies the following conditions:

- The do action is done by the grabbing sequence or its descendants.

- The `is_relevant()` method of the sequence *do*ing it returns 1.

If no sequence is grabbing the sequencer, then the sequencer will choose the first do action that satisfies the following condition:

- The `is_relevant()` method of the sequence *do*ing it returns 1.

If there is no do action to choose, then `get_next_item()` is blocked, and the sequencer will try to choose again (that is, reactivate the scheduling algorithm) when one of the following conditions happens:

- Another do action is added to the queue.

- A new sequence grabs the sequencer, or the current grabber ungrabs the sequencer.

- Any one of the blocked sequence's `wait_for_relevant()` task returns.

When calling `try_next_item()`, if the sequencer does not succeed in choosing a do action before the time specified by `uvm_driver::wait_for_sequences()` elapses, then `uvm_driver::try_next_item()` returns with null.

8.6   Interrupt Sequences

A DUT might include an interrupt option. Typically, an interrupt should be coupled with some response by the agent. Once the interrupt is serviced, activity prior to the interrupt should be resumed from the point where it was interrupted. Your verification environment can support interrupts using sequences.

To handle interrupts using sequences:

1. Define an interrupt handler sequence that will do the following:

   a. Wait for the interrupt event to occur.

   b. Grab the sequencer for exclusive access.

   c. Execute the interrupt service operations using the proper items or sequences.

   d. Ungrab the sequencer.

2. Start the interrupt handler sequence in the sequencer or in the default sequence. (You can configure the sequencer to run the default sequence when the simulation begins.)

Example 8–1   Handling Interrupts using Sequences

1. Define an interrupt handler sequence:

```
1  // SEQUENCE: interrupt_handler_seq: On interrupt, grab the sequencer
2  // and execute a read_status_seq sequence.
3  class interrupt_handler_seq extends uvm_sequence #(apb_transfer);
4    ... // Constructor and `uvm_sequence_utils macro go here
5    read_status_seq interrupt_reset_seq;
6    virtual task body();
7      forever begin
8        @p_sequencer.interrupt;
9        grab(p_sequencer);
10       `uvm_do(interrupt_reset_seq)
11       ungrab(p_sequencer);
12     end
13   endtask : body
14 endclass : interrupt_handler_seq
```

2. Start the interrupt handler sequence in the sequencer. The example below does this in the sequencer itself, in the run phase:

```
1  class apb_sequencer extends uvm_sequencer;
2    ... // Constructor and `uvm_sequencer_utils macro go here
3    interrupt_handler_seq interrupt_seq;
4    virtual task run();
5      interrupt_seq =
6          interrupt_handler_seq::type_id::create("interrupt_seq");
```

```
7      fork
8        interrupt_seq.start(this);
9      join_none
10     super.run();
11   endtask : run
12 endclass : apb_sequencer
```

- In this example, we cannot use any of the `uvm_do macros, since they can be used only in sequences. Instead, we use utility functions in the sequencer itself to create an instance of the interrupt handler sequence through the common factory.

- The example demonstrates interrupt serving on the bus. It is usually more desirable to serve interrupts at the register abstraction level, as most of the interrupt service routines involve reading and writing registers and the serving routine logic becomes protocol-independent. Please see Chapter 9 "Register and Memory Package" to learn more about writing and executing register sequences.

8.7   Protocol Layering

Some verification environments require the layering of data items of different protocols. Examples include TCP over IP, and ATM over Sonet. Other applications such as register and memory packages provide for traffic to be sent by way of a lower-layer bus component. Sequence layering and virtual sequences are two ways in which sequencers can be composed to create a layered protocol implementation.

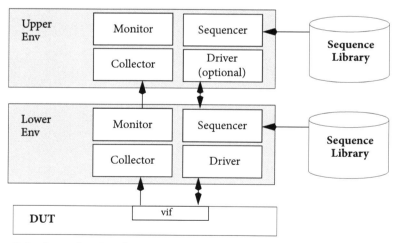

Figure 8-1   Layering Environments

The example environment in Figure 8-1 connects the lower env sequencer to the upper env driver. In most cases, the driver is not necessary and the lower sequencer will request data items directly from the upper sequencer. The following sections discuss options for layering stimulus.

8.7.1 Layering of Protocols

The classic example of protocol layering can be described by generic upper- and lower-levels (or layers) of a protocol. An array of bytes may be meaningless to the lower-level protocol, while in the upper-level protocol context, the array provides control and data messages to be processed appropriately.

For example, assume that there are two environments/sequencers that can be layered on top of each other as illustrated in Figure 8-1. The requirements for such layering include:

- Layering protocol environments without up-front planning of the lower and upper layers. This refers to the need to decouple layers without dependencies or knowledge of what needs to be connected.

- Layer randomization control. While the traffic from the upper layer is used by the lower layer, you still need to control randomization of all layers simultaneously. For example, you need to allow randomization, allow for directed and mixed traffic, and you need to be able to leverage a sequence library at each sequencer layer.

- Multi-sequencer operations and control. For example, multiple high layers driving a single low-layer sequencer.

- Performance optimization. In some cases, layers are mainly mediators between other layers and do not require allocation or randomization of data.

- Upper layers have access to lower layers. Upper layers may need to grab control or reset activity of lower layers.

8.7.2 Layering and Sequences

Layering is best implemented with sequences. There are two ways to do layering using sequences:

- Layering inside a single sequencer, which applies to simple cases. See "Layering Inside One Sequencer" on page 186 for details.

- Layering multiple sequencers, which applies to all layering cases. See "Layering of Several Sequencers" on page 187 for details.

Consider a low-layer sequencer driving `lower_env_items`, which are defined as:

```
class lower_env_item extends uvm_sequence_item;
  rand bit[`DATA_SIZE-1:0] payload[];
  rand int pl_size;
  constraint c_pload { pl_size < `MAX_PL;
                       payload.size() == pl_size; }
  ... // Constructor and UVM automation macros go here.
endclass : lower_env_item
```

The lower environment will have its own sequence library capable of generating low-level random sequences of `lower_env` items. This set of random sequences will be used to verify the lower-layer protocol and connection to the DUT. A low-level sequence base class is defined as:

```
class lower_env_base_seq extends uvm_sequence #(lower_env_item);
```

```
    ... // Constructor and `uvm_sequence_utils macro
    virtual task body();
      ...
    endtask : body
  endclass : lower_env_base_seq
```

Now consider a simple upper-layer data item which contains one or more `lower_env` items.

```
  class upper_env_item extends uvm_sequence_item;
    rand int unsigned max_item_size; // maximum pl_size of lower item
    rand int unsigned num_items;     // maximum number of lower items
    rand lower_env_item item[];   // array of lower items
    constraint c_item { num_items == item.size();
                        num_items inside {[1:10]};}
    constraint c_item_size { max_item_size inside {[10:20]}; }
    ... // Constructor and UVM automation macros go here.
    function void post_randomize();
      foreach(item[i]) begin
        item[i] = lower_env_item::type_id::create($psprintf("item[%0d]", i));
        assert(item[i].randomize with {pl_size <= max_item_size; }))
        else `uvm_error("RNDFAIL", "item randomization failed")
      end
  endclass : upper_env_item
```

Let's consider the options for layering the `upper_env_item` in a verification environment.

8.7.2.1   Layering Inside One Sequencer

For simple cases, you can layer inside one sequencer by generating a data item of the upper layer within a lower-layer sequence. Do this by creating a new sequence for the lower-layer sequencer. Figure 8-2 below depicts the architecture for using a single sequencer to layer the stimulus.

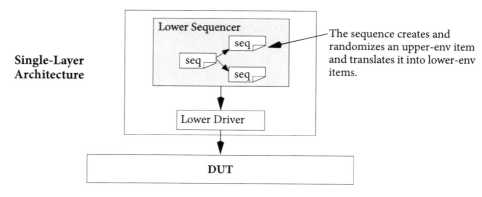

Figure 8-2   Single-Layer Sequencer Architecture

For example:

```
1  class upper_env_item_seq extends uvm_sequence #(lower_env_item);
```

```
2     ... // Constructor and UVM automation macros
3     upper_env_item u_item;   // Contains an array of lower_env_items
4     task body();
5       // Create a upper-level item.
6       `uvm_create(u_item)
7       ... // Randomize it here with appropriate constraints.
8       for(int i = 0 ; i< u_item.num_items; i++)
9         `uvm_send(u_item.item[i])
10    endtask : body
11  endclass: upper_env_item_seq
```

The `upper_env_item_seq` sequence generates a single `upper_env_item` and sends it in chunks of one or more `lower_env_items`. In this simple example, the upper item is comprised of lower items, so the lower items are automatically created when the upper item is randomized. In many cases, the lower item will have additional fields that will need to be generated, randomized and sent. For this, you will need to create the lower item and populate it with data from the upper item before randomizing and sending.

8.7.2.2 Layering of Several Sequencers

This approach to layering several sequencers uses multiple sequencers as shown in Figure 8-3, below.

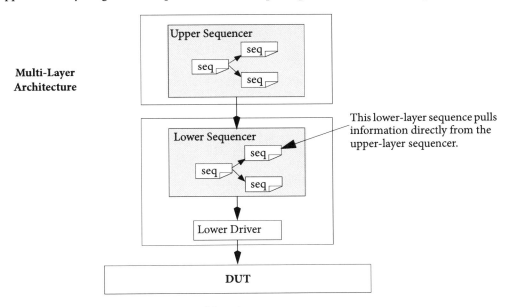

Figure 8-3   Multi-Layer Sequence Architecture

Taking the `upper_env_item` and `lower_env_item` example, there is a lower-layer sequence and a upper-layer sequence (complete with their sequencers). The lower-layer sequence pulls data from the upper-layer sequencer (or from the upper-layer driver). Each sequencer is encapsulated in a UVC so that layering can be done by connecting together the UVCs. "Using Layered Sequencers" on page 192, goes into more details on this topic.

8.7.3 Styles of Layering

This section discusses various styles you can use in layering.

8.7.3.1 Basic Layering

The most general case of layering consists of the driver accepting `layer1` items, in which:

- The `layer1` items are constructed from `layer2` items in some way. The `layer2` items are, in turn, constructed from `layer3` items, and so on.

- For every `layerN` and `layerN+1`, there is a mechanism that takes `layerN+1` items and converts them into `layerN` items.

You can also have multiple kinds of `layer1` and `layer2` items. In different configurations, you might want to layer any kind of `layer2` item over any kind of `layer1` item.

The remainder of this section describes possible variations, and complications, depending on the particular protocol or on the desired test-writing flexibility.

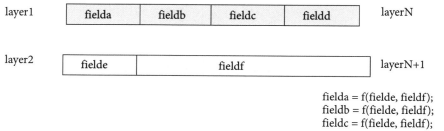

Figure 8-4 Layering of Protocols

8.7.3.2 One-to-One, One-to-Many, Many-to-One, Many-to-Many

A conversion mechanism might need to cope with the following situations (see Figure 8-5 on page 189):

- One-to-one—One upper-layer item must be converted into one low-layer item.

- One-to-many—One large upper-layer item must be broken down into many low-layer items.

- Many-to-one—Many upper-layer items must be combined into one large low-layer item (as in Sonet, for example).

- Many-to-many—Multiple upper-layer items must be taken in and converted into multiple lower-layer items. For example, upper-layer packets are 10 bytes long, and low-layer packets are three to 35 bytes long. In this case, there could be remainders.

One-to-One

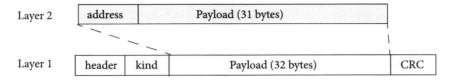

Many-to-One

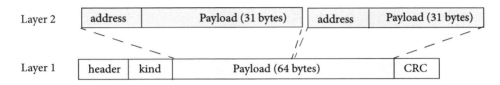

Many-to-Many

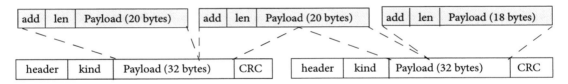

Figure 8-5   Layer Mapping

8.7.3.3   Different Configurations at Pre-Run Generation and Run Time

A system might need to support different modes of operation as defined by topology, data type, or other application-specific requirements. For example, in one environment, you may have only `layer1` items. In another environment, `layer1` items might be dictated by `layer2` items. You may also want to decouple the layers further, for example, so that `layer2` items could drive either `layer1` items or `layer1` cells (on another interface) or both.

At times, you might have a mix of inputs from multiple sources at run time. For example, you may want to have one low-layer sequencer send items that come from several high-layer sequencers.

8.7.3.4   Timing Control

In some configurations, the upper-layer items drive the timing completely. When upper-layer items are created, they are immediately converted into lower-layer items.

In other configurations, the lower-layer sequences pace the operation. When a lower-layer `uvm_do` macro is executed, the corresponding upper-layer item should appear immediately, in zero time.

Finally, there is the case where items are driven to the DUT according to the timing of the lower-layer sequences, but the higher-layer sequences are not reacting in zero time. If there is no data available from the high-layer sequences, then some default value (for example, a *zero filler*) is used instead. In this case, the upper sequencer `try_next_item()` would be used by the lower-level sequence.

8.7.3.5   Data Control

In some configurations, the upper-layer items completely dictate which low-layer items reach the DUT—in which case, the lower layer simply acts as a slave.

Often, however, both layers influence what reaches the DUT. For example, the high layer might influence the data in the payload while the lower layer influences other attributes of the items reaching the DUT. In these cases, the choice of sequences for both layers is meaningful.

8.7.3.6   Controlling Sequences on Multiple Sequencers

In the most general case, you have a graph consisting of several sequencers, some of which may control sequence execution on other sequencers and some may generate items directly. Some low-layer driver sequencers are connected to the DUT, some upper-layer driver sequencers are layered above them, and some top-level sequencers feed into all of the driver sequencers below them.

In the example configuration shown in Figure 8-6, Most-General Case of Using Virtual Sequencers, a low-layer sequencer (L1B) receives input from multiple high-layer sequencers (two instances of L2A) as well as from a controlling sequencer.

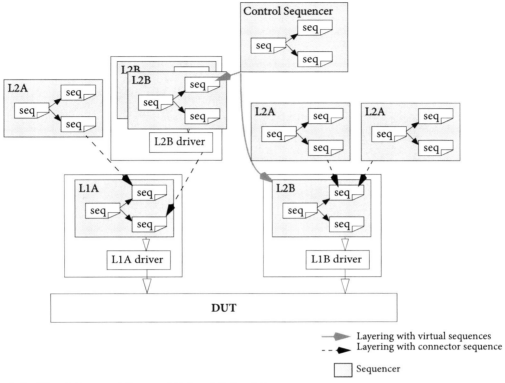

Figure 8-6 Most-General Case of Using Virtual Sequencers

8.7.4   Using Layered Sequencers

Figure 8-7 shows the layering of sequencers.

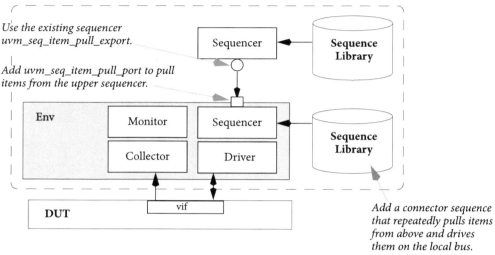

Figure 8-7   Layered Sequencers

These layered sequencers operate as follows:

- Upper-layer sequencers operate as usual, generating upper-layer data items and sending them through the `seq_item_pull_export`. In most cases, you will not need to change the upper-layer sequencer or sequences that will be used in a layered application.

- The lower-layer sequencers connect to the upper-layer sequencer(s) from which information must be pulled. The pulled information (a upper-layer item) is placed in a property of the sequence and is then used to constrain various properties in the lower-layer item(s). The actual connectivity between the layers is done in the same manner as the connection between a sequencer and a driver. To connect to the upper-layer sequencer, you must declare a corresponding `uvm_seq_item_pull_port` in the lower-layer sequencer (see Example 8–2 on page 193). The connection itself is performed at the time the containing component's `connect()` method is invoked.

- The lower-layer sequencers send information to a lower-layer driver that interacts with a DUT's physical interface.

Assuming you already have created (or are reusing) upper-layer and lower-layer sequencers, follow these steps below to create the layering.

To layer sequencers:

1. Create a lower-layer sequence that does the following:

    - Repeatedly pulls upper-layer items from the upper-layer sequencer
    - Translates them to lower-layer items

- Sends them to the lower-layer driver

To preserve late generation of the upper-layer items, pull the upper-layer items from within the lower-sequence's `pre_do()` task. This ensures that the upper-layer item will be randomized only when the lower-layer driver is ready to start processing the matching lower-layer items.

2. Extend the lower-layer sequencer, and add a TLM interface that will allow it to connect to the upper-layer sequencer. You will need to register a factory override for the new sequencer type to be used instead of the original one.

3. Connect the lower-layer sequencer to the upper-layer sequencer using the same technique as when connecting a driver to a sequencer.

4. Configure the lower-layer sequencer's default sequence to be the sequence you created in Step 1 above.

Example 8–2   Layered Sequencers

For this example, the lower-layer components are likely to be encapsulated inside an agent modeling the interface protocol. This example shows how to achieve layering without introducing the recommended reuse structure, to keep the code compact.

```
1   // Upper-layer classes
2   class upper_item extends uvm_sequence_item;
3     ...
4   endclass : upper_item
5   class upper_sequencer extends uvm_sequencer #(upper_item);
6     ...
7   endclass : upper_sequencer
8   // Lower-layer classes
9   class lower_item extends uvm_sequence_item;
10    ...
11  endclass : lower_item
12  class lower_sequencer extends uvm_sequencer #(lower_item);
13    uvm_seq_item_pull_port #(upper_item) upper_seq_item_port;
14    ...
15    function new (string name, uvm_component parent);
16      super.new(name, parent);
17      upper_seq_item_port = new("upper_seq_item_port",this);
18      `uvm_update_sequence_lib_and_item(...)
19    endfunction : new
20    ...
21  endclass : lower_sequencer
22  class lower_driver extends uvm_driver #(lower_item);
23    ...
24  endclass : lower_driver
```

Now create a lower-layer sequence that pulls upper-layer items and translates them to lower-layer items:

```
1   class upper_to_lower_seq extends uvm_sequence #(lower_item);
2     ... // Constructor and UVM automation macros go here.
3     upper_item u_item;
4     lower_item l_item;
5     virtual task body();
6       forever begin
7         `uvm_do_with(l_item,
8             { ... }) // Constraints based on u_item
9       end
10    endtask : body
11    // In the pre_do task, pull an upper item from upper sequencer.
12    virtual task pre_do(bit is_item);
13        if (is_item) p_sequencer.upper_seq_item_port.get_next_item(u_item);
14    endtask : pre_do
15    // In the post_do task, signal the upper sequencer we are done.
16    // And, if desired, update the upper-item properties for the
17    // upper-sequencer to use.
18    virtual function void post_do(uvm_sequence_item this_item);
19      p_sequencer.upper_seq_item_port.item_done(this_item);
20    endfunction : post_do
21  endclass : upper_to_lower_seq
```

Example 8–3   Layering Sequences

The following example illustrates connecting a lower-layer sequencer with an upper-layer sequencer.

Note   The lower-layer sequencer is likely to be encapsulated inside an interface UVC, therefore, it will be encapsulated in an env and an agent. This does not change the layering scheme but changes the path used to connect the sequencers to each other in the tb file. The connection of the upper sequencer to the lower sequencer will typically happen in the tb env, whereas the connection from the lower sequencer to its driver will occur in the connect() phase of the agent.

```
1   // This code resides in an env class.
2   lower_driver    l_driver0;
3   lower_sequencer l_sequencer0;
4   upper_sequencer u_sequencer0;
5   function void build();
6     super.build();
7     // Make lower sequencer execute upper-to-lower translation sequence.
8     set_config_string("l_sequencer0", "default_sequence",
9       "upper_to_lower_seq");
10    // Build the components.
11    l_driver0 = lower_driver::type_id::create("l_driver0", this);
12    l_sequencer0 = lower_sequencer::type_id::create(("l_sequencer0", this);
13    u_sequencer0 = upper_sequencer::type_id::create(("u_sequencer0", this);
14  endfunction : build
15  // Connect the components.
```

```
16  function void connect();
17    // Connect the upper and lower sequencers.
18    l_sequencer0.upper_seq_item_port.connect(u_sequencer0.seq_item_export);
19    // Connect the lower sequencer and driver.
20    l_driver0.seq_item_port.connect(l_sequencer0.seq_item_export);
21  endfunction : connect
```

Summary

This chapter describes additional techniques for generation of random stimulus in UVM verification environments. We introduce fine-grain control of sequence generation, techniques for creating and executing sequences in parallel, and suggest how to handle interrupts. We also discuss options for protocol layering when conversions of one-to-one, one-to-many, many-to-one, and many-to-many are required.

9   Register and Memory Package

Almost all devices have registers and memories that need to be controlled, checked, and covered as part of the verification task. In verifying a device under test, you often need to perform the following tasks:

- Capture the attributes and dependencies of a register.

- Randomize the device configuration and the initial register values.

- Execute bus transactions to write an initial configuration to the DUT.

- Read and write registers and memories as part of the normal run-time operation.

- Debug and analyze register activities.

- Check the device by comparing register and memory values to a shadow device model.

- Collect coverage metrics of device modes.

Register Packages provide a methodology and automation to enable productive and reusable register-related verification logic. For example, you may want to integrate register models and configuration sequences of some subsystems into a full system. If each of the subsystems use a different register solution, or if the register package does not support vertical reuse, then a full system integration may require significant source code editing.

Another advantage to incorporating a register model into your verification environment is the fact that your registers are not tied to a protocol. You define the model and can drive it from your current protocol using layering, and then a year from now, if the protocol changes, your register model won't change.

While you may be able to introduce a simple register array as a register package, implementing a complete set of requirements for a register package can be a seemingly endless task. At the beginning of the project, a simple user-created register package may be fine, but a complete package like Cadence's uvm_rgm provides the ability to expand to meet the needs of a growing project, and can save users tremendous effort.

Note   Since (at the time of this writing) no package was selected to be the formal UVM register package, we are using the uvm_rgm package to demonstrate how to use register packages. This register package is a scalable solution and is employed by many users in multiple application domains. The Cadence register package is built on open standards, delivered in open source format, and is accessible from the contribution area at **www.uvmworld.org**.

9.1   Register-Related Terminology

In addition to the basic UVM elements (`env`, `agents`, and `sequencers`), register packages introduce new terminology with which you should be familiar. The following table lists common register package terms.

Term	Description
Register Field	A collection of one or more consecutive bits holding a value. Fields have many attributes, such as hard reset value, access policy (read-only, write-only, read-write, read-clear), and so on.
Register	Represents a single register in the DUT. In the `uvm_rgm` package, a *register* is a collection of one or more register fields, which are typically accessed by a single transaction on the DUT bus.
Register File	Represents a number of DUT registers. A register file contains a collection of registers at different addresses. A register file can also contain other register files.
Memory	Represents a DUT memory. A memory contains a specified number of address locations, all of the same size and characteristics (the memory element).
Address Map	Represents the address space. The address map contains the register files and the memory blocks (if any) in the address space. In a simple environment with only one register file, an address map may seem redundant. However, address maps gain importance in environments with multiple register files and memories, structuring the objects in a tree-like hierarchy. An address map can hold other address maps, which hold register files and memories.
Register Database (RGM_DB)	The root component for all registers and memories in the design. The `RGM_DB` inherits from `uvm_component` and is instantiated in the testbench class. The `RGM_DB` contains the root address maps of a verification environment.
Register Operation (RGM_OP)	RGM operations are classes that model read and write accesses to registers and memories.
Register Sequence (RGM_SEQ)	A sequence of read/write operations that is intended to be applied to registers and memories using the register sequencer.
Register Sequencer (RGM_SEQR)	A dedicated sequencer for register (and memory) operations. The functionality of the `RGM_SEQR` resembles that of a sequencer.

9.2   Register Package Overview

Like in many class libraries, using a register package requires that you become familiar with the library APIs and use model. The following sections give you an overview of the flow, main concepts, and components of register packages.

9.2.1   Register Packages Usage Flow

The procedure you follow to use register packages is illustrated in Figure 9-1. The goal is to automate the process of specifying changes to a running simulation. In general, the steps you take to accomplish this are as follows:

1.   From the device specification, capture the device registers in Accellera IP-XACT format (the standard for capturing and integrating design IP).

    This can be done manually using an XML editor, though some companies choose to write scripts that parse their internal documentation and produce standard IP-XACT.

    Note   For more information, see "Creating an IP-XACT File" on page 202.

2.   Use the IP-XACT converter utility in the uvm_rgm package to create SystemVerilog register database classes, including: register fields, registers, register files, address maps, and a register database. This utility is provided as part of the register package. The generated register classes are building blocks for memory and register read and write sequences.

3.   Connect the generated register classes to the existing testbench.

4.   Write register and memory sequences to generate stimulus.

5.   Add coverage and checking to your register code.

Note   The Cadence uvm_rgm package helps you to generate automatic coverage and checking. These built-in facilities can be customized and tuned, as needed.

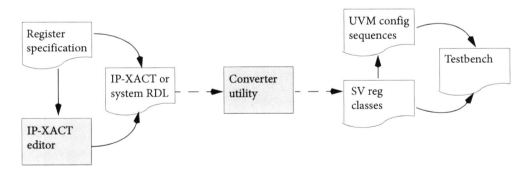

Figure 9-1   uvm_rgm Package Usage Flow

9.2.2   uvm_rgm Hook-Up and Data Flow

There are many ways to use the automation provided in the Cadence uvm_rgm register package. However, you can maximize your productivity and increase the robustness and reuse of your testbenches by following the proven guidelines outlined in this section.

Figure 9-2 illustrates the proper hookup of uvm_rgm elements in a testbench. As recommended by the UVM, the illustration shows monitoring done independent of the randomization and injection components. This means that coverage and checking are accomplished once a register's activity is collected by the monitor. The separation of stimulus injection from monitoring provides the following benefits:

- Allows coverage collection and checking, regardless of the device that is accessing registers

- Ensures that only traffic which made it to the DUT is taken into account

A further discussion of the merits of separating checking from generation can be found in Chapter 5.

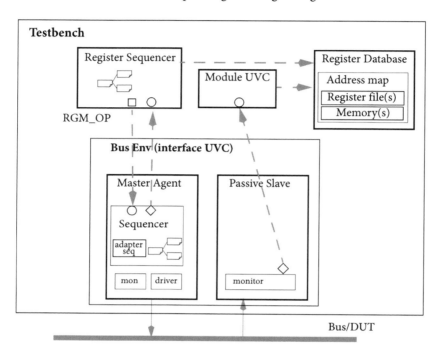

Figure 9-2   uvm_rgm Architecture Example

9.2.3   The Register Database (RGM_DB)

The entire register and memory model is generated within an RGM database component. Unlike the address map and register files—which are UVM objects and in some cases need to be allocated dynamically—the RGM_DB is a UVM component that can be placed directly into your testbench. The RGM_DB is a uvm_component that provides all of the traditional services of any other uvm_component, such as the configuration mechanism, test phases and messaging control. The RGM_DB serves as the *root* of the register tree and the top-most address map is contained within the RGM_DB.

The register database serves as a shadow model of the registers and memory in the DUT. Each register in the register database shadows a register in the DUT and reflects the current state of the DUT registers as they are written and read.

9.2.4   Randomization and Injection

9.2.4.1   The Register Sequencer and Sequences

The `uvm_rgm` package uses the familiar UVM sequence mechanism to randomize and drive register and memory sequences. Consequently, register and memory operation sequences behave much like any other UVM sequence. This means you can randomly select a register object from the `RGM_DB`, randomize it, set the access direction (read or write), and execute the register access operation. An API and set of macros are defined to perform read and write operations on registers.

Some of the operations the sequence mechanism allows you to implement include:

- Creating reusable sequences that support different configuration modes
- Using an existing sequence as a sub-sequence
- Traversing through all of the register in the address range

9.2.4.2   The Bus Interface UVC

The `uvm_rgm` sequencer is layered on top of an existing master sequencer. The master emulates the CPU as it programs, controls, and supervises other devices on the bus. Every read and write operation is translated into protocol-specific bus transactions. This isolation between register operation and protocol specific bus transactions allows reuse of the same register operation sequences, even if the specification changes to use a different bus. The bus interface sequencer is extended to support register sequence operations using the UVM factory.

9.2.5   Monitoring

9.2.5.1   The Interface UVC Monitor

As mentioned before, the monitoring path is independent from the injection facilities. We use the protocol-specific bus monitor to detect a bus transaction. At that point, the transaction information is sent to the module UVC via a TLM connection. The interface UVC monitor, used as a reusable component, is unaware of whether the transaction information collected is general bus traffic or a specific register access. This knowledge should be partitioned into the module UVC.

9.2.5.2   The Module UVC

It is recommended that you use a module UVC in this flow. The module UVC receives the transactions collected by the interface UVC monitor and decides what action to execute on the register and memory model. In the case of a write access to a register or memory location, the shadow register, or memory location is updated in the `RGM_DB` structure. Therefore, the content of the shadow register in the `RGM_DB` structure is synchronized with the DUT registers. When a read access is detected on the bus, the monitor accesses the `RGM_DB` structure and compares the read result from the DUT to the value in the `RGM_DB` shadow model. If it does not match, a DUT error is issued. In addition, the RGM_DB structure can collect coverage on the register accesses and values (when coverage collection is enabled).

9.3 Using the uvm_rgm Package

This section provides a step-by-step introduction to using the uvm_rgm register package for register and memory verification.

9.3.1 Defining the Register and Memory Models

First, you need to define the uvm_rgm model (register fields, registers, register files, address map, and register database). This is done using an XML IP-XACT file. The input format, which is a SPIRIT consortium standard, is translated into corresponding SystemVerilog classes and used in the testbench.

9.3.2 Creating an IP-XACT File

IP-XACT files are a standard format for capturing and integrating design IP. They are structural in nature and allow for describing a desired register database name, address spaces, register files, registers, and fields. Like any XML file, you can read and edit these files with an ASCII editor. In addition, you can read these files using free or commercial editors that provide a table view and extra editing and validation capabilities.

Cadence has extended the IP-XACT to enable more automation than is usually specified for register and memory verification. For example, you can specify coverage directives, constraints (for register randomization), an hdl_path variable (for directly accessing the register signals), and more.

Note If you already have a standard register specification format, you might want to create a script that parses the specifications and creates the corresponding IP-XACT file. Some companies start with an IP-XACT format and generate their specifications, C header files, register description, and even HW implementation.

9.3.2.1 XML Structure

XML is a text markup language like HTML, but was created to store data rather than just display text. The XML format is hierarchical and includes *start tags* followed by *end tags*, both contained between angle brackets. End tags are named exactly like the corresponding start tags but are preceded by a forward slash. For example:

```
<note>
<to>Ben</to>
<from>Gal</from>
<heading>Reminder for Shai</heading>
<body>Use UVM and prosper!</body>
</note>
```

IP-XACT introduces standard tags to capture design and register model attributes.

9.3.2.2 IP-XACT Structure

The structure of the IP-XACT file consists of the following:

- A header with some document detail such as the vendor name, the SPIRIT IP-XACT version, a project name, and so on.

- An array of memory maps that specify the memory and register descriptions. Each memory map is an address space that can hold memory blocks (register files), registers, or fields.

The XML code below illustrates the IP-XACT descriptions for a memory map, a register file, registers, fields, and their attributes.

```
<spirit:memoryMap>
    <spirit:name>memory_map_name</spirit:name>
<spirit:addressBlock>
    <spirit:name>regfile_name</spirit:name>
    <spirit:baseAddress>0</spirit:baseAddress>
    <spirit:range>16</spirit:range>
    <spirit:width>8</spirit:width>
<spirit:register>
    <spirit:name>register_name</spirit:name>
    <spirit:addressOffset>0x0</spirit:addressOffset>
    <spirit:size>8</spirit:size>
    <spirit:access>read-write</spirit:access>
    <spirit:reset>
        <spirit:value>0x00</spirit:value>
        <spirit:mask>0xff</spirit:mask>
    </spirit:reset>
<spirit:field>
    <spirit:name>field_name</spirit:name>
    <spirit:bitOffset>0</spirit:bitOffset>
    <spirit:bitWidth>2</spirit:bitWidth>
    <spirit:access>read-write</spirit:access>
    <spirit:values> <!-- required only for enumerations -->
        <spirit:value>0</spirit:value>
        <spirit:name>LEFT</spirit:name>
    </spirit:values>
```

Notes

- The easiest way to create an IP-XACT format is to start from an existing IP-XACT file.

- Use an XML editor for easy visualization of IP-XACT files (see the following section for details).

- Some companies use XML as the format for describing design blocks and leverage this for their register descriptions and some write scripts to convert their own register specification format to XML.

9.3.2.3 IP-XACT Vendor Extensions

The IP-XACT specification is not complete for register automation needs. Some of the missing capabilities include: constraints, coverage directives, and backdoor paths. That said, the standard does support extensions that enable us to add the missing functionality. For example:

```
<spirit:vendorExtensions>
  <vendorExtensions type>ua_lcr_c</vendorExtensions:type>
  <vendorExtensions hdl_path>lcr</vendorExtensions:hdl_path>
  <vendorExtensions:constraint>c_char_lngth {value.char_lngth != 2'b00;}
  </vendorExtensions:constraint>
</spirit:vendorExtensions>
```

Note   The uvm_rgm package introduces useful *vendor* extensions. We strongly recommend that you leverage the vendor extensions to enable additional automation, but this is not mandatory.

9.3.2.4 Leveraging XML and IP-XACT Editors

One of the benefits of using a standard is the number of free, commercial third-party applications which support that standard.

Some of the benefits of using applications that support the XML standard are that they:

- Ensure a clean XML syntax before running the parser script.

- Provide an intuitive view that allows collapsing and enhancing sub-trees.

- Support edit-time and on-demand standard validation.

- Enable automatic correlation between the Spirit and generated SystemVerilog classes.

Note   You can download the Eclipse application from **www.eclipse.org**.

9.3.2.5 Building the Register-Model Procedurally

In some cases, you will need to build the register model using the full procedural language capabilities. For example, you may need to create arrays with complex iterator logic that is not supported by IP-XACT. The uvm_rgm package provides you with the means to capture such models. Please review the *Register and Memory Model User Guide* for additional information.

9.3.3 Creating uvm_rgm SystemVerilog Classes

The following example shows the XML description for the line control register for the UART Controller device.

Example 9–1   UART Controller Line Control Register XML Description

```
1   <spirit:register>
2     <spirit:name>ua_lcr</spirit:name>
3     <spirit:addressOffset>0x3</spirit:addressOffset>
```

```
 4      <spirit:size>8</spirit:size>
 5      <spirit:access>read-write</spirit:access>
 6      <spirit:reset>
 7         <spirit:value>0x03</spirit:value>
 8         <spirit:mask>0xff</spirit:mask>
 9      </spirit:reset>
10       // FIELD DESCRIPTIONS
11      <spirit:field>
12         <spirit:name>char_lngth</spirit:name>
13         <spirit:bitOffset>0</spirit:bitOffset>
14         <spirit:bitWidth>2</spirit:bitWidth>
15      </spirit:field>
16      <spirit:field>
17         <spirit:name>num_stop_bits</spirit:name>
18         <spirit:bitOffset>2</spirit:bitOffset>
19         <spirit:bitWidth>1</spirit:bitWidth>
20      </spirit:field>
21      <spirit:field>
22         <spirit:name>p_en</spirit:name>
23         <spirit:bitOffset>3</spirit:bitOffset>
24         <spirit:bitWidth>1</spirit:bitWidth>
25      </spirit:field>
26      <spirit:field>
27         <spirit:name>div_latch_access</spirit:name>
28         <spirit:bitOffset>7</spirit:bitOffset>
29         <spirit:bitWidth>1</spirit:bitWidth>
30      </spirit:field>
31      <spirit:vendorExtensions>
32         <vendorExtensions:type>ua_lcr_c</vendorExtensions:type>
33         <vendorExtensions:compare_mask>0xff</vendorExtensions:compare_mask>
34        <vendorExtensions:hdl_path>uart_regs.lcr</vendorExtensions:hdl_path>
35        <vendorExtensions:constraint>c_char_lngth {value.char_lngth != 'b00;}
36           </vendorExtensions:constraint>
37   </spirit:vendorExtensions>
38   </spirit:register>
```

Example 9–2   UART Controller XML Description for the Reg File, Address Map

```
 1    <?xml version="1.0"?>
 2    <spirit:component
 3     xmlns:spirit="http://www.spiritconsortium.org/XMLSchema/SPIRIT/1.4"
 4     xmlns:xsi="http://www.w3.org/2001/XMLSchema-instance"
 5     xmlns:vendorExtensions="$UVM_RGM_HOME/builder/ipxact/schema"
 6     xsi:schemaLocation="http://www.spiritconsortium.org/XMLSchema/SPIRIT/1.4
 7        http://www.spiritconsortium.org/XMLSchema/SPIRIT/1.4/index.xsd
 8        $UVM_RGM_HOME/builder/ipxact/schema
```

```
 9        $UVM_RGM_HOME/builder/ipxact/schema/vendorExtensions.xsd">
10      <spirit:vendor>Cadence_Design_Systems</spirit:vendor>
11      <spirit:library>uart_ctrl_lib</spirit:library>
12      <spirit:name>uart_ctrl_reg_db</spirit:name>
13      <spirit:version>1.0</spirit:version>
14          <!-- START OF ADDRESS MAP DEFINITION -->
15      <spirit:memoryMaps>
16        <spirit:memoryMap>
17          <spirit:name>addr_map</spirit:name>
18          <spirit:addressBlock>
19          <!-- UART Controller Register File -->
20            <spirit:name>uart_ctrl_rf</spirit:name>
21            <spirit:baseAddress>0x00</spirit:baseAddress>
22            <spirit:range>0xFFFF</spirit:range>
23            <spirit:width>8</spirit:width>
24            <!-- Include each register description for the register file-->
25            <spirit:register> <!--LINE CONTROL REG--> </spirit:register>
26            <spirit:register> <!--INTERRUPT ENAB REG--> </spirit:register>
27            <spirit:vendorExtensions>
28             <vendorExtensions:type>uart_ctrl_rf_c</vendorExtensions:type>
29                <vendorExtensions:hdl_path>rf1</vendorExtensions:hdl_path>
30            </spirit:vendorExtensions>
31          </spirit:addressBlock>
32        </spirit:memoryMap>
33      </spirit:memoryMaps>
34      <spirit:vendorExtensions>
35      <vendorExtensions:type>uart_ctrl_addr_map_c</vendorExtensions:type>
36        <vendorExtensions:hdl_path>addr_map</vendorExtensions:hdl_path>
37      </spirit:vendorExtensions>
38  </spirit:component>
```

9.3.3.1 Using the IP-XACT Utility

The `uvm_rgm` package provides a Java utility to automate the creation of SystemVerilog classes using the IP-XACT description. To convert the input IP-XACT to SystemVerilog classes, use the following command:

```
$JAVA_HOME/bin/java -jar $UVM_RGM_HOME/builder/ipxact/uvmrgm_ipxact2sv_parser.jar
                    -i INPUT_FILE [Options]
```

The `uvmrgm_ipxact2sv_parser.jar` script also has an option to create a simple test to do a quick sanity check of your register database files. The option is: `-qt testname`. It will create an instance of the register database, execute a hard reset and print the register database and its sub-components. We suggest you use this option to test your register descriptions while you are mastering the IPXACT format.

9.3.3.2   The Generated SystemVerilog Code

The IP-XACT utility, `uvmrgm_ipxact2sv_parser.jar`, converts the IP-XACT register description file into a set of SystemVerilog classes for register verification. Included in the output file are the following:

- Enumerated types—A type declaration for each unique enumeration

- Field declarations

- Registers—A class for every unique register type

- Register files—Contain instances of registers for each register file

- Address maps—Contain one or more register files

- A top-level `RGM_DB` class (example) that contains the top-level address map

The generated code is UVM-compliant and tuned for performance and the memory footprint of large systems. It leverages much of the UVM automation and adds additional register-related automation by deriving the classes from the `uvm_rgm` base classes. Most of the code is not intended to be read by humans, but some of the public attributes are accessible for further user-defined coverage and generation. The code below illustrates an example of a generated register class:

Example 9–3   UART Controller Line Control Register SystemVerilog Description

```
1   class ua_lcr_c extends uvm_rgm_sized_register #(8);
2     typedef struct packed {
3       logic div_latch_access;
4       logic [2:0] rsv;
5       logic p_en;
6       logic num_stop_bits;
7       logic [1:0] char_lngth;
8     } pkd_flds_s;

9     `uvm_object_utils(ua_lcr_c)

10    `uvm_rgm_fld_utils_begin(pkd_flds_s)
11      `uvm_rgm_fld_int(0, div_latch_access, REG_RD, REG_WR, 7, 1, "")
12      `uvm_rgm_fld_int(1, rsv, REG_RD_RSV, REG_NO_WR, 4, 3, "")
13      `uvm_rgm_fld_int(2, p_en, REG_RD, REG_WR, 3, 1, "")
14      `uvm_rgm_fld_int(3, num_stop_bits, REG_RD, REG_WR, 2, 1, "")
15      `uvm_rgm_fld_int(4, char_lngth, REG_RD, REG_WR, 0, 2, "")
16    `uvm_rgm_fld_utils_end

17    constraint c_char_lngth { value.char_lngth != 2'b00; }

18    covergroup compare_and_update_cg;
19      option.per_instance=1;
20      coverpoint value.char_lngth;
21      coverpoint value.num_stop_bits;
```

```
22      coverpoint value.p_en;
23      coverpoint value.div_latch_access;
24   endgroup

25   virtual function void compare_and_update_sample();
26      compare_and_update_cg.sample();
27   endfunction

28   covergroup update_cg;
29     option.per_instance=1;
30     coverpoint value.char_lngth;
31     coverpoint value.num_stop_bits;
32     coverpoint value.p_en;
33     coverpoint value.div_latch_access;
34   endgroup

35   virtual function void update_sample();
36      update_cg.sample();
37   endfunction

38   virtual function void set_cov_inst_name();
39      compare_and_update_cg.set_inst_name($psprintf("%s.compare",
   get_full_name()));
40      update_cg.set_inst_name($psprintf("%s.update", get_full_name()));
41   endfunction

42   function new(input string name="unnamed-ua_lcr_c");
43      super.new(name);
44      set_reset_value(uvm_rgm_hard_reset, 8'h3, 8'hff);
45      set_reset_value(uvm_rgm_soft_reset, 8'h0, 8'h0);
46      set_compare_mask(8'hff);
47      compare_and_update_cg=new;
48      update_cg=new;
49   endfunction
50 endclass : ua_lcr_c
```

Note   Be aware of the following:

- The register class is derived from the `uvm_rgm_sized_register` class, which provides additional register automation not present in `uvm_object`.

- The fields are defined in a packed `struct` using SystemVerilog types that can easily be constrained, assigned, or sampled for coverage. You can read more about such control and extensions in the following sections.

- If the coverage attribute in IP-XACT was enabled for a specific field, a coverpoint is automatically created and sampled on register update/compares, and on updates.

- Implementing a class field for every field is inefficient for memory utilization and run-time performance. The `uvm_rgm_field` macros provide the same facilities with significant memory reduction.

Example 9–4   UART Controller Register File, Address Map and Register Database

```
1   // Register File Definition
2   class uart_ctrl_rf_c extends uvm_rgm_register_file;
3    // Register definitions (Only TWO are shown)
4      rand ua_ier_c ua_ier;
5      rand ua_lcr_c ua_lcr;

6      `uvm_object_utils(uart_ctrl_rf_c)

7      function new(input string name="unnamed-uart_ctrl_rf");
8        super.new(name);
9        set_size(`UVM_RGM_AWIDTH'hffff);
10       ua_ier = ua_ier_c::type_id::create("ua_ier");
11       ua_ier.set_hdl_path("ua_ier_reg");
12       add_register(`UVM_RGM_AWIDTH'h8, ua_ier, "ua_ier");
13       ua_lcr = ua_lcr_c::type_id::create("ua_lcr");
14       ua_lcr.set_hdl_path("ua_lcr_reg");
15       add_register(`UVM_RGM_AWIDTH'h3, ua_lcr, "ua_lcr");
16     endfunction
17   endclass : uart_ctrl_rf_c

18   // Address Map definition
19   class uart_ctrl_addr_map_c extends  uvm_rgm_address_map;
20     rand uart_ctrl_rf_c uart_ctrl_rf;

21     `uvm_object_utils(uart_ctrl_addr_map_c)

22     function new(input string name="unnamed-uart_ctrl_addr_map");
23       super.new(name);
24       set_size(`UVM_RGM_AWIDTH'h10000);
25       uart_ctrl_rf = uart_ctrl_rf_c::type_id::create("uart_ctrl_rf");
26       uart_ctrl_rf.set_hdl_path("rf1");
27       add_register_file(`UVM_RGM_AWIDTH'h0, uart_ctrl_rf, "uart_ctrl_rf");
28     endfunction
29   endclass : uart_ctrl_addr_map_c

30   // Register Database Definition
31   class uart_ctrl_reg_db extends uvm_rgm_db;
32     rand uart_ctrl_addr_map_c addr_map;

33     `uvm_component_utils(uart_ctrl_reg_db)
34     function new(string name = "unnamed-rgm_rdb", uvm_component parent);
35       super.new(name,parent);
```

```
36    endfunction : new

37    virtual function void build();
38      super.build();
39      // Create the address map
40      addr_map = uart_ctrl_addr_map_c::type_id::create("addr_map", this);
41      uart_ctrl_addr_map.set_hdl_path("addr_map");
42      add_addr_map(addr_map);
43    endfunction : build
44 endclass : uart_ctrl_reg_db
```

9.3.3.3   Extending the Auto-Generated uvm_rgm Classes

You may want to extend the generated register classes to modify the coverage or to add environment specific fields. We do not recommend modifying the automatic generated SystemVerilog code. The reasons for keeping the code untouched are:

- In the event of specification changes, you will want to regenerate the register model.

- uvm_rgm generated code may be modified over time for the purposes of code optimization and adding additional features. Directly editing the code prevents you from leveraging future uvm_rgm releases.

We recommend using the UVM factory to extend auto-generated code. The built-in UVM factory allows for code enhancements without intrusively modifying the generated code. This is done by deriving a class from the generated base class and updating the derivative as needed. (See "UVM Factory" on page 62 for more details.)

The next section describes how to integrate the generated classes into your verification environment.

9.4   Connecting uvm_rgm Components in a Testbench

Registers provide a great opportunity for reuse, as most devices are targeted for reuse, or comprised of pre-verified sub-components. The appropriate hook-up of register components to a testbench should preserve the potential for planned and unexpected reuse needs. Only the register package integrator needs to know how to connect the uvm_rgm components to the testbench. The uvm_rgm integration should allow test writers to focus on writing sequences and tests using the register package.

9.4.1   Connecting Register Components to a Testbench

In "Using the IP-XACT Utility" on page 206, you generated your SystemVerilog registers, register file(s), address map(s), and register database from your IP-XACT file. The uvm_rgm library provides a register sequencer that you can use. By this point you will also need a functioning interface bus UVC. With these pieces available, you can connect the register database components to your verification environment.

Perform the following steps to connect these components in the testbench:

1. Add the register database component (`uart_ctrl_reg_db`) in your testbench component.

2. Create an adapter sequence for the master sequencer. This sequence will take register operations and convert them to bus-specific protocol on the interface UVC bus.

3. Extend the interface bus UVC master sequencer to add the infrastructure required (this will be used to provide register operations to be driven to the bus).

4. Instantiate the register components in the testbench and connect the TLM ports between the components.

The following sections cover the steps needed to connect register sequences to a testbench.

9.4.2 Adding the Necessary Infrastructure to the Bus Master Sequencer

As mentioned earlier, the register sequencer provides register operations to an interface UVC master sequencer. Upon receiving the register operation, the master sequencer will convert the register operation to the appropriate bus transfer, which will then be sent to the interface driver. Traditional UVM sequencers do not posses the ability to receive the register operations or perform the necessary conversion of the register operation to the bus transfer. Your existing UVC's master sequencer must be modified to add some new TLM ports to enable this communication. You must also write some new logic to perform the register operation to bus transfer conversion. To minimize the knowledge and level of effort required by the user, the `uvm_rgm` package employs a standard (consistent with normal UVM sequence layering) means of layering the register sequencer. Figure 9-3 on page 212 illustrates the connections between the register sequencer and the bus master sequencer.

The master sequencer is extended to have:

- A `uvm_blocking_put_imp`. This will allow the interface sequencer to receive register operations from the register sequencer. You will need to implement a `put()` function that will be called when those operations are received.

- An `uvm_analysis_port` which provides a port that the interface sequencer can use to send responses back to the register sequencer. This allows the register sequences running on the register sequencer to receive the results for read operations and make decisions based on the result of those read values.

- An adapter sequence that provides the method to:
  - Convert the register operation requests into bus transfers, and send them to the interface driver—commonly called `execute_op()`
  - Process the responses to the bus transfers sent to the driver, and generate and return those responses to the register sequencer by way of the analysis port mentioned above.

You can have the register sequencer take full control over the bus master sequencer by setting the bus master sequencer's count attribute to zero, or you can interleave register operations with other bus transactions.

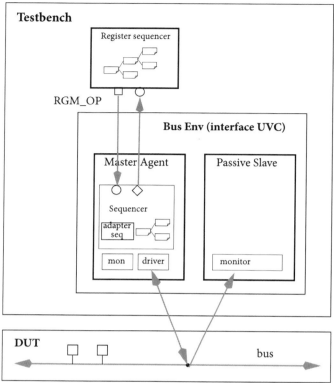

Figure 9-3   Layering a Register Sequencer on Top of a Master Sequencer

The code snippet below demonstrates adding the necessary infrastructure to a bus master sequencer.

```
1   `uvm_blocking_put_imp_decl(_reg)

2   class apb_rgm_master_sequencer extends apb_master_sequencer;

3     uvm_blocking_put_imp_reg #(uvm_rgm_reg_op, apb_rgm_master_sequencer)
4       reg_req_export;
5     uvm_analysis_port #(uvm_rgm_reg_op) reg_rsp_port;

6     apb_rgm_adapter_seq adapter_seq;

7     `uvm_sequencer_utils(apb_rgm_master_sequencer)

8     function new(string name, uvm_component parent);
9       super.new(name, parent);
10      reg_req_export = new("reg_req_export", this);
11      reg_rsp_port = new("reg_rsp_port", this);
12      `uvm_update_sequence_lib_and_item(apb_transfer)
```

```
13      adapter_seq =
14         apb_rgm_adapter_seq::type_id::create("adapter_seq", this);
15      endfunction : new

16      task run();
17         adapter_seq.start(this);
18         super.run();
19      endtask

20      task put_reg(uvm_rgm_reg_op t);
21         adapter_seq.execute_op(t);
22      endtask

23 endclass : apb_rgm_master_sequencer
```

The adapter sequence implements the execute_op() task called by the master sequencer's put_reg() implementation. This execute_op() task converts a register operation into a bus transaction and executes it (by way of uvm_do) on the local bus. By default, the register sequencer is operating in *push* mode, once this task completes, the register sequencer unblocks and continues. The adapter sequence also executes the process_response() task that runs forever. This process gets responses as they arrive and returns that response data to the register sequencer via the master sequencer's reg_rsp_port.

Note   This conversion from register operation to bus data item will vary and is specific to the bus interface protocol used.

Example 9–5   Adapter Sequence for APB Sequencer

```
1   class apb_rgm_adapter_seq extends uvm_sequence #(apb_transfer);
2     uvm_rgm_reg_op cur_op;

3     `uvm_object_utils(apb_rgm_adapter_seq)
4     `uvm_declare_p_sequencer(apb_rgm_master_sequencer)

5     function new(string name="apb_rgm_adapter_seq");
6       super.new(name);
7     endfunction : new

8     virtual task body();
9       process_responses();
10    endtask

11    virtual task process_responses();
12      while (1) begin
13        get_responses(rsp)
14        cur_op.set_reg_value(rsp.data);
15        p_sequencer.reg_rsp_port.write(cur_op);
16      end
```

```
17    endtask

18    virtual task execute_op(uvm_rgm_reg_op op);
19      cur_op = op;
20      p_sequencer.uvm_report_info(get_type_name(),
21        $psprintf("%s executing the following operation :\n%0s",
22        get_sequence_path(), op.sprint()), UVM_FULL);
23      `uvm_create(req)
24      req.addr = op.get_address();
25      if(op.get_direction()==OP_WR)
26      begin
27        req.data = op.get_reg_value();
28        req.direction = APB_WRITE;
29      end
30      else req.direction = APB_READ;
31      `uvm_send(req)
32    endtask : execute_op
33 endclass : apb_rgm_adapter_seq
```

Note Instead of using the `uvm_sequence_utils`, we use the `uvm_object_utils` and the `uvm_declare_p_sequencer` in order to avoid registering the adapter sequence in the sequencer. This prevents it from being randomly picked and executed again in the sequencer random traffic.

9.4.3 Instantiation and Connection to the Testbench

Following the UVM guidelines, the reusable component instantiation and connection is done in the testbench class. The steps you take to instantiate and connect the testbench are:

1. Instantiate the register database, the register sequencer, the bus UVC, and any other interface or module UVC you need.

2. Instantiate an analysis port implementation in order to retrieve bus transactions from the bus monitor and update or compare (and update) the value with the register database shadow value. This is typically done inside the module UVC.

3. Connect the component's ports and exports as shown in Figure 9-4, Testbench Instantiation and Connection, below.

4. Set up an initial reset operation for the shadow model. See "Reset Handling" on page 217 for an example.

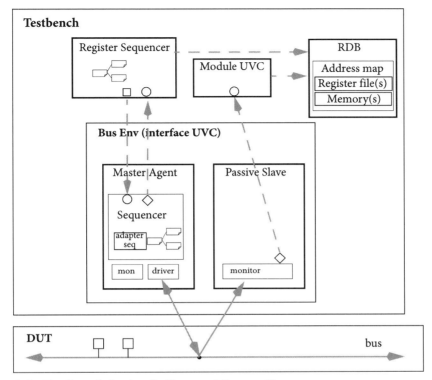

Figure 9-4   Testbench Instantiation and Connection

Example 9–6   UART Controller Testbench with Register Database Components

```
1   class uart_ctrl_env extends uvm_env;
2     uart_ctrl_config cfg;           // Configuration Object
3     apb_env apb0;                   // APB UVC
4     uart_env uart0;                 // UART UVC
5     uart_ctrl_env uart_ctrl0;       // Module UVC
6     uart_ctrl_virtual_sequencer virtual_sequencer; //Virtual Sequencer

7     uart_ctrl_reg_db rdb;                  // Register Database
8     uvm_rgm_sequencer reg_sequencer; // Register Sequencer

9   // UVM Component Utils and Constructor
10    `uvm_component_utils(uart_ctrl_tb)
11    function new (string name, uvm_component parent=null);
12      super.new(name, parent);
13    endfunction
14    // Additional Class Functions
15    extern virtual function void build();
```

```
16    extern virtual function void connect();
17    extern virtual task run();
18    extern virtual function void update_config(uart_ctrl_config cfg);
19    extern virtual task reset_rdb();
20  endclass : uart_ctrl_tb

21  function void uart_ctrl_tb::build();
22    super.build();
23    // Configure UVCs (not shown here)
24    // override the master sequencer
25    set_inst_override_by_type("*apb0.master.sequencer",
                           apb_master_sequencer::get_type(),
                           apb_rgm_master_sequencer::get_type());

26    // Create the interface UVCs, module UVC and virtual sequencer (not shown)
27
28    rdb = uart_ctrl_reg_db::type_id::create("rdb", this);
29    reg_sequencer =
                uvm_rgm_sequencer::type_id::create("reg_sequencer",this);
30    endfunction : build

31  function void uart_ctrl_tb::connect();
32    apb_rgm_master_sequencer apb_sqr_ptr; //pointer to APB master SEQR
33    super.connect();
34    // Connect Virtual Sequencer APB, UART and Register Sequencer
35    virtual_sequencer.rgm_seqr = reg_sequencer;
36    virtual_sequencer.apb_seqr = apb0.master.sequencer;
37    virtual_sequencer.uart_seqr = uart0.Tx.sequencer
38    // Register Sequencer Layering - Connect the TLM ports
39    if (!$cast(apb_sqr_ptr, apb0.master.sequencer))
40      `uvm_fatal("CASTFAIL", Failed to cast the APB master sequencer")
41    reg_sequencer.req_port.connect(apb_sqr_ptr.reg_req_export);
42    apb_sqr_ptr.reg_rsp_port.connect(reg_sequencer.rsp_export);

43    // Assign the address map (container of the register sequencer)
44    reg_sequencer.set_container(rdb.uart_ctrl_addr)map);
45    if (!$cast(uart_ctrl0.addr_map_ptr, rdb.uart_ctrl_addr_map))
46      `uvm_fatal("CASTFAIL", Failed to cast the Address Map to the rdb AM")

47    // TLM port connection to module UVC for RGM update, compare and update
48    apb0.bus_monitor.item_collected_port.connect(uart_ctrl0.apb_in);
49    // Connect TLM Ports for other testbench components (not shown)
50  endfunction : connect
```

Notes

- "Updating the Register Database Model" on page 223 describes how the module UVC is used to update the shadow register database based on the bus operations seen in the bus monitor. The module UVC contains whitebox knowledge and references to the device, which enables it to make intelligent decisions about whether a value should be compared to and updated into the register database shadow. We recommend the use of a module UVC for this purpose. However, it is possible to perform that function within the testbench class by creating the analysis_imp locally in the testbench. See "Updating the Register Database Model" on page 223 for more details on updating the shadow register database.

- It is possible to update the database from multiple agents, as needed.

9.4.4   Reset Handling

Whenever a device is going through a hard reset, its registers are set to predefined values. In this case, the shadow registers should keep in sync with the actual values. Reset values for each field are provided in IP-XACT format and, using the IP-XACT utility, added to the uvm_rgm classes. You can reset a register, register file, or even the entire address map using the built-in reset method and specifying which type of reset to execute. The example below shows an initial shadow model reset that is typically required for all devices.

```
1   // Testbench task to reset the register database
2   task uart_ctrl_tb::reset_rdb();
3     forever begin
4       wait (top.reset === 1);
5       `uvm_info(get_type_name(), "Resetting RDB Shadow Registers", UVM_LOW)
6         rdb.uart_ctrl_addr_map.reset(uvm_rgm_hard_reset);
7     end
8   endtask : reset_rdb

9   // Start the reset_rdb() task in the testbench run() task
10  task uart_ctrl_tb::run();
11    fork
12      super.run()
13      reset_rdb();
14    join_none
15  endtask : run
```

Note   Failing to reset the shadow model will cause a run-time error message when the first comparison between the shadow value and the actual device value takes place. This is probably the most common mistake users make in initial integration.

9.5   Controlling Register Scenarios

As part of the regular register activity, you might need to apply the following to the device:

- Drive the device's initial configuration to enable operation modes.
- The device configuration may need to be changed multiple times during a run. For example, a DMA may be configured for several different tasks on the same run.

- Normal run-time operations of reading and moving values between registers and other memory locations. For example, some devices require polling status registers or serving interrupts by reading and writing to a certain register.

Users typically want to write and read registers using the register's name or address (ideally, the register's name, since addresses can change throughout the course of a project). Instead of inventing a new solution, uvm_rgm leverages the standard sequence mechanism. To do this, you create UVM sequences of register reads and write that leverage the uvm_rgm register operation class. This allows you to easily model read and write scenarios with the desired mix of randomness and directed operations. The following section describes basic register sequence capabilities.

9.5.1   Register Operations

The data item for register sequences is a uvm_rgm_reg_op class that contains the register, the address on which to operate, and attributes, such as direction (read or write) and the access mode (through the bus—frontdoor, or using the hdl_path—backdoor).

Note   Setting the access mode to frontdoor sends a transaction on the bus to access a register. Setting the access mode to backdoor bypasses the bus logic and goes directly into the HDL signal that holds the register value. In reality, such access is not possible but it can save simulation cycles and help testing in verification.

The following code snippet shows the fields present in the uvm_rgm_reg_op class definition (accessor functions are provided but not shown here for the properties):

```
1   class uvm_rgm_reg_op extends uvm_sequence_item;

2     // operation hdl connection
3     protected uvm_rgm_hdl_connection_t hdl_connection = FRONTDOOR;

4     // operation address
5     protected uvm_rgm_addr_t address;

6     // operation direction
7     protected uvm_rgm_op_direction_t direction;

8     // operation register variable
9     protected uvm_rgm_register_base reg_var[$];

10    `uvm_object_utils_begin(uvm_rgm_reg_op)
11      `uvm_field_int(address, UVM_DEFAULT)
12      `uvm_field_enum(op_direction_t, direction, UVM_DEFAULT)
13      `uvm_field_object(reg_var, UVM_DEFAULT)
14    `uvm_object_utils_end
15    ...
16  endclass : uvm_rgm_reg_op
```

Note   Although a register operation is executed, we are really randomizing the defined registers and their field values. For performance and capacity requirements, the register database types (rdb, address map, register file) only include the register-specific information and do not include all the `rgm_reg_op` fields and methods.

9.5.2   Register Read/Write Sequences

Register sequences are derived from the class `uvm_rgm_sequence` (created to provide additional automation and convenience when writing register sequences), which in turn is derived from the `uvm_sequence`. You can read or write registers by name or by address. In a register sequence, you may need to apply constraints for constrained random tests or in a directed way, set a field to a specific value. A set of functions and macros allow you to perform register operations with or without additional constraints.

There are multiple ways to write and read registers:

- Single-step operation mode, which is easiest to write and understand

- Two-step operation mode (not shown here)

- Low-level manual means to cause a register operation to be executed (not shown here)

Example 9–7   Register Sequence

The following example shows the single-step operation mode.

```
1   class rd_wr_reg_seq extends uvm_rgm_sequence;
2     ua_lcr_c lcr_reg;
3     ua_ier_c ier_reg;

4     `uvm_sequence_utils(rd_wr_reg_seq, user_reg_sequencer)
5     function new(string name="rd_wr_reg_seq");
6       super.new(name);
7     endfunction

8     virtual task body();
9       `uvm_info(get_type_name(), "Executing...", UVM_MEDIUM)
10      `rgm_write_by_name_with(lcr_reg, "uart_ctrl_rf.ua_lcr",
11                             {value.div_latch_access == 1'b1)
12      `rgm_write_by_name(ier_reg, "uart_ctrl_rf.ua_ier" )
13      #1000; // Allow time to pass or execute other sequences
14      `rgm_read(lcr_reg)
15      `rgm_read_by_name(ier_reg,"uart_ctrl_rf.ua_ier")
16    endtask
17  endclass : rd_wr_reg_seq
```

Notes

- The `rgm_write_by_name` and `rgm_write_by_name_with` macros perform a write operation after finding the register in the string argument ("`uart_ctrl_rf.ua_lcr`").

- The `rgm_read` macro performs a read operation using its register argument. The `rgm_read_by_name()` macro will find the register in the database and then execute the read into the register argument.

- Within the register database, you can traverse through the address space and register-file hierarchies and use the `get_reg_by_addr` for a specific register file. For example, to get the register in *offset* 5 within the DMA and print it, use the following code:

```
uvm_rgm_register_base base_reg;
base_reg = rdb.addr_map.dma_rf.get_reg_by_addr(5);
base_reg.print();
```

  The function call returns the register at that address. When you print it, you will get all the fields defined for that register.

- To get all the registers in the register file and print, use the following code:

```
uvm_rgm_register_base base_regs[$];
rdb.addr_map.dma_rf.get_all_regs(base_regs);
foreach (base_regs[i]) base_regs[i].print();
```

  `get_all_regs()` is a void function which returns a queue of registers via the `base_regs` reference argument to the function.

- You can call the `get_reg_response()` task to retrieve the response to a specific register read. This is shown in "Read-Modify-Write Sequence" below.

- A full set of register sequence tasks and macros can be found in the *UVM Register and Memory Reference* provided with the `uvm_rgm` register package.

9.5.2.1   Read-Modify-Write Sequence

Many times you need to read a certain address, review the field values, modify a few fields, and write the result back to the register. The following example illustrates how to create this scenario:

```
1    class read_modify_write_seq extends uvm_rgm_reg_sequence;
2      ua_lcr_c lcr_reg;
3      uvm_rgm_register_base reg_rsp_var;

4      `uvm_sequence_utils(read_modify_write_seq, reg_sequencer)
5      function new(string name="read_modify_write_seq");
6        super.new(name);
7      endfunction

8      virtual task body();
9        `uvm_info(get_type_name(),"Executing...", UVM_MEDIUM)
10       `rgm_read_by_name(lcr_reg, "uart_ctrl_rf.ua_lcr")
11       get_reg_response(req);
12       $cast(lcr_reg, req)
13       // invert the div_latch_access bit
14       lcr_reg.value.div_latch_access = !lcr_reg.value.div_latch_access;
```

```
15          `rgm_write_send(lcr_reg)
16      endtask
17  endclass : read_modify_write_seq
```

Line 10: The rgm_read_by_name call executes a read on the APB bus.

Lines 11-12: The get_response() and $cast() calls retrieve the result into the lcr_reg register.

Line 14: Then the div_latch_access field of that register is inverted.

Line 15: The rgm_write_send call will execute a write operation without randomizing the value of lcr_reg.

9.5.3   Multi-Register Sequence Operations

In many cases, you want to perform operations on a subset of registers, or on all registers in the address map or register file. For example, perhaps a certain sequence would like to write to all writable registers in a register file. To achieve this, all of the containers (register files and address map) need to provide a get_all_regs() function, as follows:

Syntax

virtual function void **get_all_regs**(ref **uvm_rgm_register_base regs**[$], input bit clone = 1);

Description

regs   Returned queue of all the registers in the container

clone   Returns the clone of all the registers if 1

Example 9–8   Multi-Register Sequence

The following example shows how to fetch all of the registers in an address map and read their values:

```
1   class read_all_reg_seq extends uvm_rgm_built_in_base_seq;

2   `uvm_sequence_utils(read_all_reg_seq, uvm_rgm_sequencer)
3   function new(string name="unnamed-rgm_read_all_reg_seq");
4     super.new(name);
5   endfunction

6   uvm_rgm_register_base r_list[$];
7   virtual task body();
8     `uvm_info(get_type_name(), "Read all registers sequence starting...")
9     uart_ctrl_rf.get_all_regs(r_list);
10    // Perform the reads
11    foreach(r_list[j])
```

```
12          `rgm_read(r_list[j])
13    endtask
14 endclass : read_all_reg_seq
```

Notes

- By default, `get_all_regs()` creates a copy of all registers. You can also access these registers by reference by setting the clone bit to 0. We recommend that you avoid getting a register by reference and randomizing it. Avoiding this is a good practice that prevents corruption of the shadow model and overlooking bugs.

- A full set of built-in functions are provided in the uvm_rgm package. Please see the *UVM Register and Memory Reference*.

9.5.4   Sequences Reuse

UVM sequences are reusable, and register sequences are a perfect candidate for reuse. In module-level environments, you create multiple configuration sequences for multiple devices. In an integrated system-level environment, it is desirable to use these configuration sequences and combine them into system configuration sequences. The `uvm_rgm` sequences can be executed on multiple register file instances or with a different address offset in a larger system. To direct a sequence for a different location in the address hierarchy, use the `set_config` statement. This insulates the `body()` of the sequence from becoming invalid when the hierarchical context is added to a larger address map at some offset or instance name.

9.6   Using uvm_rgm for Checking

The `uvm_rgm` package provides built-in checking capabilities, which are flexible enough to accommodate many checking strategy requirements.

9.6.1   Using the Shadow Model for Checking

The register model gets updated as read/write transfers are identified by the bus monitor, sent to the module UVC monitor and compared/updated against the register database shadow model.

In some cases, a register is modified by the DUT and should not be compared. In that case, you need to set the comparison mask in the IP-XACT file to zero (0). The register compare mask can be set to any value of masking and compare selected fields as needed.

9.6.2   Advanced Register Checking

Many times, the DUT will modify register values during simulation time (status registers, for example). When this is the case, the shadow model is not in sync with the actual DUT register values. Masking the comparison will remove the error message, but still the question remains: *How do we verify status registers or read-only registers?* Also, a scoreboard may need to know the DUT configuration for a certain check. This can be achieved in the following manner:

- For these types of checks, a reference model or a *predictor* is required to determine the expected value. This predictor can be:
  - Cycle accurate, updating the shadow model to always match the DUT registers
  - Partially accurate, only checking equivalency at certain times or on a subset of the registers

For implementing the reference model or for updating the shadow register model values, the uvm_rgm containers provide a set of functions to set or get register values.

9.6.2.1 Get Register Functions

The following list shows the syntax for the get_reg_by_name() and get_reg_by_addr() methods:

- virtual function **uvm_rgm_register_base get_reg_by_name**(string name, bit clone_bit=1);
- virtual function **uvm_rgm_register_base get_reg_by_addr**(uvm_rgm_addr_t addr, bit clone_bit=1);

Note For other get_* methods, see the *uvm_rgm User Guide*.

Example 9–9   Updating a Get Register Field in the Register Database

The following example demonstrates how to update a field inside of the lcr_reg register on an interrupt event signal (Users integrating an example like this could trigger the interrupt event when an interface sees the appropriate interrupt signal transition.):

```
1   class uart_ctrl_env extends uvm_env;
2     ...
3     event interrupt;

4     virtual task update_reg_model();
5       forever begin
6         uvm_rgm_register_base lcr_reg;
7         @interrupt;
8         lcr_reg = addr_map_ptr.uart_ctrl_rf.get_reg_by_name("ua_lcr");
9         lcr_reg.set_field_value("div_latch_access", 0);
10      end
11    endtask : update_reg_model
12  endclass
```

9.7   Updating the Register Database Model

Every operation (reads and writes) performed on the DUT's registers through the bus, is observed by the bus monitor, which sends the transaction to the module UVC. The module UVC then performs a corresponding update, or compare (and update) of the shadow model. That way, there is constant alignment between the DUT's status and the registers' model, which resides inside the register database.

This task should be done by the integrator in charge of connecting the register model with the UVC.

To keep the model up to date with the DUT, do the following:

1. Update the module UVC (or create a new one if it does not exist). The module UVC is in charge of updating the register model after each transaction that is captured by the bus interface UVC monitor.

2. Using a `uvm_analysis` port, connect the bus interface UVC monitor to the module UVC such that the transactions collected are forwarded to the module UVC.

3. When each write transaction is received by the module UVC, the module UVC should update the register model by calling the `RGM_DB update_bv()` method, providing the address and data. This keeps the register model in sync with what was written into the DUT.

4. When each read transaction is received by the module UVC, the module UVC should compare the data to what is contained in the register model by calling the `RGM_DB compare_and_update_bv()` method. The `compare_and_update_bv()` method, as indicated by the name, also updates the register model to the data that was provided after the compare has taken place.

9.7.1   Updating the Module UVC

The module UVC is the component in charge of updating the register model after each interface UVC transaction related to the registers is detected. This task should be done by the integrator.

The module UVC keeps the shadow model aligned with the DUT's register status by notifying the register model after each UVC register transaction is received. This is done by calling the `update_bv()` method after each write transaction and calling `compare_and_update_bv()` after each read transaction.

The following example shows updates to the module UVC we introduce in Chapter 10 "System UVCs and Testbench Integration" in the section "Module UVC Architecture" on page 232.

When an APB transaction is received the register model is updated according to the operation direction (read or write).

```
1   class uart_ctrl_env extends uvm_env;
2   // Instances of the uart_ctrl config, monitor are not shown here

3     uvm_analysis_imp #(apb_transfer, uart_ctrl_env) apb_in;

4     uart_ctrl_addr_map_c addr_map_ptr;   // pointer to the address map

5     `uvm_component_utils(uart_ctrl_env)

6     function new (string name, uvm_component parent);
7       super.new(name, parent);
8       apb_in = new("apb_in", this);
9     endfunction

10    function void write(apb_transfer transfer);
11      if(apb_slave_cfg.check_address_range(transfer.addr)) begin
12        if (transfer.diretion == APB_WRITE) begin
```

```
13            `uvm_info(get_type_name(),
                  $psprintf("Write: calling update() with addr=%0h data=%0h",
                  transfer.addr, transfer.data), UVM_MEDIUM)
14            addr_map_ptr.update_bv(transfer.addr, transfer.data, 1);
15          end
16          else if (transfer.direction == APB_READ) begin
17            `uvm_info(get_type_name(),
18            $psprintf("Read: calling compare_and_update() with addr=%0h, data=%0h",
19            transfer.addr, transfer.data), UVM_MEDIUM)
20            addr_map_ptr.compare_and_update_bv(transfer.addr,
                                                 transfer.data, 1);
21          end
22          else `uvm_error("ex_rgm_mod_uvc", "Unsupported access!!!")
23        end
24      endfunction : write

25 endclass : uart_ctrl_env
```

9.8   Collecting Coverage of Register Activities

Many device operation modes translate directly into register control modes. This makes register field values coverage a good indicator of a complete verification.

9.8.1   Using uvm_rgm Automatic Coverage Facilities

The uvm_rgm automatically creates coverage groups for fields that are marked to be covered by way of the vendor extensions in IP-XACT.

Syntax

<**vendorExtensions**:coverage_en>true</vendorExtensions:coverage_en>

Once a field is tagged for coverage, a coverage point is created in the register coverage groups.

Example 9–10   Generated Coverage Group

The following example demonstrates a generated coverage group for a register that has a default single field named value. The auto-generated coverage is collected when you call the update() or compare_and_update() routines. Just the covergroup information is shown here.

```
1   class ua_lcr_c extends uvm_rgm_sized_register #(8);
2     typedef struct packed {
3       logic div_latch_access;
4       logic [2:0] rsv;
5       logic p_en;
6       logic num_stop_bits;
```

```
7      logic [1:0] char_lngth;
8    } pkd_flds_s;

9    covergroup compare_and_update_cg;
10     option.per_instance=1;
11     coverpoint value.char_lngth;
12     coverpoint value.num_stop_bits;
13     coverpoint value.p_en;
14     coverpoint value.div_latch_access;
15   endgroup

16   virtual function void compare_and_update_sample();
17     compare_and_update_cg.sample();
18   endfunction

19   covergroup update_cg;
20     option.per_instance=1;
21     coverpoint value.char_lngth;
22     coverpoint value.num_stop_bits;
23     coverpoint value.p_en;
24     coverpoint value.div_latch_access;
25   endgroup

26   virtual function void update_sample();
27     update_cg.sample();
28   endfunction

29   virtual function void set_cov_inst_name();
30     compare_and_update_cg.set_inst_name($psprintf("%s.compare",
   get_full_name()));
31     update_cg.set_inst_name($psprintf("%s.update", get_full_name()));
32   endfunction

33   function new(input string name="unnamed-ua_lcr_c");
34 ...
35     compare_and_update_cg=new;
36     update_cg=new;
37   endfunction
38 endclass : ua_lcr_c
```

9.8.2   User-Defined Coverage

What if you want to cross the register field values with other testbench attributes? Or describe a sophisticated coverage model while exploiting SystemVerilog coverage attributes? As was mentioned before, we do not recommend editing the auto-generated code. For such needs, you can extend the register class, define a desired coverage group, and use the UVM factory to instantiate the new register class.

The following example demonstrates a user-defined coverage group:

```
1   class ua_lcr_cov_c extends ua_lcr_c;

2     covergroup lcr_modes_cg;
3       coverpoint num_stop_bits;
4       coverpoint char_lngth;
5       cross num_stop_bits, char_lngth;
6     endgroup

7     function update_sample();
8       super.update_sample();
9       lcr_modes_cg.sample();
10    endfunction

11  endclass : ua_lcr_cov_c
```

Once this is done, you can use the standard factory overrides (`type` and/or `instance`) to replace the `ua_lcr_c` instances with `ua_lcr_cov_c` instances.

9.9   Controlling Coverage-Sampling Time

Sampling registers as soon as they are written may not be correct for some applications. For example, if a DUT is configured for a certain operation mode, but an *abort* function is called right after, then the question arises: *Was this operation mode really tested?*

The solution for this issue is to not add the `.sample()` function of the covergroup to the `update_sample()` (and/or the `compare_and_update_sample()`) method. Rather, you should manually trigger the sample at the appropriate time. Whatever block is aware of this condition can use the `get_reg_by_name()` or `get_reg_by_address()` to get the desired register object and then call the coverage group `.sample()` function.

Summary

This chapter is a quick overview of a register package. It uses the Cadence `uvm_rgm` package as an example for register packages. Many more capabilities exist in `uvm_rgm` than are shown here. For example, a user can:

- Do backdoor operations for both Verilog and VHDL relying on a `hdl_path` string. This can enable you to write directly to the field or the string.

- Define in IP-XACT write and read FIFO registers that hold multiple values and indirect registers (registers that are not mapped in the address map and can only be accessed indirectly).

- Write sequences in complete register-level or field-level granularity.

- Take advantage of an advanced tagging mechanism to control register-related activities.

- Use the pre_access() and post_access() hooks, which are provided to implement side effect behaviors triggered by accessing a register.

- Implement a shadow memory model.

- Use built-in tests that allow for the execution of predefined register tests without writing SystemVerilog code (which writes to all registers inside a container). Various filters allows flexible control over these built-in tests.

For more information about register packages and the uvm_rgm, please read the documentation provided with the Cadence uvm_rgm package on the **www.uvmworld.org** website.

10   System UVCs and Testbench Integration

Chapter 7 "Simple Testbench Integration" introduced a testbench that instantiates scoreboard checking and coverage directly within the top testbench class. But what if you want to reuse this logic in a cluster-level environment, which later might be reused in a larger subsystem that is eventually part of an even larger system? This chapter reviews this requirement and the solution of how to keep device-specific verification encapsulated for reuse, and which logic should be placed within the testbench top and the module UVC container.

Note   In this chapter we use the term *system* to describe system-level hardware integration. The topic of software UVCs and hardware and software co-verification is beyond the scope of this book.

10.1 Introduction

Interface UVCs are developed for a designated protocol and can be used in verification of any device which uses that protocol. But where do you place device-specific coverage? Where do reference models or scoreboards reside? These concerns and many more are not related to an interface and usually involve an association across multiple interfaces. Module UVCs are verification component containers that organize DUT-specific verification logic and enable integration of modules or clusters into a larger environment. The types of reuse that module UVCs enable are:

- Blocks to module, modules to cluster, clusters to system

- Between projects with whitebox and blackbox reuse

- TLM to cycle-accurate to post-silicon

Similar to the interface UVC, the module UVC has a standard architecture and configuration attributes. Like interface UVCs, module UVCs provide a proven recipe to the module UVC developer and a consistent, easy integration for the testbench integrator. Figure 10-1, UART Controller DUT and UART Controller Module UVC, depicts the architecture of a reusable module UVC. The terms *module UVC* and *system UVC* are interchangeable. A module UVC is a system UVC for a single module, and the way to configure and instantiate them is the same. Both module UVCs and system UVCs support further integration into a larger system.

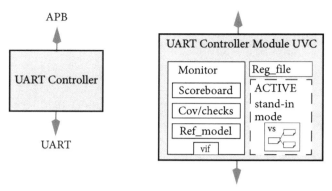

Figure 10-1   UART Controller DUT and UART Controller Module UVC

Figure 10-2, UART DUT and Module UVC Integrated into a Larger System, illustrates a module UVC created for a UART controller device. When the UART is integrated into a larger system, some of the external interfaces of the module UVC become internal to the larger system.

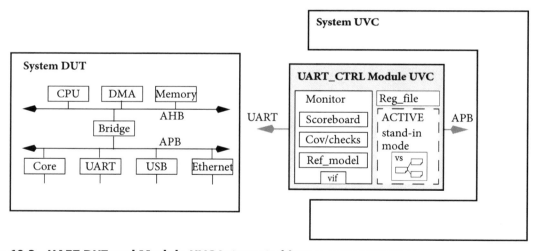

Figure 10-2   UART DUT and Module UVC Integrated into a Larger System

Figure 10-3, Testbench Architecture with UART Controller Module UVC, shows a module UVC in passive mode integrated within a testbench. A module UVC can also be active in stand-in mode. In this mode the module UVC emulates a subsystem design, stand-in mode is used to enable simulation before all of the DUT is implemented, in some cases to speed up the simulation. This chapter focuses on a module UVC architecture that maximizes reuse in the event of vertical reuse. Later we show how the testbench integrator leverages the module and system UVCs for system-level integration.

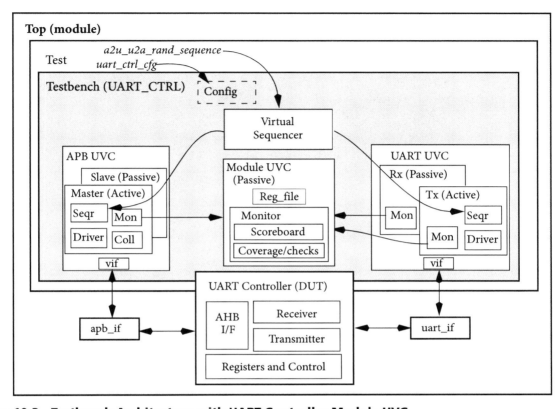

Figure 10-3   Testbench Architecture with UART Controller Module UVC

10.2   Module and System UVC Architecture

Module and system UVCs share the same high-level topology and standard attributes. Both can be further reused in larger systems. Their architecture and sub-components are similar with the only difference being that system UVCs integrate more than a single module. The following sections review the module UVC structure and then show how it scales to a larger system.

10.2.1   Reuse in Module and System UVCs

The role of the module or system UVC is to encapsulate knowledge about its related device and add the components needed to verify the system. The goal is to follow a solid formula that allows planned and unplanned reuse. In an interface UVC, we reuse traffic generation and protocol-specific checks and coverage. In a module UVC, we reuse:

- Device-specific checks
  - Scoreboards and internal checks
  - Reference model

- Device specific coverage
- Fine-tuning of interface UVCs' coverage definitions
- Cross-coverage
- Internal coverage

- Relationships between participating UVCs

  - Configuration dependencies
  - Connections between scoreboards and appropriate monitors

Note   The virtual sequencer is not part of the module UVC, as some of the interfaces controlled in the module level might become internal to the DUT and cannot be driven in the larger system.

10.2.2 Module UVC Architecture

In general, a module UVC includes:

- Configuration information

- A monitor for collecting and interpreting events and transactions going to or from the DUT. As always, a monitor is responsible for coverage and checking. In order to achieve that, a monitor can have scoreboards, reference models, and a virtual interface to access the internals of the module.

- Memory blocks and register files. These are usually pointers to components in the testbench.

- The ability to emulate the DUT functionality in stand-in mode described later in "Stand-In Mode" on page 252.

- A virtual sequencer and a register sequencer are declared in the module UVC package, but instantiated in the testbench.

Note   The module UVC does not contain the interface UVCs. The module UVC is connected via references and TLM ports to other UVCs (in particular to the related interface UVC's monitors). If two subsystems integrate all of their external interfaces, the interfaces that connect the subsystems are duplicated in the integrated system. For example, if our UART controller module UVC contains an instance of the APB interface UVC, a system that instantiates two UART controller devices on the same APB bus ends up with two instances of the APB UVC. A block diagram of the UART controller module UVC is presented below.

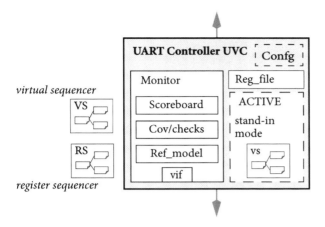

Figure 10-4   Module UVC Architecture and Components

10.2.3   System UVC Architecture

Figure 10-5 illustrates a system UVC architecture that instantiates two module UVCs.

Note   From an integrator's point of view, it does not matter if the integrated subsystem is an atomic module UVC or a composition of other sub-components. In order to achieve this, a system UVC contains the same sub-components and configuration attributes as the module UVC. The main difference between these components is that a system UVC contains more than a single DUT module integration.

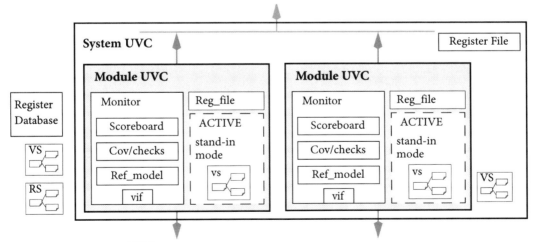

Figure 10-5   A System UVC

10.3 Sub-Components of Module and System UVCs

The next sections describe in more detail each of the module UVC sub-components.

10.3.1 Monitor

The monitor in a system or module UVC is a critical component in the verification environment. It collects data related to the activity in the module or system. This information is made available to checkers, scoreboards, and coverage collectors. The monitor collects most of its information from the relevant interface UVCs via TLM connections. Some additional information relating to the internal state of the module or system may be derived either from a virtual interface to the DUT (whitebox access) or from a reference model. The connection from the monitor to the corresponding interface UVC monitors is done using the interface UVC TLM analysis ports, as illustrated in Figure 10-6, below.

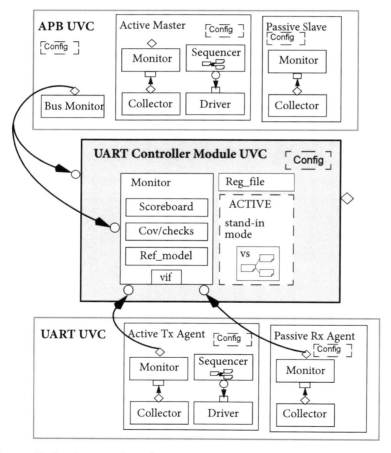

Figure 10-6   Connecting the UART Controller UVC and Monitor with Interface UVC TLM Ports

Module UVC Monitor Example

The following code example, taken from the UART controller module UVC, shows how the module UVC monitor uses information collected from other monitors.

Example 10–1   UART Controller Module Monitor

```
1   // TLM Port Declarations
2   `uvm_analysis_imp_decl(_rx)
3   `uvm_analysis_imp_decl(_tx)
4   `uvm_analysis_imp_decl(_apb)

5   class uart_ctrl_monitor extends uvm_monitor;

6     virtual interface uart_ctrl_if vif; // Optional interface to DUT

7     uart_ctrl_config cfg;                   // UART Controller config info

8     uart_ctrl_tx_scbd tx_scbd;          // Tx Scoreboard
9     uart_ctrl_rx_scbd rx_scbd;          // Rx Scoreboard
10    uart_ctrl_env_cover uart_cover;     // Coverage Component

11    // TLM Connections to the interface UVC monitors
12    uvm_analysis_imp_apb #(apb_transfer, uart_ctrl_monitor) apb_in;
13    uvm_analysis_imp_rx #(uart_frame, uart_ctrl_monitor) uart_rx_in;
14    uvm_analysis_imp_tx #(uart_frame, uart_ctrl_monitor) uart_tx_in;
15    // TLM Connections to other Components (Scoreboard, Ref model)
16    uvm_analysis_port #(apb_transfer) apb_out;
17    uvm_analysis_port #(uart_frame) uart_rx_out;
18    uvm_analysis_port #(uart_frame) uart_tx_out;

19    `uvm_component_utils(uart_ctrl_monitor)

20    function new (string name, uvm_component parent);
21      super.new(name, parent);
22      create_tlm_ports(); // Create TLM Ports
23    endfunction: new

24    // Additional class methods
25    extern virtual function void create_tlm_ports();
26    extern virtual function void build();
27    extern virtual function void connect();
28    extern virtual function void write_rx(uart_frame frame);
29    extern virtual function void write_tx(uart_frame frame);
30    extern virtual function void write_apb(apb_transfer transfer);
31    // More class methods update_config, assign_vi
32 endclass : uart_ctrl_monitor
```

Whitebox and Blackbox Verification Modes

Testbench development is often started with a reference model of the DUT or using a stand-in mode (see "Stand-In Mode" on page 252). In this case, you can develop the testbench blackbox aspects that rely mostly on the interface UVC's input. Later, when the device implementation matures, you can move to the whitebox implementation-specific checks and coverage. A blackbox operation mode is also more reusable if you swap device implementation with a different implementation. The module UVC should support both whitebox and blackbox operation modes. The module UVC virtual interface that touches the device internals is used only in whitebox operation mode.

You can have more abstraction in the monitor, both in the connection to the interface verification components and the whitebox DUT access. As you gather monitor information from the interface UVC, it is possible to use an abstract interface UVC implementation that is not protocol specific. Generic payload is an example of this use model. This allows verification of a device before the actual interface protocols are determined and also makes the system UVC reusable in case of future modifications of the interface protocols.

You can make the whitebox operation more reusable if, instead of a virtual interface, you use an interface class to set and get the needed signal values.

10.3.1.1 Scoreboard

In Chapter 7 "Simple Testbench Integration", the scoreboard components were placed directly in the testbench. For module-to-system reuse, scoreboards are placed within the monitor that can access multiple interface UVCs monitor information. If a broader end-to-end checker exists, it should be possible to turn off local scoreboards to speed up the simulation. The monitor `build()` method creates and configures the scoreboard(s) and the monitor `connect()` method is used to connect the monitor TLM ports to the scoreboard ports, as shown in the example below:

Example 10–2   UART Controller Monitor build() and connect() Methods

```
1   function void uart_ctrl_monitor::build();
2     super.build();
3     uart_cover = uart_ctrl_cover::type_id::create("uart_cover",this);
4     if (cfg == null) begin
5       cfg = uart_ctrl_config::type_id::create("cfg", this);
6       set_config_object("tx_scbd", "cfg", cfg);
7       set_config_object("rx_scbd", "cfg", cfg);
8     end
9     tx_scbd = uart_ctrl_tx_scbd::type_id::create("tx_scbd",this);
10    rx_scbd = uart_ctrl_rx_scbd::type_id::create("rx_scbd",this);
11  endfunction : build

12  function void uart_ctrl_monitor::connect();
13    super.connect();
14    apb_out.connect(tx_scbd.apb_match);
15    uart_tx_out.connect(tx_scbd.uart_add);
```

```
16    apb_out.connect(rx_scbd.apb_add);
17    uart_rx_out.connect(rx_scbd.uart_match);
18 endfunction : connect
```

10.3.1.2 Coverage

Module and system UVCs have access to the interface UVCs transactions, state variables in the testbench, or reference model and DUT internals. As part of the testbench integration, further constraints and extensions on the interface UVC-provided coverage may be required.

For more information, see "Coverage" on page 248.

10.3.1.3 Reference Model

A reference model emulates the DUT functionality and, given the input to the DUT, can predict the expected result. The reference model can also provide status and state information. This information is useful for generating traffic, coverage and checking.

A reference model can be implemented at three levels of precision:

- It can provide transaction-level functionality. Such reference models provide transaction-level valid output for a given input. This information can be used for scoreboards to compare the actual to predicted, or for functional stand-in mode. The transaction level functionality is the most commonly used reference model; this model is provided by the architects as a golden model to the DUT behavior.

- Reference models can also be cycle accurate. Such models perform cycle-accurate emulation and provide the expected result per cycle. These can be used in stand-in mode and scoreboard, but typically are overkill for scoreboarding.

- It can provide rough justification by checking the validity of the DUT behavior given some input and output. The DUT internals might be used for justification.

10.3.2 Memory Blocks and Register Files

A device is typically mapped into the system memory map. The module UVC can be configured from a higher-level environment to its actual location within the system map. To be reusable, all module UVC operations work on a local context and assume a correct context to be set from outside. Vertical reuse of register and memory configuration sequences also relies on the register package ability to provide the context (typically an address offset) to configuration sequences.

10.3.3 Active Stand-In Mode

In some cases, the system is not fully available. You may still want verify the rest of the system or start developing your testbench. For this, a user needs to emulate the DUT behavior. The active stand-in mode of operation uses a virtual sequencer, buffers, and sequences to control the ports of the DUT and data structures. Section 10.8, "Stand-In Mode," on page 252 has further details on how to implement the module UVC stand-in mode.

10.3.4 The Module UVC Class

The example below shows the class definition of the UART controller module UVC.

Example 10–3 UART Controller Module UVC

```
1   class uart_ctrl_env extends uvm_env;
2     // Component configuration classes
3     uart_ctrl_config cfg;
4     // Module monitor (includes scoreboards, coverage, checking)
5     uart_ctrl_monitor monitor;
6     // Pointer to the Register Database address map
7     uart_ctrl_addr_map_c addr_map_ptr;

8     // TLM Connections
9     uvm_analysis_port #(uart_config) uart_cfg_out;
10    uvm_analysis_imp #(apb_transfer, uart_ctrl_env) apb_in;

11    `uvm_component_utils(uart_ctrl_env)
12  function new(input string name, input uvm_component parent=null);
13      super.new(name,parent);
14      // Create TLM ports
15      uart_cfg_out = new("uart_cfg_out", this);
16      apb_in = new("apb_in", this);
17    endfunction

18    // Additional class methods
19    extern virtual function void build();
20    extern virtual function void connect();
21    extern virtual function void write(apb_transfer transfer);
22    extern virtual function void assign_vi(virtual interface
    uart_ctrl_internal_if int_if);
23    extern virtual function void update_config(uart_ctrl_config
    uart_ctrl_cfg);
24  endclass : uart_ctrl_env
```

10.4 Module UVC Configuration

The UVC configuration is a reusable aspect that must be encapsulated with the UVC. When a UVC becomes part of a system, some of its configuration is fixed according to the specific use in the system. Configuration of large systems can be challenging, as the system may contain multiple components and interfaces that need to be configured in a coherent way. The integrator of a system may not be familiar with all the subsystem configuration options that need to be integrated. Similar to the recommendation in interface UVCs, the module UVC and DUT configuration attributes are encapsulated within a configuration object. The object allows randomizing legal settings by capturing configuration attribute dependencies in constraints. As modules and system UVCs are integrated, their configuration classes are integrated as well and the system attributes and dependencies are controlled via constraints. Both the testbench integrator and the test writers can apply more constraints on the configuration class.

10.4.1 Standard Configuration Modes

Both the DUT and the module UVC need to be coherently configured for the desired operation mode. As well as DUT-specific configuration attributes such as bus speed or number of channels, some configuration attributes are generic and commonly used in all module UVCs. Standardizing these provides a consistent user experience for the integrator and test writers. The reuse attributes in a module UVC are active and passive modes, and whitebox versus blackbox configuration modes. As discussed, it is best to capture the configuration class within an object—to be randomized, printed, sent between components and encapsulated as needed. The module UVC configuration class contains the interface UVCs configuration classes. The standard attributes of a module UVC include:

- **Active and Passive Modes**—The active mode implements the stand-in mode, where the module UVC plays the role of the DUT (for example, when the DUT is not available). The active mode enables an additional virtual sequencer used to drive the external interfaces on the DUT's behalf.

- **Whitebox and Blackbox Modes**—The UVC also supports whitebox versus blackbox modes. In a blackbox verification mode, the UVC ignores the internal implementation of the DUT and assumes only knowledge of the interfaces and generics that are not implementation specific. In this mode, the module UVC is reusable for a different implementation of the DUT. In a whitebox mode, the UVC is aware of the DUT implementation whether is it RTL, SystemC or other implementation. For example the UVC can access FIFOs and signals and cover their state. The verification in this mode is both more thorough and more specific.

- **Level of Abstraction**—The same module UVC allows verifying a DUT that is going through a refinement process from high-level models to RTL and into gate-level description. The is achieved by using a level of abstraction knob on every component.

The example below shows a partial implementation of the UART UVC config class. This configuration object is included in the reusable files for the UART interface UVC. Example 10–5 on page 240 shows the composite UART controller configuration object.

Note   The APB configuration class is shown in the Interface UVCs Chapter, Example 5–12 on page 104.

Example 10–4   UART Configuration Class (Partial)

```
1    class uart_config extends uvm_object;
2      //UART topology parameters
3      uvm_active_passive_enum  is_tx_active = UVM_ACTIVE;
4      uvm_active_passive_enum  is_rx_active = UVM_PASSIVE;

5      // UART device parameters
6      rand bit [7:0] baud_rate_gen; // Baud Rate Generator Register
7      rand bit [1:0] nbstop;        // Number stop bits (mode_reg[7:6])
8      rand bit [1:0] ua_chmode;     // Channel mode    (mode_reg[9:8])
9      rand bit       rx_en ;        // RX Enable (control_reg[2])
```

```
10   rand bit       tx_en ;           // TX Enable (control_reg[4])

11   // Constraints
12   constraint c_num_stop_bits { nbstop inside {[0:2]};}

13   // Constructor and uvm_object_utils and uvm_field_* macros

14 endclass : uart_config
```

Example 10–5   UART Controller Configuration Class

```
1   class uart_ctrl_config extends uvm_object;
2     apb_config apb_cfg;
3     uart_config uart_cfg;
4     `uvm_object_utils(uart_ctrl_config)
5     function new(string name=uart_ctrl_config");
6       super.new(name);
7       uart_cfg = uart_config::type_id::create("uart_cfg");
8       apb_cfg = apb_config::type_id::create("apb_cfg");
9     endfunction : new
10 endclass : uart_ctrl_config
```

10.4.2 Module UVC Reconfiguration

As the device is being configured in run time, the testbench and module UVCs might require reconfiguration. Typically module UVCs acquire their configuration directly from the bus, exactly like the DUT. This ensures that the module UVC and the DUT are in synch, and that the reconfiguration works in passive mode. For example, module UVC senses configuration changes by translating bus transactions to register operations and adjusting its operation as needed.

Users may need to reflect configuration changes to a module UVC. In the case of reconfiguring an existing module, use of set_config_* is not appropriate because it does not trigger the field modification. (For example, someone still needs to call the apply_config_settings or get_config to update the configurable values.) Similar to interface UVCs, we recommend defining an update_config() task that receives a configuration object argument, verifies that the configuration is consistent, and applies the configuration on the components and its sub-components. Shown below are the update_config() methods for the UART controller module UVC and the UART controller monitor.

Example 10–6   UART Controller update_config() Methods

```
function void uart_ctrl_env::update_config(uart_ctrl_config uart_ctrl_cfg);
  `uvm_info(get_type_name(), {"Updating Config\n", uart_ctrl_cfg.sprint},
UVM_HIGH)
  cfg = uart_ctrl_cfg;
  monitor.update_config(uart_ctrl_cfg);
endfunction : update_config
```

```
function void uart_ctrl_monitor::update_config(uart_ctrl_config uc_cfg);
  `uvm_info(get_type_name(), {"Updating Config\n", uart_ctrl_cfg.sprint},
UVM_HIGH)
   cfg = uc_cfg;
   tx_scbd.slave_cfg = uc_cfg.apb_cfg.slave_configs[0];
   tx_scbd.uart_cfg = uc_cfg.uart_cfg;
   rx_scbd.slave_cfg = uc_cfg.apb_cfg.slave_configs[0];
   rx_scbd.uart_cfg = uc_cfg.uart_cfg;
endfunction : update_config
```

10.5 The Testbench

The testbench class instantiates, configures, and connects the interface UVCs, module UVCs, register sequencer and database, and the virtual sequencer. The reusable components are set for a default operation mode that can be altered by a specific test for verification purposes. With a UVM testbench, instantiation is relatively easy, as each component provides a set of high-level configuration parameters to build itself. At the same time, designing a testbench requires understanding of the system verification needs and can involve a lot of creativity.

Figure 10-7 below illustrates the components and connections for the UART controller example testbench.

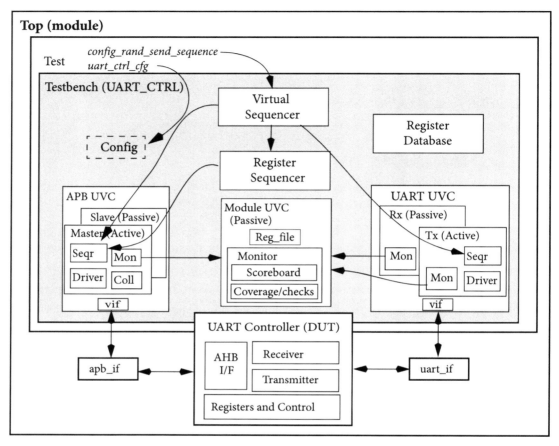

Figure 10-7 UART Controller Testbench Topology

Before designing a testbench, the verification architect needs to create a proper strategy for stimuli creation, checking, and coverage. An ideal testbench provides easy, high-level, abstract simulation control that hides from the test writers the detailed mechanics, and at the same time, allows fine control for specific test scenarios that require it.

Here are some guidelines for designing a testbench:

- Consider the high-level scenario that the simulation requires. Usually there is a high-level operation that is performed repeatedly to verify a design. In our UART controller example, we need to reset the UART controller, configure the controller, through APB transactions, to a certain operation mode, and start sending traffic from the serial UART interface, and back. The UART can be reconfigured multiple times within a given simulation.

- Create a strategy to enable high-level operation with minimal effort or knowledge of the testbench. For example, a high-level sequence can allow randomizing the configuration class; the rest of the testbench activity, such as register configuration, running traffic through the external interfaces, is performed automatically. Consider how this high-level API should be translated into the desired simulation operations.

- By default, the testbench should create legal simulations while self-checking is active and coverage is collected. Users can touch different aspects of the configuration or generation to steer the simulation to areas of interest.

- Think of all stimulus requirements and operation modes (for example, with software or without, and whether acceleration is planned).

- If performance is potentially an issue, create safe ways to cut corners and improve the simulation speed without the risk of missing bugs. For example, you can disable local checkers, use backdoor operations to memory and registers to save bus operations, avoid long memory allocation using sparse memories, simplify randomization, and more.

10.5.1 The UART Controller Testbench Strategy

Observe the testbench topology in Figure 10-7, UART Controller Testbench Topology. All UVM users are likely to draw this testbench topology if asked. The great thing about UVM is that the high-level encapsulation and guidelines spell out much of the correct architecture for users. Many times, the users already have this high-level picture in mind, and they just need to understand all the capabilities and flexibility that this architecture provides for their projects.

The example below illustrates a testbench class declaration.

Example 10–7 UART Controller Testbench

```
1   class uart_ctrl_tb extends uvm_env;
2     // UVC Components
3     apb_env   apb0;   // APB UVC
4     uart_env uart0;   // UART UVC
5     uart_ctrl_env uart_ctrl0; // Module UVC

6     // Virtual sequencer
7     uart_ctrl_virtual_sequencer virtual_sequencer;

8     // Configuration Class for the testbench
9     uart_ctrl_config cfg;

10    // The register database
11    uart_ctrl_rdb rdb;

12    // register_seqencer for read/write operations on registers and memories
13    uvm_rgm_sequencer reg_sequencer;

14    // Provide implementations of virtual methods: get_type_name and create
15    `uvm_component_utils(uart_ctrl_tb)
```

```
16    // Constructor - required UVM syntax
17    function new(input string name, input uvm_component parent=null);
18      super.new(name,parent);
19    endfunction

20    // Additional class methods
21    extern virtual function void build();
22    extern virtual function void connect();
23    extern virtual task run();
24  endclass : uart_ctrl_tb
```

10.5.1.1 Configuration and Reconfiguration Mode

As mentioned above, it is best to repeatedly randomize a configuration object, configure the testbench and the DUT accordingly, and send external traffic to verify this configuration. The configuration includes attributes that determine topology and run-time operation modes. The topology-related configuration attributes are randomized before build, and cannot be modified after the testbench is created. Other run-time parameters can be re-randomized to reconfigured, but need to be consistent with the fixed topology settings. One solution is to build a class that has config and reconfig randomization modes. In the config mode, both topology and run-time attributes are randomized. In the reconfig mode, the topology attributes are have their rand_mode() setting on 0, and only the run-time parameters are randomized. The constraints between all attributes maintain the configuration consistency.

10.5.1.2 The System-Level Virtual Sequence

The initial testbench configuration is randomized as part of the testbench build() phase in order to set the testbench topology. The reconfiguration needs to happen during run time and to propagate to the rest of the testbench. This makes the virtual sequencer that controls the entire environment the ideal location for configuration randomization.

The virtual sequencer of the testbench should have a top sequence that takes a system configuration object and translates it to the needed testbench operations. For example, the sequence:

- Re-randomizes the configuration run-time attributes as needed

- Executes a register sequence that programs the DUT's register file and initiates memories

- Configures the module and interface UVCs as needed using update_config()

- Executes sequences on interface UVCs. This can be optional, as the UVCs should have a project-specific default.

- Coordinates parallel threads that execute some test specific operation (for example, to wait for some event and trigger a soft reset to check correct DUT reaction to this scenario.)

The following example illustrates a typical UART controller virtual sequence:

Example 10–8   UART Controller Virtual Sequence

```
1   class concurrent_u2a_a2u_rand_trans_vseq extends uvm_sequence;
2     rand int unsigned num_a2u;
3     rand int unsigned num_u2a;

4     function new(string name="concurrent_u2a_a2u_rand_trans_vseq");
5         super.new(name);
6     endfunction : new

7     // Register sequence with a sequencer
8    `uvm_sequence_utils(concurrent_u2a_a2u_rand_trans_vseq,
                          uart_ctrl_virtual_sequencer)

9     constraint c_num_a2u {(num_a2u <= 20);}
10    constraint c_num_u2a {(num_u2a <= 10);}

11    // REGISTER sequence
12    uart_cfg_rgm_seq uart_cfg_dut;     // CONFIGURE DUT
13    // APB sequences
14    apb_to_uart_wr a2u_seq;
15    read_rx_fifo_seq rd_rx_fifo;
16    // UART sequence
17    uart_transmit_seq u2a_seq;

18    virtual task body();
19      uvm_test_done.raise_objection(this);
20      // configure UART DUT
21     `uvm_do_on(uart_cfg_dut, p_sequencer.rgm_seqr)
22      fork
23       // Write UART DUT TX FIFO from APB UVC and transmit data from UART UVC
24        `uvm_do_on_with(a2u_seq, p_sequencer.apb_seqr,
                          {num_of_wr == num_a2u;})
25        `uvm_do_on_with(u2a_seq, p_sequencer.uart_seqr,
                          {num_of_tx == num_u2a;})
26      join
27      // Read UART DUT RX FIFO from APB UVC
28     `uvm_do_on_with(rd_rx_fifo, p_sequencer.apb_seqr,
                        {num_of_rd == num_u2a;})
29      uvm_test_done.drop_objection(this);
30    endtask : body
31 endclass : concurrent_u2a_a2u_rand_trans_vseq
```

10.5.1.3 Register Operations

A main register sequence accepts the testbench configuration and translates it into register operations in a procedural way. Some register attributes come directly from the configuration class, while others are randomized on the register level. Because SystemVerilog does not allow constraining an object handle, the virtual sequence creates the top register sequence, assigns the configuration objects and then randomizes and sends the register sequence for execution.

10.5.2 Virtual Sequencer and Register Sequencer

These components are defined with the UVC code but instantiated in the testbench. The assumption is that the virtual sequencer is not reusable at the next level of integration because some of the external interfaces become internal to the larger system (exceptions are discussed later). The configuration sequences and the register model are reusable, but only the top-level DUT knows when and how to hierarchically locate the register models and when to program the subsystem using the configuration sequences.

10.5.3 Interface UVC Extensions

As you move to a system or project specific environment, some system constraints may be required on the interfaces UVCs. For example, the system may not support all types of transactions on the bus. The module UVC extends the interface UVC, and adds fields, constraints or other desired logic to adjust the interface UVC logic for system needs.

10.6 Sequences

Driving the verification environment is done using sequences. Reusing sequences from the various components of the environment saves effort when building the verification environment. For multi-interface and system-level control, we use a virtual sequencer.

The virtual sequencer coordinates the stimulus generation across multiple UVCs. Figure 10-8, UVCs within SoC Design, illustrates a larger SoC design with a virtual sequencer driving stimulus on each interface UVC.

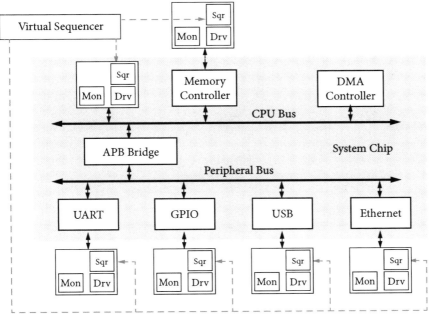

Figure 10-8   UVCs within SoC Design

10.6.1   Developing Reusable Sequences

VIP developers familiar with a protocol should be encouraged to create sequences representing interesting, protocol-specific scenarios. We recommended using random fields to parameterize the sequence activities to make them generic. The integrator chooses which sequences will be reused per specific requirements. The developer needs to help the integrator understand which sequences are applicable to what scenarios and what is fundamental to the UVC work. The default sequence should be set by the developer (whether random or by a template method). Infinity minus should be implemented here (that is, make all the possibilities applicable).

Module-level sequences are not always reusable on the system level. In general, mixing random sequences can break a design. For example, inputs that are accessible at the module level might not be accessible at the system level. However, if you know the interfaces that are likely to remain external on the next level of integration, you can create a dedicated virtual sequencer for these and another virtual sequencer to control these and the rest of the sequencers. When you move to the next level of integration, the virtual sequences of the external interfaces are still usable. Figure 10-9, Reusable Virtual Sequences, illustrates this concept.

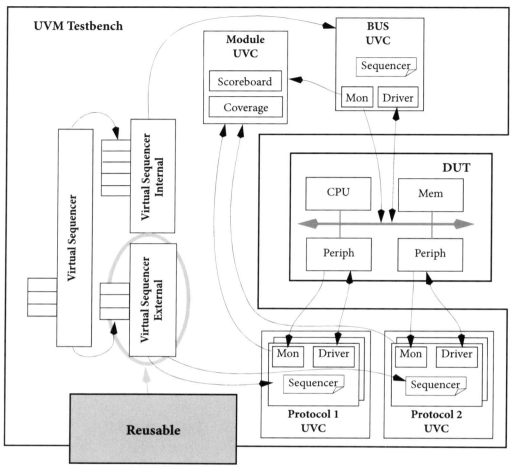

Figure 10-9   Reusable Virtual Sequences

Register sequences are highly reusable and are, by default, context-independent. The register sequencer resides in the testbench outside of the module UVC, as typically there is one CPU that programs the assembled sub-devices.

10.7 Coverage

Coverage definitions can be reused from module to system, while adding system-specific coverage definitions. Interface UVCs collect coverage of traffic on the specific protocol they monitor. Module UVC coverage is collected in its monitor, based on information from interface UVCs and from the DUT/reference model. System-level coverage is based on information in all module and interface UVCs in the system. Coverage results can be crossed to show interactions and combined states. In modules and systems, a massive amount of coverage can be quickly collected via reuse, crosses, and association. The challenges are to identify the meaningful coverage that represents the verification goals, and avoid defining combinations that are sometimes not reachable by the system. Special attention should be paid regarding the impact of coverage on performance.

10.7.1 Module UVC Coverage

The module and system UVCs provide coverage data in different categories, such as:

- Basic traffic coverage for each of the interfaces—Note that not all interface coverage is relevant or interesting to the system. The system may not make use of all interface capabilities. As SystemVerilog does not allow coverage extensions, duplicating the coverage groups and inserting the needed modifications might be required. Eliminating existing coverage can be done at collection time or at review time (using filter on the existing database); for performance reasons, the first is recommended.

- Crossing traffic coverage for all interfaces

- Internal coverage (for example, internal states)

- Sequence coverage—*Have we tried all of the sequences that we were targeting?*

- Register coverage—Register coverage is interesting, as it reflects the device operation modes. Specifically, it is important to identify crosses of operation modes that should be verified. It is also important to check that the device was sufficiently exercised before declaring the device operation mode to be verified

- Performance-related coverage, such as delays and throughput

- Configuration coverage, such as all operation modes

- Reset and recovery

- Hot configuration (where applicable)

- Error conditions and recovery

Example 10–9   Module UVC DUT Coverage

The following example shows functional coverage collection for the UART Rx FIFO. This coverage group is placed in a coverage component, uart_ctrl_cover, which is instantiated and connected in the UART controller monitor. Creating a separate UVM component for coverage collection is optional. For simplicity, only the Tx coverage group is shown.

```
1   class uart_ctrl_cover extends  uvm_component ;

2     virtual interface uart_ctrl_internal_if vif;
3     bit coverage_enable = 1;

4     int unsigned mod_tx_fifo_ptr;

5     // Required macro for UVM automation and utilities
6     `uvm_component_utils(uart_ctrl_cover)

7     virtual task run();
```

```
8       fork
9         collect_tx_coverage();
10      join
11    endtask : run

12    virtual task collect_tx_coverage();
13      // Extract & re-arrange to give a more useful input to covergroups
14      // Calculate percentage fill level of TX FIFO
15      forever begin
16        @(vif.tx_fifo_ptr)
17        mod_tx_fifo_ptr = ( vif.tx_fifo_ptr * 100 / `UA_TX_FIFO_DEPTH);
18        if (coverage_enable) dut_tx_fifo_cg.sample();
19      end
20    endtask : collect_tx_coverage

21    // DUT TX covergroup
22    covergroup dut_tx_fifo_cg;
23      tx_level : coverpoint mod_tx_fifo_ptr {
24                           bins EMPTY = {0};
25                           bins HALF_FULL = {[50:99]};
26                           bins FULL = {100}; }
27    endgroup

28    function new(string name , uvm_component parent);
29      super.new(name, parent);
30      if (coverage_enable) begin
31        dut_tx_fifo_cg = new();
32        dut_tx_fifo_cg.set_inst_name ({get_full_name(),
   ".dut_tx_fifo_cg"});
33      end
34    endfunction

35    function void assign_vi(virtual interface uart_ctrl_internal_if
   uart_int);
36      vif = uart_int;
37    endfunction : assign_vi

38 endclass : uart_ctrl_cover
```

Example 10–10 Module UVC Performance-Related Coverage

This second functional coverage example shows how you might collect throughput delay coverage for the Rx path. Simulation time is captured once a UART frame has been written into the Rx FIFO. When the FIFO is read via the APB interface, time is again captured and the number of clocks is calculated and sampled. As with the previous example, this coverage group can be placed in the module UVC monitor or an optional coverage component. For simplicity, only the Rx delay covergroup is shown.

```
1   class uart_ctrl_cover extends  uvm_component ;
2    // virtual interface, coverage_enable, uvm_component utils, etc
3    time rx_time_q[$];
4    time rx_clks_delay, clk_period;

5    uvm_analysis_imp_apb #(apb_transfer, uart_ctrl_cover) apb_in;
6    uvm_analysis_imp_rx #(apb_transfer, uart_ctrl_cover) uart_rx_in;

7    uart_pkg::uart_config uart_cfg;

8    virtual task run();
9      capture_clk_period();
10   endtask : run

11   covergroup rx_delay_cg;
12     clocks : coverpoint rx_clks_delay   {
13                          bins ZERO   = {0};
14                          bins ONE    = {1};
15                          bins TWO    = {2};
16                          bins GT_TWO = default;
17                          }
18   endgroup

19   function new(string name , uvm_component parent);
20     super.new(name, parent);
21     apb_in = new("apb_in", this);
22     uart_tx_in = new("uart_tx_in", this);
23     uart_rx_in = new("uart_rx_in", this);
24     if (coverage_enable) begin
25       rx_delay_cg = new();
26       rx_delay_cg.set_inst_name ({get_full_name(), ".rx_delay_cg"});
27     end
28   endfunction

29   function void write_rx(uart_frame frame);
30       rx_time_q.push_front($time);
31   endfunction : write_rx

32   function void write_apb(apb_transfer transfer);
33     if ((transfer.addr == uart_cfg.fifo_address) &&
34        (transfer.direction == APB_READ)) begin
35       rx_clks_delay = ($time - rx_time_q.pop_back())/clk_period;
36        if (coverage_enable) rx_delay_cg.sample();
37     end
38   endfunction : write_apb
39 endclass : uart_ctrl_cover
```

10.7.2 System-Level Coverage

System coverage is very similar to module-level coverage, with some exceptions:

- Connectivity coverage is very important.

- Crossing of all valid configurations of the modules in the system is possible.

- There is no internal state coverage on the system level. This is typically disabled and can be enabled as a problem or a concern occurs.

Lower-level coverage definitions should be reused where applicable (and fine-tuned if necessary). Irrelevant coverage goals should be filtered out at the system level.

10.7.3 Adding Coverage Definitions to System UVCs

To define new coverage groups under the module/system monitor:

- Use events from the system monitor, or from one of the lower-level monitors.

- Use data items from system monitor, or from one of the lower-level monitors.

- Duplicate coverage definitions from the interface UVC or lower-level UVCs (where needed).

10.8 Stand-In Mode

In early stages of the testbench development, the design code may not be available or may be only partially implemented. You can start the testbench integration, sequence library creation, coverage collection and more if a stand-in (active) mode is supported. In stand-in mode, the system UVC drives the simulation by playing the role of the DUT. A reference model is used to emulate the device behavior. The active mode is helpful to create a system-level testbench when the DUT and pieces of it are not available. This is highly device-specific, but for some devices with the availability of interface UVCs, the stand-in mode is surprisingly easy to implement.

The following figures illustrate both passive (normal) and stand-in (active) modes.

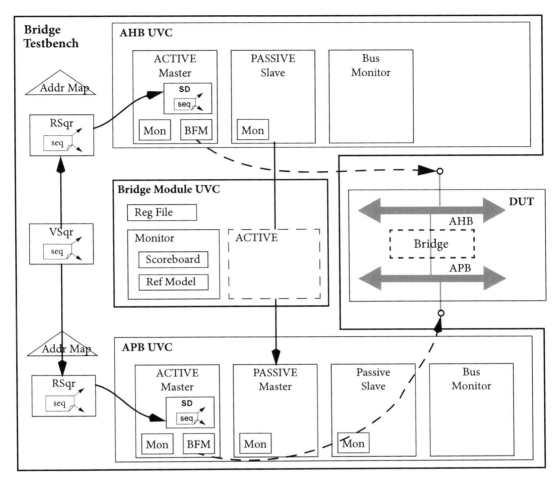

Figure 10-10   Module UVC in Passive (Normal) Mode

When the module UVC becomes active, its corresponding agents in the interface UVCs become active as well. The sequencer in the active part of the module UVC is layered on top of the sequencers in the interface UVCs. The built-in driving capabilities of the interface UVCs are used by the module UVC to drive the simulation.

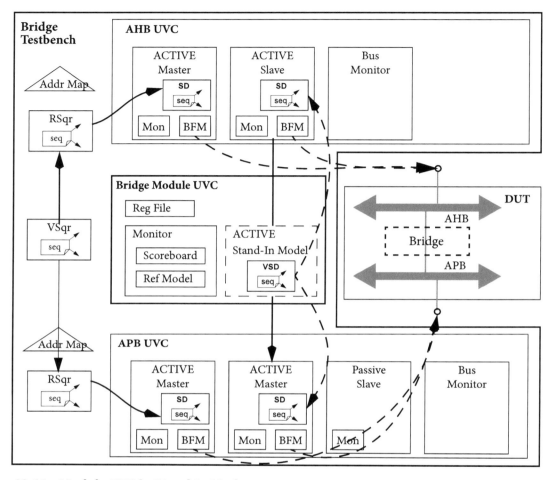

Figure 10-11   Module UVC in Stand-In Mode

Essentially, what you get is that some of the agents in the interface UVCs emulate the surrounding environment (exactly as in passive mode), and some of the agents that used to be passive help emulate the module UVC logic. In the case of a controller, the virtual sequencer may perform buffering to bridge protocol speeds.

10.9   Scalability Concerns in System Verification

A system verification environment is assembled from numerous lower-level verification environments. In large systems, the performance of the verification environment might become an issue. Proper preparation in the interface UVCs and in the module UVC allows trading off controllability for performance. For example, you may want to disable assertions and leave the end-to-end checkers to identify system malfunctions. This section discusses various techniques to speed up the simulation for project-specific needs.

10.9.1 Randomization and Stimuli Creation

Random generation is a very powerful tool for productivity (reducing the manual work of configuring the environment or DUT and creating stimulus) and improved quality (hunting for bugs in areas that are hard to foresee). However, excess use of randomization might result in scalability problems. When building a large verification environment, consider carefully how to avoid unnecessarily complex generation that might slow down the entire simulation.

The following tips show how to avoid some common pitfalls related to large verification environments. The overall effect depends on the size and complexity of the DUT.

10.9.1.1 Recycle Allocated Items

The `` `uvm_do `` macro allocates a sequence item using the factory. You can avoid the allocation using the `` `uvm_create `` once for allocation and `` `uvm_send `` or `` `uvm_rand_send `` multiple times, as mentioned in Chapter 8 "Stimulus Generation Topics".

10.9.1.2 Avoid Redundant Randomization

In some scenarios, expensive randomization provides diminishing value. In such cases, it is helpful to use procedural checking and avoid complex constraint solving. Hard-coding values can hide bugs; thus the use of this technique should be limited to scenarios in which variation is not an option.

Examples for such scenarios include:

- Iterations in the sequence `body()` when the same values or small deterministic value variations need to be created. Using a single randomization, followed by a `` `uvm_send `` can enable this.

- In layering, the randomization of the lower item might not be necessary, as it is best to only program the register on the local bus and not to exercise the local bus capabilities.

- Slaves can randomize replies that include split, retry, and other. If these scenarios were exercised on the module level, you can create a simple sequence that always returns the desired value without randomization in the slave sequence.

10.9.2 Coverage

Coverage is handled similar to checking. While it serves an important role during module verification, some coverage may be traded off for performance during system-level verification.

All coverage definitions and related code should be implemented under a `coverage_enable` monitor flag.

10.9.2.1 Grouping Coverage

As in checking, coverage definitions can also be structured in logical groups, under various `has_*_coverage` flags, like `has_whitebox_coverage` or `has_error_coverage`. Error coverage and whitebox coverage are important at the module level. On the other hand, for system-level verification, they could create holes in the coverage. There might be no simple way to create all error cases or activate all internal states in a specific system. Therefore, this kind of coverage should be implemented under special flags so that it can be disabled at the system level, using the configuration mechanism.

10.9.2.2 Determining the Appropriate Tradeoff

System verification has its own specific coverage goals implemented in the testbench and various subsystem UVCs. These include connectivity and interoperability, which must be active during system verification, but can be turned off (for example, for HW/SW co-verification).

10.9.3 Messages

UVCs typically produce a lot of useful information for module-level verification. Some of that information might be redundant in system verification. Extensive use of messages and string manipulation can significantly slow down your simulation. Make sure you use the message macros and do not directly call the message routines.

10.10 Module UVC Directory Structure

The module UVC is developed and maintained as reusable UVM package with additional subdirectories. The objective is to encapsulate all reusable code, examples, and documentation for verification of the system in a consistent manner so that it can be shared within and between projects.

In particular, the module UVC package contains examples of how to reuse this as a component in a larger system. The examples are contained in one or more testbench directories, the contents of which are described in Figure 10-12 on page 257. A testbench example should be used as the basis for integration of the module UVC in a larger system. A testbench is sometimes called an SVE (Simulation and Verification Environment).

Note   The standalone verification testbench and test is part of the reusable module UVC package. Many times a bug is uncovered in a large integration that requires further isolated tests. It is useful in such cases to have available the tests and sequences used at the subsystem level.

The figure below illustrates the recommended directory structure of a module or a system UVC.

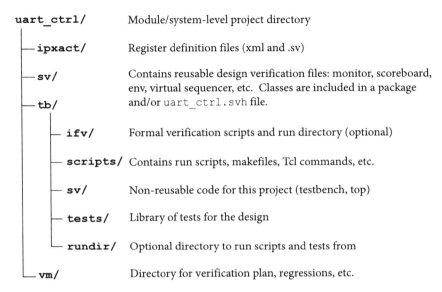

```
uart_ctrl/        Module/system-level project directory

  ipxact/         Register definition files (xml and .sv)

  sv/             Contains reusable design verification files: monitor, scoreboard,
                  env, virtual sequencer, etc.  Classes are included in a package
  tb/             and/or uart_ctrl.svh file.

      ifv/        Formal verification scripts and run directory (optional)

      scripts/    Contains run scripts, makefiles, Tcl commands, etc.

      sv/         Non-reusable code for this project (testbench, top)

      tests/      Library of tests for the design

      rundir/     Optional directory to run scripts and tests from

  vm/             Directory for verification plan, regressions, etc.
```

Figure 10-12   UART Controller Directory Structure

Summary

This chapter tackles the requirements of developing complex testbenches and provides recommendations on how to make testbench components reusable for cluster-level and system-level verification. We introduce the module UVC verification component, which organizes DUT-specific verification logic, follows a consistent architecture, and allows configuration using the UVM configuration mechanism. We also describe the creation of reusable virtual sequences, DUT-specific coverage, and DUT-specific checking. All of these are collected into a common package and directory structure similar to the package we introduced for interface UVCs.

11   The Future of UVM

Any discussion of the UVM must also look toward the future. The UVM is a great step forward for the industry for enabling SystemVerilog VIP to be shared and reused within and between companies. It also provides a standard way in which commercial VIP should be developed so that it can easily be plugged into any project which is based on the UVM. As seen in the previous chapters, the UVM covers most of the fundamental methodology required for building reusable SystemVerilog Verification Environments for RTL designs. There are still some fundamental capabilities that are required to complete this methodology, as well as some more significant areas in which the UVM can be extended in order to truly be "universal" and have an even bigger impact on the industry. This chapter gives an overview for both the short-term and longer term areas in which the UVM will likely be enhanced.

11.1 Commercial UVM Verification IP

Throughout this book, we review the process of creating UVCs and how they might be reused within a central company repository. An additional opportunity to accelerate testbench creation is to adopt commercial VIP for standard protocols, because many of the standard protocols are extremely complex and require a large investment to learn the protocol and develop a UVC from scratch. Cadence Design Systems and other VIP providers can leverage the UVM to offer commercial-grade plug-and-play UVCs for standard industry protocols. The typical advantage of a commercial UVC is that it will be used on projects in different companies to verify many designs, which increases the maturity of the UVC much more quickly than what can typically be achieved by an internally-developed UVC. Just like design IP that has already been silicon-proven is of more value, verification IP which has been "hardened" by being used to successfully verify lots of designs provides similar value.

In addition to being used to verify many different designs, there are several other considerations for choosing the right commercial VIP to ensure the most productivity benefits.

- In order to easily integrate the VIP into your verification environment, it should be checked to ensure it is truly UVM compliant. A VIP that is based on a different methodology or that only loosely follows the UVM will likely require a lot of work to integrate into a UVM verification environment.

- UVCs for specific interface protocols should adhere to the standard UVM architecture; use randomization and sequences for stimulus, including a sequence library of common, useful sequences; provide functional coverage, protocol checks, and monitoring of transactions on the interface for higher-level scoreboard and reference model checks.

- It is often the case when designing a new IP with interfaces based on standard protocols that the design may not support all of the features of the protocol. Therefore, it is very important for a commercial UVC to be highly configurable so that it is easy to enable or disable various features of driving, checking, and covering the protocol.

11.2 Class Library Enhancements

The OVM has been used successfully on countless projects by hundreds of companies over the past few years. The feature set of UVM is a superset of OVM, so it is reasonable to say that the UVM provides a comprehensive solution for building reusable verification environments. However, there are outstanding requests from users for further enhancements to the class library and methodology with various priority levels. Some of the higher priority enhancements that have been requested are described in this section.

11.2.1 Register Package

Since practically all designs are configured and controlled by writing and reading the registers to program the device for specific operation modes, an essential verification activity requires being able to generate constrained-random stimulus for writing registers, as well as the ability to check and cover registers in order to ensure they have been programmed correctly. There are currently multiple register packages available for the UVM that provide various capabilities for modeling registers and generating register configuration stimulus. In order to ensure further reuse and consistency of modeling register configuration, the UVM should include a single register package or at least specify the API for a single register package. At the time of the writing of this book, no single register package has been selected as the official UVM package or API. The IP-XACT format includes register-related features and allows facilitating reuse of register models, so it should be a requirement for the UVM register package to leverage IP-XACT for describing the definition of registers to be modeled. This book includes the Cadence-contributed register package and has concepts that can be universally applied.

11.2.2 Run-Time Phases

Run-time phases are arguably the most needed enhancement to complete the UVM class library. They are required to coordinate the execution at simulation run time of components that were designed in isolation and without up-front planning. The point of run-time phases is to provide hooks for testbench developers to define logic that will be executed during specific "phases" of simulation. For example, the UVM might define a specific phase for reset that could call a task at a specific phase in simulation. A testbench developer could then define all the reset-related logic for a specific DUT to execute during the reset phase and place this logic inside this task. These built-in tasks will then be called automatically in a specific order during simulation to execute each phase and the corresponding logic defined within that phase. Some of the requirements regarding run-time phases include the following:

- Ability to reset the phases and re-execute them for the entire system or a subsystem

- Ability to assign verification components to part of a specific "domain" so that phases can be coordinated for verification components that are part of the same domain. This might be needed, for example, to reset a subset of the system.

- Ability to extend standard phases for specific needs, which is important for seamless simulation coordination

- Ability to synchronize an arbitrary set of components without advanced planning

- Support for run-time phases by the sequencers and sequences, as different traffic may be required at different phases

11.2.3 Multi-Language Integration

Today, practically all designs are designed or verified using more than a single language. One of the main reasons for this fact is that different languages are optimized for different tasks. For example:

- Verilog and VHDL are optimized for RTL design.

- SystemVerilog and *e* are optimized for constrained-random verification.

- SystemC is optimized for high-level modeling.

- PSL and SVA are optimized for assertion-based verification.

Furthermore, there may be cases where one team is more efficient and has more expertise in using a specific language for a specific task. As we continue to evolve design and verification, we will continue to define new languages to further optimize these tasks. Therefore, for UVM to be truly "universal," and applicable for use in most real-world verification environments, it is essential for UVM to expand beyond SystemVerilog to also support other languages and integration of verification IP and models that are not written in SystemVerilog—namely *e* verification IP and SystemC models. The figure below shows an example of a typical multi-language environment where the UART UVC and the testbench might be written in SystemVerilog and the desire is to reuse an existing APB UVC that is written in *e*.

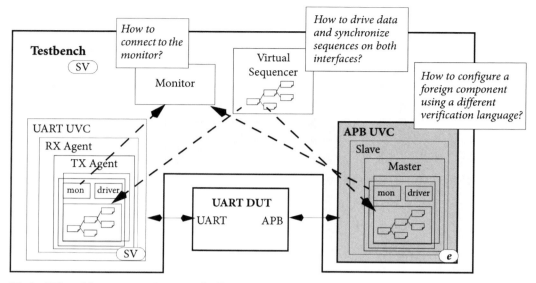

Figure 11-1 Mixed-Language Reuse Challenge

Some of the requirements for extending the UVM to support multi-language integration include:

- Passing of transactions between languages, based on the TLM communications API, including SystemVerilog, *e*, and SystemC

- Ability to instantiate and configure a verification component defined in one language from another language

- Ability to override the UVM factory from another language

- Providing a common format and control of debug messages across languages

- Ability to support common data types and automatic conversion of data types across languages

- Test phases with cross-language test flow coordination and synchronization

- Debugging—Consistent debug views, regardless of implementation language

- Register modeling that allows a common register model to be accessed across multiple languages

Some of these requirements may end up being simulator-specific rather than class library features, but many of these requirements will need enhancements to the UVM library infrastructure as well as requiring the definition of new UVM libraries for *e* and SystemC. Since the UVM methodology is derived largely from the original *e* Reuse Methodology (*e*RM)—and *e*RM was already updated to be aligned with OVM with the introduction of the OVM *e*—it should not be a large task to extend UVM to include support for *e*. Cadence also introduced a subset of OVM capabilities for SystemC, so hopefully this will also accelerate the inclusion of SystemC models within the UVM in the not so distant future.

11.3 Multi-Domain UVM

The main focus of the UVM to date has been for RTL verification. Over the last several years, more of the verification has expanded beyond RTL simulation to include more formal verification; more verification earlier in the design cycle, based on high-level SystemC models; more need for robust analog mixed-signal verification; and more use of hardware acceleration for system-level verification, including hardware/software verification. A significant issue in this expanding verification flow is that there little to no consistency in terminology, testbench infrastructure, or tests. Furthermore, as you move from verifying your high-level SystemC model, to RTL simulation, through formal verification—and later, hardware/software acceleration and emulation—there is very little to no verification reuse. The momentum behind the OVM brought unrelated experts from such areas as ESL, hardware acceleration/emulation, formal verification, and analog-mixed signal verification to discuss a consistent flow that enables further reuse and consistency across these different domains. We expect this momentum to carry under the wider UVM umbrella. The UVM was architected to consider future extension into many of these domains, so it is important not to compromise the UVM concepts, as it is enhanced to support these different domains. For example, in acceleration, the interface UVC and agent encapsulation should be preserved. There is great promise to further optimize and unify verification beyond RTL simulation by extending the application of UVM to other domains.

Summary

A lot of verification expertise has been accumulated throughout the last decade which has been leveraged to define the UVM as a highly productive and reusable solution for constructing SystemVerilog Verification Environments. The core methodology of UVM has been in practical use by many customers for many years and has been proven in both SystemVerilog and *e* to be a very efficient approach for building testbenches and reusing verification components. The convergence that UVM provides within the industry is a new opportunity to end debate about competing methodologies and enable a worldwide VIP ecosystem. As we look toward the future, UVM offers a strong foundation for further unifying and optimizing verification across multiple languages and domains.

The Authors

Sharon Rosenberg – Solutions Architect, Cadence

Sharon Rosenberg leads the multi-language testbench methodology development team in the Front-End Verification Division at Cadence Design Systems. He has been involved with *e*RM and OVM since the very early days, is an Accellera sub-committee member, and is a key contributor in the development of the overall verification methodology that has become UVM.

Sharon started his verification career in defining and implementing the *e* verification language at Verisity Design. In his 14 years of experience, Sharon took part in multiple verification projects as a consultant engineer, led a Core Competency deployment team, and now leads a Solutions Architecture team. Sharon has a BS in Computer Science from Bar-Ilan University, Ramat-Gan, Israel.

Kathleen A. Meade – Staff Solutions Engineer, Cadence

Kathleen A. Meade is a Staff Solutions Engineer in the Front-End Verification Division at Cadence Design Systems. She has worked with customers on simulation and functional verification for more than 18 years in various roles, including a Field Applications Engineer, Core Competency Engineer, and Solutions Deployment.

Before joining Cadence in 1992, Kathleen worked at the GE Simulation and Control Systems Department as a design engineer on flight simulation systems. She received her BSE from the University of Connecticut and MSCE from the University of Central Florida.

Contributors

Tom Anderson, Anil Raj Gopalakrishnan, Phu Huynh, Vishal Jain, Dorit Kerem, Zeev Kirshenbaum, Gabi Leshem, John Rose, Justin Sprague, Stuart Swan, Andrey Schwartz, Michael Stellfox, Umer Yousafzai.

Acknowledgements

John Choroszy, Dave DeYoreo, Suzie Im, Ben Kauffman, Dayna Musto, Adam Sherer, Amy Witherow.

Index

Symbols

A

B

C

D

G

H